ἓν οἶδα ὅτι οὐδὲν οἶδα

—After SOCRATES

WILLIAM D. GRAY, Ph.D. (University of Pennsylvania), is Professor of Botany at Southern Illinois University. He previously taught at The Ohio State University and Iowa State University, and has been a guest lecturer at universities and before industrial and professional groups throughout the United States as well as in Canada, India, and Africa. Dr. Gray serves as a consultant to government and industry and has published scores of papers on mycology and related subjects in the professional journals.

CONSTANTINE J. ALEXOPOULOS, Ph.D. (University of Illinois), is Professor of Botany, University of Texas. He has also taught at the University of Iowa and Michigan State University. Dr. Alexopoulos is Past President of the Mycological Society of America and of the Botanical Society of America, and he holds the Botanical Society's Certificate of Merit. He is the author of a basic mycology textbook and of numerous articles on Myxomycetes and fungi, and has contributed to the *Encyclopaedia Britannica*.

BIOLOGY OF
THE MYXOMYCETES

William D. _avid_ Gray
SOUTHERN ILLINOIS UNIVERSITY

Constantine J. Alexopoulos
UNIVERSITY OF TEXAS AT AUSTIN

THE RONALD PRESS COMPANY • NEW YORK

Library of Congress Catalog Card Number: 68–57149
PRINTED IN THE UNITED STATES OF AMERICA

To
GEORGE W. MARTIN
whose long years of dedicated teaching
and scholarly research have inspired
students of the Myxomycetes throughout
the world.

Preface

Thirty-seven years ago when one of the authors (W.D.G.) first became interested in the Myxomycetes, there would have been little justification for writing such a book as that attempted here. While deBary's early treatise had given us a good general picture of the Myxomycetes, there had been few investigators working on these organisms at any one point in time, and the majority of writings in the field were concerned with taxonomy or the listing of species collected in some designated area. Although the various taxonomic books all contained brief accounts of the life histories, etc., only the little volume of the Frys (Rt. Honourable Sir Edward and Agnes) attempted to deal with all aspects of the Myxomycetes—such as they were known in 1899. Needless to say this little book, containing 22 illustrations and a bibliography of 23 references, did not provide a very comprehensive treatment of the group.

Tremendous progress has been made in all areas of biology, and the rather specialized area of mycology that deals with the study of Myxomycetes is no exception. The number of active workers in this field has increased many fold. This is due not only to a greatly enlarged scientific community but also to the fact that the Myxomycetes provide excellent experimental material for attacking a wide variety of biological problems. As the attitudes and techniques of biochemistry have become increasingly sophisticated, Myxomycetes have been used to a greater and greater extent in deeply probing attempts to elucidate the biochemical reactions that precede and accompany many of the observable physiological and morphological events occurring in a living system.

In view of the much-increased interest in the Myxomycetes it now seems justifiable to attempt such a book as the present one—not to answer all of the questions but rather to bring together into one volume as many of the pertinent facts as are presently known, together with the theories proposed to explain various phenomena observed in the laboratory and in nature. Thus we have attempted to cover in reasonable depth the biology of the Myxomycetes, and particularly the ultrastructural, biochemical, and physiological aspects. Such a work may well be of value not only to the student who is beginning to develop an interest but knows little about the Myxomycetes, but also to the more experienced investigator whose areas of interest in the group may have been channeled along very narrow lines.

We wish to express our thanks to all who have assisted us. Various investigators have been most generous in supplying us with reprints of their papers, with prints of published illustrations, and, in some instances, with information and illustrations as yet unpublished. Dean John Ward of Oregon State University read the section on morphogenesis, and Dr. Arthur Cohen of Washington State University read the chapter on Myxamoebae, Swarm Cells, and Microcysts. Special thanks are due George Burson, Dan Irwin, and Su-hwa Lee of the Southern Illinois University Cartographic Service and Marilyn Andresen of the Southern Illinois University Audio-Visual Services for their assistance in the preparation of many of the charts and line drawings. Thanks are also due Mrs. Merideth Blackwell and Wallace LeStourgeon, graduate students in Mycology at the University of Texas at Austin, the former for her invaluable assistance in the preparation of the bibliography, the latter for technical assistance in photography. Grateful thanks are hereby expressed to the National Science Foundation for its long-term support of the myxomycete research of one of the authors (C.J.A.). We wish also to thank our wives for their assistance, patience, and understanding through the several years during which this book has been in preparation and for their aid in the compilation of the indexes.

WILLIAM D. GRAY
CONSTANTINE J. ALEXOPOULOS

Carbondale, Illinois
Austin, Texas
October, 1968

Contents

BIOLOGY OF
THE MYXOMYCETES

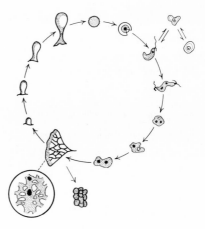

1

Introduction

The Myxomycetes or plasmodial slime molds constitute a natural group of fungus- or protozoan-like organisms comprising about 425 known species with a unique life cycle which sets them apart from all others to which the term slime molds has also been applied. The combined animal- and fungus-like characteristics of this group are reflected in the name applied to them by Anton deBary, who must be considered the first of the great investigators to become interested in these anomalous organisms. DeBary proposed the name Mycetozoa for the group, in which he included the plasmodial slime molds, and while this name admits the fungus characteristics, it definitely places the major emphasis on the group's animal affinities.

Link (1833) first applied the name Myxomycetes (which places major emphasis on their fungal affinities) to the plasmodial slime molds, and, although the Listers as well as a number of their followers clung to the name Mycetozoa, most investigators today use the class name Myxomycetes. The more common and widespread use of the latter name may be due to a more general acceptance of the view that the plasmodial slime molds have closer affinities with the fungi than with the animal kingdom, or it may be due merely to the fact that in the biological sciences the burden of the study of these organisms has been left largely to the mycologists.

SUMMARY LIFE CYCLE

The somatic stage of the Myxomycetes is a free-living, acellular, multinucleate, mobile assimilative phase, the plasmodium, which becomes converted into one or more fruiting bodies which produce the spores. Typically, a slime mold is found either in the assimilative or in the reproductive stage, and only in rare instances may both of these stages coexist in the same individual. When the spores germinate they give rise to flagellated swarm cells or to non-flagellated myxamoebae. These divide repeatedly by binary fission and produce large populations of cells. Compatible cells then fuse, and a plasmodium eventually results (Fig. 1).

COMPARISON OF MYXOMYCETES WITH OTHER SLIME MOLDS

The Myxomycetes (plasmodial or acellular slime molds) thus differ from the Acrasiales (cellular slime molds) in that there is formation of a true multinucleate plasmodium, in that flagellated swarm cells are typically a part of their life cycle (although their formation may be suppressed in certain environments), and in that fusion of cells behaving as gametes appears to be a prerequisite for the completion of the life cycle of most species that have been critically investigated. They differ from the Plasmodiophoromycetes (endoparasitic slime molds) in lacking a zoosporangial stage and in their free-living rather than endoparasitic habit, and from the Labyrinthulales (net slime molds) by not having the characteristic spindleform cells which glide through a network of slimy tubes often called a filoplasmodium. Whether these four types of organisms are in any way related cannot be stated with certainty, but at this stage of our knowledge such relationship is at best doubtful.

In 1967, L. S. Olive summarized our knowledge of a new group of organisms, the Protostelida, which have amoeboid uninucleate to multinucleate protoplasts, reticulate in two genera (*Schizoplasmodium, Schizoplasmodiopsis*), and have anteriorly flagellated cells in one genus (*Cavostelium*). The possibility that this group represents a form ancestral to the Acrasiales and the Myxomycetes is presented.

BRIEF HISTORY OF MYXOMYCETE STUDY

The Myxomycetes or plasmodial slime molds have been known to biologists for some 300 years. Lister (1925) gives a history of the early reports concerning these organisms, beginning with Panckow's descrip-

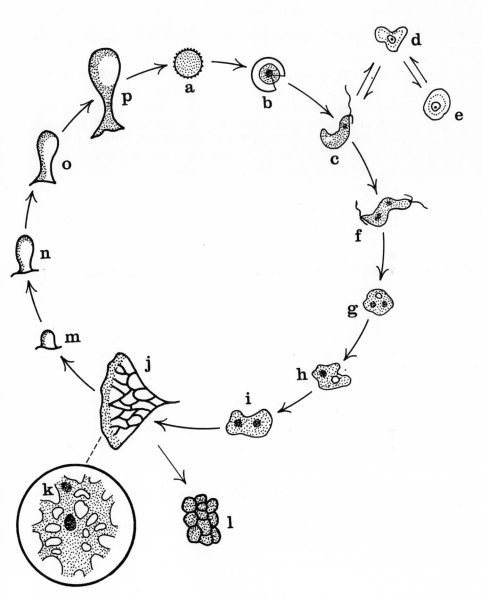

Fig. 1. General life cycle of the endosporous Myxomycetes. a. spore; b. germinating spore; c. swarm cell; d. myxamoeba; e. microcyst; f. swarm cells fusing; g. zygote before karyogamy; h. zygote; i. binucleate plasmodium; j. mature fan-shaped plasmodium; k. detail of portion of plasmodium; l. sclerotium showing macrocysts; m–o. developing sporangium; p. mature sporangium.

tion and illustration of *Lycogala epidendrum* in 1654. Seventy-five years after Panckow, Micheli in 1729 called attention to the group in his monumental *Nova Plantarum Genera* in which he described a number of species and made one of the first references to the plasmodium [1] by noting that *Mucilago* passes through a "mucilaginous stage." Although Linnaeus' *Species Plantarum* has been designated as a starting point for the naming of Myxomycetes, the father of taxonomy contributed little to our knowledge of these organisms. As Martin (1966) succinctly states, "Linnaeus, 1753, named and described five species—surely a scanty harvest for a starting point. . . ." Fries (1829) was probably the first to fully comprehend the important connection of the plasmodium to the fruiting stage and to emphasize that many individual sporangia develop from a single plasmodium. It is to deBary, however, that we are indebted for our first knowledge of the developmental cycle of the Myxomycetes. He germinated the spores, observed the interconversion of swarm cells and myxamoebae, studied the plasmodium, and described the development of the fruiting bodies. [For an appraisal of deBary's contributions to our knowledge of the Myxomycetes see Martin (1958). For an early but very complete study of the plasmodium, Cienkowski's paper (1863b) should be consulted.] In 1875, Rostafinski, deBary's student, produced the first important taxonomic monograph of the Myxomycetes, which may be considered the beginning of modern taxonomy without detracting anything from the important works of such men as Gleditsch, Batsch, Sowerby, Persoon, Fuckel, Schweinitz, and others, who preceded him.

Shortly after deBary and Cienkowski laid the foundations for the study of the biology of the Myxomycetes, the experimental era was ushered in by Hofmeister (1867), Rosanoff (1868), and Baranetzki (1876), who studied the effects of external factors on the movement of plasmodia.

Special credit must be given to several investigators working in the twentieth century. For example, although earlier workers had undoubtedly maintained crude plasmodial cultures of several species of Myxomycetes, it was the work of Howard (1931b) that provided a simple method of cultivating *Physarum polycephalum* and thus made this common species an easily available experimental organism for many investigators. Camp's (1936) development of a moist chamber method for cultivating *P. polycephalum* provided a technique for producing still larger quantities of plasmodia of this species with even greater ease. In a series of papers extending over a period of several years, Seifriz

---

[1] G. Lister (1912) also cites Jean Marchant's description in 1727 of "the pale-yellow foam-like masses" of *Fuligo septica,* which probably refers to the fruiting plasmodium of that species.

repeatedly called attention to the great potential of *P. polycephalum* as an excellent organism for many types of biological investigations and thus did much to popularize the use of this species, and Kamiya made important contributions to the area in the development of sophisticated and very sensitive apparatus which has been very useful in the study of protoplasmic streaming and plasmodial locomotion. In the present decade the work of Rusch and his associates at the McArdle Laboratory, University of Wisconsin, has attracted considerable attention since these investigators have developed methods for the pure culture of plasmodia of *P. polycephalum* in chemically defined medium.

In spite of the fact that the skeleton life history of the Myxomycetes was worked out by deBary and his contemporaries, the nuclear life cycle is still controversial today, many cytological problems are still awaiting solution, and the physiology and biochemistry of these fascinating organisms are just beginning to be explored.

The problem of whether Myxomycetes are more closely related to fungi than to animals has still not been solved but is being approached from a number of different points of view. For example, Korn, *et al.* (1965) have reported that *Physarum polycephalum* has qualitatively the same pattern of unsaturated fatty acids as a soil amoeba (*Acanthamoeba* sp.) but does not contain the unique diunsaturated fatty acids which are characteristic of the cellular slime mold *Dictyostelium discoideum*.

REVIEW ARTICLES

Not counting the rather superficial little book of the Frys (1899) in which the authors coyly express a preference for the pet name "myxies" because it rhymes with "pyxies," six serious review articles summarizing our knowledge of the biology of the Myxomycetes have been written in the last 37 years: Martin (1940), Hawker (1952), Alexopoulos (1963, 1966), von Stosch (1965), and Gottsberger (1966). Increased activity in the area of myxomycete investigations may be demonstrated by comparing the number of literature citations in some of these review articles. In 1899, the Frys cited 23 references, but 41 years later Martin, in the first comprehensive review paper, listed 204 references. Alexopoulos' review (1963), which covered the 23-year period immediately following Martin's paper, has a bibliography of 393 references, and a great many additional papers have appeared since the 1963 publication date. Much of what has been written in the various review articles will necessarily be repeated in this book, and information has been drawn freely from these reviews. In addition to the reviews listed above, the excellent review of Rusch (1968) on *P. polycephalum* should also be consulted.

For the student whose orientation is primarily biochemical, this review will be most helpful.

NOMENCLATURE

Understandably, as taxonomists have continued to study the Myxomycetes more critically, species concepts have changed over the years. Thus, new species have been named, new genera have been proposed, species have been transferred to different genera, species names have been relegated to synonymy, and so on. For example, the very common "wasps' nest" slime mold, formerly called *Hemitrichia vesparium*, is now to be found under the name *Metatrichia vesparium*. In the present work, names of all organisms are those accepted by Martin and Alexopoulos (1969); hence, in many instances species names referred to are not those used by the original investigators whose works are being cited.

2

Spores

With the exception of the three exosporous species of the genus *Ceratiomyxa*, the spores of all species of Myxomycetes are formed within some type of spore case. During the final stages of the fruiting process individual spores are delimited by successive cleavages of protoplasm, and as the fruiting structure matures the spores round up, the spore walls are formed, and spore pigment, if present, develops. For the most part the mature spores of these organisms are roughly spherical, although in some species they are typically oval or elliptical in outline.

MORPHOLOGY

Size of Spores

Spore sizes vary from species to species, and within limits in the species themselves. The spores of the majority of species are probably 10 microns or less in diameter; however, they may be as small as 4 microns, as in *Stemonitis smithii*, or as large as 20 microns, as in *Fuligo megaspora*. Ranges of spore sizes are commonly listed for each species in the standard taxonomic works such as Martin (1949), Macbride and Martin (1934), Lister (1925), Hagelstein (1944), and Martin and Alexopoulos (1969), and spore measurements are very necessary in any identification work. The recent work of Solis (1962) is quite suggestive, since this worker found that the size ranges of spores of *Physarum nicaraguense* from sporangia that developed on elm bark were different from those of spores from sporangia that had developed on cornmeal agar. Plasmodia were obtained by sowing spores on cornmeal agar and then transferring them to sterilized elm bark. The spores (200) developed on elm bark measured from 7–12 microns, with a median of 10 microns; 200 spores developed on agar under the same temperature and light conditions measured 8.5–14.5 microns with a median of 13 microns. Since little work has been performed in which the effects of various environmental factors upon spore size have been considered, in all probability the now recognized ranges of spore sizes may have to be altered for many species when carefully controlled cultural studies have been conducted. Like many other studies so necessary for our complete understanding of the Myxomycetes, such studies as those just alluded to must await the development of adequate culture techniques for a far greater number of species than are now being cultured.

Pigmentation

In color, spores may vary from colorless as in *Cribraria splendens* or *C. intricata* through tan, brown, yellow, purple, red, or pink to black as in *Badhamia macrocarpa*. The color of the spores (both in mass and in transmitted light) is another very useful characteristic in all identification work. As a matter of fact, the initial separation into orders of the subclass Myxogastres is based in large part upon spore color. Thus, the spore masses of members of the orders Physarales and Stemonitales are usually black or deep violaceous (rarely ferruginous or pallid), while the spore masses of members of the Liceales, Trichiales, and Echinosteliales are usually brown or yellow, although they are sometimes rosy but very rarely blackish-brown. The chemical nature of the pigments of myxomycete spores as such has never been established; however, Solacolu (1932) studied the pigments of mature fructifications of 26 species, and some spore pigments were undoubtedly included. Solacolu concluded that myxomycete pigments were not anthocyanins but were similar to the pigments that occur in higher fungi. In view of the variety of pigments that have been isolated from various true fungi (Gray, 1959; p. 305), Solacolu's conclusions, while throwing little or no light upon the exact nature of myxomycete spore pigments, might conceivably be used as evidence of a closer relationship of Myxomycetes to other fungi.

Lepeschkin (1923) analyzed the plasmodium of *Fuligo septica* and believed the plasmodial pigments to be related chemically to the anthocyanins. Seifriz and Zetzmann (1935) suggested that the plasmodial pigment of *Physarum polycephalum*, which behaves as a natural indicator of acidity, belongs to the group of respiratory pigments known as flavones, lyochromes, or flavins. Plasmodial pigments will be treated more fully in a later chapter, but it should be noted that, in view of the remarkable sequence of morphological events and the striking color changes that occur in the transformation of the plasmodium into fruiting bodies with mature spores, it would be rather surprising if it were demonstrated that spore pigments are chemically identical to plasmodial pigments.

The Spore Wall

The appearance of the spore wall differs considerably throughout the class. Thus, in *Lindbladia tubulina,* the spores are smooth or nearly so; in *Cribraria microcarpa,* minutely spinulose; in *Fuligo cinerea,* coarsely spinulose; in *Trichia botrytis,* minutely warted; in *Trichia affinis* and others, reticulated with an episporic network. In some species spore wall markings are quite constant and, hence, may serve as useful taxonomic characters. Alexopoulos (1958, 1960b) has shown that the unique spores of two of the four then known species of *Echinostelium* remain constant in their wall markings even when sporangia develop upon different substrates under different conditions. On the other hand, spore wall markings appear to be quite variable in some species. In a taxonomic study of three species of *Trichia,* which are separated principally on the basis of spore markings, Farr (1957a, 1958) found a complete gradation in wall markings from the completely and conspicuously reticulate markings of *T. favoginea* to those of *T. persimilis,* in which the spores are marked by elongate warts forming an irregular or fragmentary reticulation. Furthermore, Farr reported that such variation could be found in the spores of a single specimen. However, she produced no experimental evidence in support of her thesis and had no way of knowing whether the variations she found were genetically stable.

The chemical nature of the spore wall material has not been established with certainty, but on the basis of results obtained from the microchemical tests which he performed on the fruiting bodies of a number of myxomycete species, Boic (1925) concluded that the ground substance of the spore wall is pure cellulose. However, Kiesel (1930) later reported that plasmodia contain a material he termed myxoglucosan, which resembles cellulose and may be the basis for reports that spore walls contain cellulose. Goodwin's paper (1961) demonstrated the presence of cellulose in the spore walls as well as in the capillitium and stalks of three species of *Comatricha,* using both the iodine-potassium-iodide-sulfuric acid and the chlor-zinc-iodide reagents; however, a chitin test yielded negative results. Koevenig (1964) has described preliminary electron microscopy studies on the walls of germinating *Physarum gyrosum* spores and has reported that the electron micrographs suggest a tripartite wall with an electron-dense middle layer. Pigmentation of the spore wall obscured tests designed to determine its chemical nature, but results suggested the presence of a polysaccharide. Addition of cellulase to the germination fluid resulted in a shift from the split method to the pore method of germination. As a result of his more extensive electron microscope observations on *Didymium nigripes*, Schuster (1964a) reported that the spore walls of this species consist of an outer thin component and an inner thick component. From the results of his microchemical tests, Schuster suggested that the inner wall is cellulose-containing and the outer component might contain chitin. According to Ulrich (1943) chitin is not present in the Myxomycetes except possibly in the capillitium of *Stemonitis fusca*. This reviewer states, however, that keratin-like proteids have been reported in the capillitium, spore walls, and cysts of Myxomycetes. At present, our knowledge of the chemical composition of the fruiting structures of Myxomycetes is so incomplete that all statements regarding the composition of these structures must be placed in the category of hypotheses. However, since the affinities of the Myxomycetes have never been definitely established, it is imperative that there be further studies of the type conducted by Schuster and by Koevenig with the objective of establishing with certainty the chemical nature of the spore wall.

Number of Nuclei

It is impossible to generalize on the number of nuclei in myxomycete spores. With regard to the nuclear number in spores of the exosporous *Ceratiomyxa*, there seems to be general agreement. Thus, Olive (1907b), Jahn (1908), Wilson and Ross (1955), and McManus (1958) all report four nuclei per spore in *Ceratiomyxa*. It has often been assumed that spores of the Myxogastres are uninucleate, and there are sufficient reports of a number of species of this subclass to indicate that uninucleate spores are very common. Lister (1925) states that in most Mycetozoa each spore is provided with one nucleus, and Alexopoulos (1962) comments that spores are generally uninucleate. Skupienski (1929), in the report on his studies on *Didymium nigripes*, illustrates spores with only one nucleus, as do Howard (1931a) and Guttes, Guttes, and Rusch (1961) for *Physarum polycephalum*. Koevenig (1964) found the spores of *P. gyrosum* to be characteristically uninucleate, and he never observed the emergence of more than one protoplast from a spore. Similarly, Schuster (1964a), who made electron microscope observations on spore formation in *D. nigripes*, states that the protoplasm in the developing sporangium cleaves to give ultimately uninucleate spheres—the incipient spores. In her studies on *Clastoderma debaryanum*, McManus (1961b) found in the spore only one body that she considered to be a nucleus. In contrast to the above reports, Smith (1929b) observed two nuclei in some spores of several species of *Arcyria,* and Carroll (in Alexopoulos, 1966) has shown that there are at least eight nuclei in some spores of *Arcyria cinerea.* Dangeard (1947) found two or four nuclei in some maturing spores of *Didymium clavus.* In view of these divergent reports it would be best not to generalize regarding the nuclear number in spores. Since von Stosch (1935) has reported that meiosis occurs in the maturing spore of the heterothallic *D. nigripes,* with one nucleus disintegrating after each division, thus producing a uninucleate spore, and since Aldrich (1967) has noted disintegration of three of four nuclei in spores of *P. flavicomum,* it is possible that divergent views on the number of nuclei in a spore may be in part due to observations made by different investigators on spores at different stages of maturity.

Basal Bodies

The presence of basal bodies (centrioles) in myxomycete spores was first signalled by von Stosch (1935) who reported them in *Didymium iridis.* Schuster (1965b) failed to find such structures in sectioned spores of *D. nigripes* and *Physarum cinereum.* Very recently Aldrich (1967) published electron micrographs of thin sections of post-meiotic spores of *P. flavicomum* in which a basal body is clearly demonstrated (Fig. 2).

DISSEMINATION

There have been few studies concerned specifically with spore dissemination in the Myxomycetes, but as Alexopoulos (1963) has pointed out, ideas concerning this process may be based upon field observations, knowledge of the structural features of myxomycete fructifications, and knowledge obtained from organisms possessing structures similar to those of Myxomycetes. Brodie and Gregory (1953), while primarily interested in spore dispersal from cupulate plant structures, also studied spore dispersal from sporangia of seven species of Myxomycetes under conditions of known wind velocity. They found that in all experiments spores were blown from sporangia of *Badhamia utricularis, Comatricha typhoides, Craterium leucocephalum, C. minutum, Fuligo septica, Physarum nutans,* and *Trichia affinis* by a wind of velocity 0.5 meter per second. However, spores did not appear to be removed more easily from cupulate sporangia (i.e., *C. leucocephalum* and *C. minutum*) than from non-cupulate sporangia.

Ingold (1940) has described spore dissemination in *Trichia persimilis* in which, when the spores and capillitial threads have been exposed by

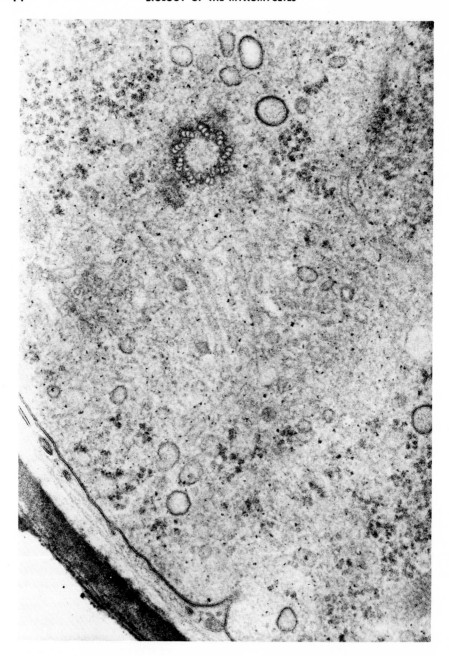

Fig. 2. *Physarum flavicomum.* Portion of post-meiotic spore showing basal body in cross-section. × 78,000. (Aldrich, 1967. Courtesy Henry Aldrich and Cell Research Institute, University of Texas at Austin.)

rupture of the peridium, the capillitial threads twist or untwist, varying with the humidity of the surrounding air. Strains which are set up between the closely massed threads are relieved as the ends spring free of the mass; spores adhering to the mass are thus thrown into the air. Although *T. persimilis* is not unique in the possession of hygroscopic elater-like capillitial threads, the majority of myxomycete species do not possess a capillitium of this type. Hence, the removal of spores from mature sporangia is more commonly due to actions other than elater movements. While wind is probably the major factor involved in spore dissemination over long distances, this has not been verified by the actual isolation and identification of myxomycete spores from the atmosphere. There is circumstantial evidence, however, that such spores are in the air. Van Overeem (1937) cultured *Physarum nutans* from rainwater collected in sterile vessels, and Pettersson (1940) reported spores of *Stemonitis fusca* and *Arcyria denudata* in rainwater. Brown, Larson, and Bold (1964) exposed synthetic agar to the air in various ways and in various parts of the United States (but chiefly in Austin, Texas), and found that myxomycete plasmodia developed not infrequently on the agar. Although spores were not actually observed on the agar, from the size of the plasmodia when first detected it seems probable that they originated from spores, although they may have developed from very small windblown sclerotial fragments. These investigators reported the isolation of "more than 16 species of Myxomycetes."

Alexopoulos (unpublished data, 1965) has isolated the following species from slides or rotorods exposed to the wind over Austin, Texas: *Arcyria incarnata, Badhamia gracilis, Diderma chondrioderma, Didymium iridis, D. nigripes, D. trachysporum, Fuligo cinerea, F. septica, Perichaena depressa, Physarella oblonga, Physarum auriscalpium, P. cinereum, P. compressum, P. gyrosum, P. pusillum, Stemonitis flavogenita,* and *S. fusca.* Koevenig (1961b) has shown that insects and other animals carry the spores of some species, but how important these agents are in spore dissemination is not known. There is no doubt that falling raindrops also aid in freeing spores from sporangia and in their transportation over short distances.

GERMINATION

In contrast to spore germination in the majority of the Eumycota, in which a more or less rigid or semirigid filamentous germ tube is formed, spore germination in the Myxomycetes results in the formation of motile protozoon-like structures (myxamoebae and swarm cells) which ultimately function as gametes. Apparently this phenomenon was first observed by deBary in 1854. This observation, followed by his elucidation of the unusual life history of the Myxomycetes (deBary, 1858), led to the removal of the major subclass (Myxogastres) from the Gasteromycetes where they had been placed by Fries (1829) and to their being considered as a separate and distinctive group.

Following deBary, a number of the earlier investigators also observed spore germination, as is evidenced by the reports of Hoffman (1859), Kent (1881), McClatchie (1894), and Durand (1894). Until recent times, however, the bulk of our information on the subject of myxomycete spore germination was provided by the works of deBary (1864), Jahn (1905), and Constantineanu (1907). More recently, extensive studies on spore germination have been conducted by Smith (1929b), Gilbert (1928a, 1928b, 1928c, 1929a, 1929b), Smart (1937), and Elliott (1949).

Initiation and Methods of Spore Germination

Although it has been the object of research by a number of investigators, there is no agreement yet with regard to what actually initiates spore germination. As had been noted earlier by deBary (1864), Jahn (1905) reported that there are two possible methods by which spores may germinate. In the first method, the spore wall ruptures in a wedge-shaped split which widens and allows the protoplasmic contents to emerge. In the second method, a small jagged aperture appears in the wall and the spore contents slowly move out through the aperture (Fig. 3). In the first method, the spore walls have the appearance of having been split open as a result of pressure within, while in the second method a portion of the spore wall seems to have been dissolved or at least softened. These observations were later confirmed by Gilbert (1928c) who reported that while some species showed transitional conditions, he also had observed the two well-defined methods of germination reported earlier by Jahn.

Jahn attributed cell-wall rupture to pressure from within, but he also believed that a glycogen-digesting enzyme was in part responsible since such an enzyme would catalyze the hydrolysis of insoluble glycogen to soluble maltose. This would bring about a reduction in water concentration in the spore contents and, hence, would lead to a condition in which water would diffuse into the spore in greater amounts. Such movement of water into the spore would create pressures that eventually could cause rupture of the cell wall.

Skupienski (1920) agreed with Jahn in part, since he regarded myxomycete spore germination as a purely osmotic phenomenon. However, this investigator did not accept Jahn's view that enzyme action might also be involved. Constantineanu (1907) did not agree that either os-

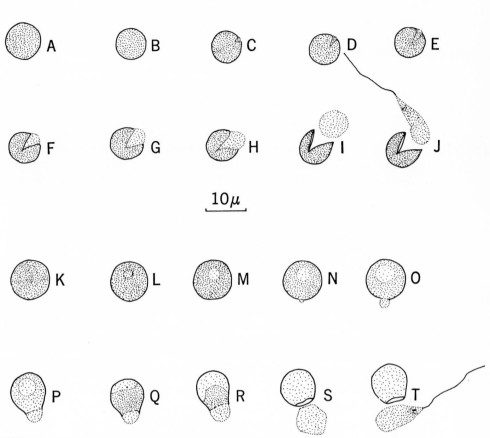

Fig. 3. A–J. Germination by the split method (*Fuligo septica*). K–T. Germination by the pore method (*Dictydiaethalium plumbeum*). (Redrawn from Gilbert, 1928c.)

motic pressure or enzyme action is initially involved in spore germination, since he found that spores germinated in higher percentages in mineral salts solution than they did in distilled water.

Pinoy (1902, 1903, 1907) advanced the hypothesis that bacterial action is necessary to soften the spore walls and, thus, to facilitate the germination of myxomycete spores. However, no other investigators have produced evidence in support of Pinoy's idea, and the hypothesis is generally considered to be unacceptable. Since McClatchie (1894) as well as Skupienski (1920) and Gilbert (1928a) reported that the spores of certain species may germinate in distilled water in less than one hour, it is difficult to understand how a few bacteria could exert such an influence in so short a period of time.

More recently, McManus (1958) has reported that in *Ceratiomyxa fruticulosa* spore germination involves the softening and gradual disappearance of the cell wall—an observation that might indicate the necessity for assuming that there are three distinct types of spore germination in the Myxomycetes.

On the basis of information now available there is no doubt that myxomycete spores germinate principally by one of the first two methods described above. One would expect that for a given species the method of germination would always be the same but that this is not necessarily true is evidenced by the work of Smart (1937). He found that if spores of *Reticularia splendens* (*E. rozeanum*), which ordinarily germinate by the pore method, are held at a temperature above that which is maximum for germination and are then placed at a temperature which is optimum for the species, the spores germinate by a wedge-shaped split. Unfortunately, the results obtained by Smart may be used to support either the osmotic pressure hypothesis or the enzyme hypothesis, since it may be argued that elevated temperature may either inactivate the responsible enzymes or lead to a faster diffusion rate of water.

The results reported by Koevenig (1964) are of considerable interest. He found that spores of *Physarum gyrosum* germinated by the split method; however, when an aqueous solution of Calbiochem 21947 cellulase (0.1% w/v) was used as the germination medium, the spores germinated by the pore method. Although the answer to the question concerning the chemical nature of the spore wall is by no means final, these results add strength to the view that the wall is, at least in part, cellulose.

At this stage of our information it is possible to state with certainty only that the very first step in the sequence of events that results in germination is the entry of water. Whether this in itself initiates germination, as implied by Skupienski, or is merely one of a series of events that ultimately leads to the initiation of germination is not known. That some unknown internal factor may be involved in the initiation of spore germination is evidenced by the observations of Wilson and Cadman (1928), who noted that single spores of *Reticularia lycoperdon* failed to germinate but that abundant germination occurred in cultures in which many spores were present. Smart (1937) investigated the germination of single spores of 15 species from 12 genera and obtained faster germination or higher percentages of germination in nearly all instances when single spores were placed in a medium in which many spores of the species under test had already germinated. Data from Smart's work are presented in Table 1. In view of his results, Smart agrees with Wilson and Cadman's hypothesis that an autocatalytic agent is excreted by spores and must be present in relatively high concentration to permit spore germination. This point needs further investigation before it can be

Table 1. Germination of single spores. (Smart, 1937.)

Species	Number of Spores Germinating Lot 1 (10 Spores) (Fresh Medium)	Lot 2 (10 Spores) (Previous Germination Medium)
Fuligo septica	9 after 3 hours	10 in 45 minutes
Badhamia utricularis	8 after 4 days	7 in 2½ days
Physarum cinereum	9 after 7 days	9 in 6 days
Physarum didermoides	7 after 8 days	8 in 5 days
Physarum polycephalum	6 after 3 days	8 in 15 hours
Stemonitis fusca	3 after 2 days	9 in 1 day
Stemonitis axifera	4 after 1 day	8 in 8 hours
Comatricha pulchella	3 after 5 days	7 in 2½ days
Dictydium cancellatum	2 after 18 days	2 after 18 days
Enteridium rozeanum	0 in 2 weeks	10 in 30 minutes
Reticularia lycoperdon	0 in 2 weeks	8 in 15 minutes
Dictydiaethalium plumbeum	0 in 2 weeks	7 in 3 hours
Lycogala epidendrum	3 after 2 days	8 in 3 hours
Perichaena depressa	8 after 2 days	9 in 1 day
Arcyria denudata	6 after 6 days	6 in 6 days

assumed that some unknown growth factor plays a major role in the initiation of germination, since Scholes (1962) found that with more dilute suspensions of spores of *Fuligo septica* rate of germination was faster and percentage of germination higher. Gehenio and Luyet (1950) have reported single spore germination for *Physarella oblonga,* and Kerr and Sussman (1958) apparently had no difficulty in obtaining germination of single spores of *Didymium nigripes.* Henney (1967) germinated a very large number of single spores of *Physarum flavicomum,* and Wollman (1966) germinated single spores of *Comatricha laxa, C. nodulifera,* and *C. typhoides.* It is important that single-spore studies be conducted with a great many additional species since only by determining whether a plasmodium will develop from a single spore or a single myxamoeba can it be determined whether a species is heterothallic (Dee, 1960; Collins, 1961; Henney, 1967).

Longevity of Spores and Germination Time

How long spores will remain viable once they have matured undoubtedly depends in part upon the environmental conditions existent at the time they were formed. In addition to this type of variation, spore longevity would also be expected to vary from species to species. Hoffman (1859) germinated spores that were four years old, and deBary (1864) germinated some that were six years old. Smith (1929a) studied 21 species representing all groups and found that some spores remained viable for 32 years; he later extended this to 44 years (Macbride and Martin, 1934). Smith found no correlation between the ages of his specimens and their percentages of germination, but Elliott (1949) obtained germination of spores from herbarium specimens as old as 61 years and noted that age reduced percentage of germination in all of the species investigated. More recently Erbisch (1964) reported germination of 68-year-old spores of *Lycogala flavofuscum*, 61-year-old spores of *Fuligo septica*, and 75-year-old spores of *Hemitrichia clavata*.

Since different investigators have frequently employed different methods for testing the germinability of spores, and none had known the exact set of environmental conditions under which the spores they were testing had developed, it is not surprising that differences of opinion regarding the longevity of spores of a particular species have been expressed. For example, deBary (1864) reported that spores of *Metatrichia vesparium* remain viable for only seven months, while Gilbert (1929a) obtained germination of spores of this species when they were four years old. Different investigators also have reported markedly different times required for germination of the same species, as is evidenced by the results of Alexopoulos (1963) and Smart (1937) which are presented in Table 2.

Table 2.   Time required for germination of myxomycete spores.
[Based on results of Smart (1937) and Alexopoulos (1963).]

	Shortest Average Time for Germination	
Species	Smart	Alexopoulos
Arcyria cinerea	8 days	24 hours
Didymium iridis	3 days	17 hours
Physarum viride	5 days	74 hours

It is quite possible that in some species the spores may not remain viable for very long periods of time. Gilbert (1935), while studying the germination of spores of *Ceratiomyxa fruticulosa*, found that spores less than two days old which had not been allowed to dry required but four hours to germinate. Spores eight days old required eight hours to germinate, and older spores required sixteen hours or more. Gilbert also noted that percentage of germination decreased sharply with increase in age. From these observations it seems probable that spores of this species do not have a great longevity. If this is correct, then this innate characteristic of the spores bears no relationship to the relative abundance and distribution of myxomycete species, since *C. fruticulosa* is worldwide in distribution and may well be the most common species of all.

Maturation Period

Spores of many filamentous fungi are capable of germination almost immediately after they are formed, while others appear to require an after-ripening or maturation period. There is evidence that similar situations involving dormancy occur in the Myxomycetes. For example, spores of *Physarum pulcherrimum* will germinate as soon as the sporangium is mature, whereas spores from similar collections of *Lycogala epidendrum* do not germinate. According to Gilbert (1929a) spores of the latter species do not germinate normally until they are at least one month old. Gilbert also cites an example in which two-week-old spores of *Arcyria oerstedtii* gave rise only to an occasional swarm cell, but three months later spores from the same collection showed 100 per cent germination. Studies similar to this should be conducted using spores from the same sporangium, since it has been the experience of most collectors to find perfectly matured as well as immature sporangia in a collection of fruiting bodies formed from a single plasmodium. Gilbert also noted a striking effect of aging upon the germinability of spores of *Reticularia splendens* (*E. rozeanum*); data obtained with this species are presented in Table 3.

Table 3. Relation of spore age to rate and percentage of germination in *Reticularia splendens (E. rozeanum).* (Gilbert, 1929b.)

Number of Specimens	Spore Age	Percentage of Germination
3	Fresh	Occasional
1	6 months	5–10%
2	1 year	90–100%
1	1 year 4 months	70–80%
1	2 years	90–100%

Since physiological maturity need not necessarily parallel morphological maturity, and in view of the reports of Gilbert, it seems evident that some myxomycete spores may require a further maturation period even though to all appearances the spores are mature. Most collectors attempt to obtain freshly formed fruiting bodies rather than old and weathered ones, and so it is quite possible that the inability to obtain spore germination of certain species may be due in part to the fact that spores were not of sufficient age. Another factor which may be responsible for the divergent findings of different investigators is that few besides Elliott (1949) have made special efforts to insure that the spore walls were thoroughly and immediately wetted. Wettability of the spore wall may vary from species to species, and reports of failure to obtain germination of the spores of a particular species may be due to the fact that the investigator did not take this point into consideration.

External Factors Inducing Germination

The effects of various external factors upon spore germination have been considered by a number of investigators. The most extensive work is that of Smart (1937), who studied spore germination in 70 species and varieties of Myxomycetes in relation to nutrition, pH, temperature, alternate wetting and drying, and light. More recently, Elliott (1949) conducted studies on the germination of spores of 59 species in 30 genera. All families except the Dianemaceae and Collodermataceae were represented in Elliott's collections, and he observed germination in all species except *Echinostelium minutum*. Although Elliot was primarily interested in obtaining swarm cells for flagellar studies, he also investigated the efficacy of various wetting agents and developed a simple technique involving the use of a one per cent solution of bile salts.

Available Nutrients. Alexopoulos (1960b) reported the successful germination of spores of *Echinostelium minutum*, but only those from sporangia that had developed on a leaf of *Ulmus americana* in moist chamber culture. When spores were taken from sporangia that had developed on a substrate other than elm leaf, Alexopoulos encountered the same difficulties previously encountered by Elliott. Olive (1960), however, obtained germination of spores of this species which had been obtained from sporangia that had developed on old milkweed pods, but he noted that when the cultures grew and fruited on Difco cornmeal-dextrose agar containing 0.1 per cent yeast extract there were also present an encapsulated yeast and a bacterium derived from the natural substrate.

Although it has been known for many years that spores of most Myxomycetes will germinate in distilled water or in tap water, Smart (1937) demonstrated that rate of germination is faster and percentage of germination greater when spores are sown in weak decoctions of natural substrata. Of the various materials that Smart used, extracts of rotting oak wood, pine wood, pine wood and bark, hay, oak leaves, pine needles, and humus favored germination in the greater number of species studied. Smart states that some vital change in the protoplasm is promoted by the presence of nutrient materials in the germination medium and that this change causes water to be absorbed by the protoplasm. This in turn creates the internal pressure that ruptures the cell wall. Constantineanu (1907), in addition to studying the effects of natural substrates upon germination, also studied the effects of various mineral solutions on this process. He placed spores in Knop's solution of acid reaction and found that in dilutions up to four per cent, percentage of germination of *Didymium squamulosum, Amaurochaete atra,* and *Fuligo septica* was higher than in distilled water. Smart repeated Constantineanu's experiments and obtained similar results with *Stemonitis splendens, S. axifera, S. fusca, Comatricha flaccida, C. typhoides, C. nigra, Arcyria denudata, A. cinerea, A. digitata (A. cinerea), Perichaena depressa, Physarum pulcherrimum,* and *P. didermoides.*

Cooke and Holt (1928) found that sugars and proteins were most favorable for spore germination in the species they studied, and Smart stated that in general the spores of most Myxomycetes germinate better in organic solutions than in inorganic ones. It should be recalled that Constantineanu did not agree that either enzyme action or osmotic pressure was primarily responsible for the initiation of spore germination and found that it was impossible to explain the difference between the influence of mineral and organic substrates on spore germination on the basis of osmotic pressure of the medium alone. Smart concluded that chemical factors are more important than osmotic factors in spore germination.

Acidity of Medium. For his studies on the relation of pH to spore germination Smart (1937) used 29 representative species. In each instance, the medium previously found most suitable for germination of the species under test was used, and 18 solutions ranging from pH 2.0 to pH 10.5 were prepared. The pH optima for all species under test were between pH 4.5 and pH 7.0, although the range in which germination of spores of all test species occurred was pH 4.0 to pH 8.0. If the species tested by Smart are representative of the class, it may be concluded that the germination of myxomycete spores in general is favored by a medium of slightly acid reaction. The graphs prepared by Smart indicate that some species have a rather broad optimum range whereas in others the optimum is quite sharply delimited (Fig. 4). Abe (1941) studied the relation of pH to spore germination in *Fuligo septica* var. *rufa, Reticularia lycoperdon,* and *Physarum gyrosum* and reported that even in very weak concentrations free acids inhibit germination; however, in buffered solutions spores germinate above pH 4.0. Thus, Abe's findings are in accord with those of Smart who reported a pH range for germination of 4.0–8.0 in all of the species he studied.

Temperature. Since temperature has a marked effect upon all biological processes, it can be assumed that it will also affect spore germination. DeBary (1884) noted that spring and summer temperatures were most favorable for spore germination in temperate climates, and Constantineanu (1907) reported that moist spores of *Dictydium cancellatum, Physarum didermoides,* and *Lycogala epidendrum* germinated more rapidly at 30° C than at 18° to 20° C and not at all at 35° C. Aside from a

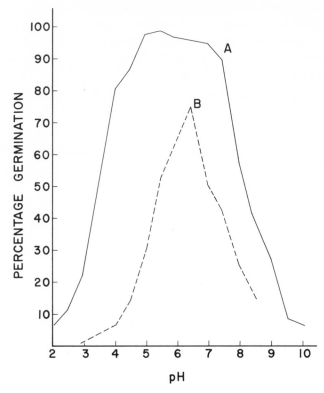

Fig. 4. The relation of pH to spore germination. A. *Fuligo septica*. B. *Comatricha laxa*. (Redrawn from Smart, 1937.)

few experiments in which Constantineanu held spores of *Didymium squamulosum* at 50° C and then measured time required for germination and percentage of germination at room temperature, little seems to have been done on the subject of temperature relations until the work of Smart appeared. This investigator established the cardinal points for spore germination in 70 species and varieties by means of hanging drop cultures which were incubated at 13 different temperature points ranging from 0° to 50° C. Smart found that optimum temperatures for spore germination of all species tested were in the range of 22° to 30° C, with the majority germinating at the higher temperatures of this range. Temperature range for germination was found to be 2° to 36° C, but Smart noted that at 10° C or lower and at 32° C or higher, rate of germination was slower and percentage of germination was greatly reduced. Differences between species were apparent; e.g., spores of *Fuligo septica* germinated over the temperature range of 2° to 36° C, while those of

Cribraria elegans germinated only in the range of 10° to 30° C. Scholes (1962) found that 30-minute exposures to low temperatures (−20° and 2° C) decreased the subsequent germination of *F. septica* spores at 25° C, and that exposures at 60° C for longer than 5 minutes resulted in failure to germinate.

Wetting–Drying Cycle. Lister (1901) and Jahn (1905) both reported that alternate wetting and drying of spores increased the percentage of germination in some species and induced germination in other species when they ordinarily would not germinate. Gilbert (1929a) secured germination in *Trichia* and *Hemitrichia* by alternate wetting and drying of spores, and Smart (1937) reported that alternate wetting and drying of the spores "stimulated" germination in certain species, especially those of the orders Trichiales and Cribrariales. Elliott (1949) found that of the species he tested, alternate wetting and drying had beneficial effects only on spore germination of *Physarum flavicomum*. Jahn believed that alternate wetting and drying activated the enzyme glycogenase which catalyzes the conversion of glycogen to maltose. Smart agreed with Jahn that alternate wetting and drying results in enzyme activation, but he favored the idea that the enzyme activated is not glycogenase but an enzyme concerned directly with softening of the cell wall.

Light. Cooke and Holt (1928) have inferred that the spores of *Stemonitis splendens* var. *flaccida* and *Comatricha flaccida* (now united under the latter name) germinate better in darkness than in light; however, Smart reported that the influence of light upon germination was negligible insofar as he was able to observe. Using the same organisms as Cooke and Holt, Smart could find no differences in time required for germination or percentage of germination between spores kept in darkness and those kept in the indirect light of the laboratory.

Areas of Needed Research

In spite of the fact that during the past century a very considerable number of investigators have concerned themselves with one aspect or another of the problem of spore germination in Myxomycetes, our knowledge of this subject is still far from complete. On the basis of present information certain generalizations seem permissible, but it should be borne in mind that as further information becomes available such generalizations may have to be revised. The spores of a sufficiently representative number of Myxomycetes have now been germinated (Table 4) to indicate that, with one or two exceptions, there probably are no special problems attendant on the germination of spores of Myxomycetes in general.

Table 4.   Species of Myxomycetes for which spore germination has been reported by one or more investigators or has been achieved in the authors' laboratories.

Amaurochaete atra (Alb. & Schw.) Rost.
Arcyria cinerea (Bull.) Pers.
Arcyria denudata (L.) Wetts.
Arcyria ferruginea Sauter
Arcyria incarnata (Pers.) Pers.
Arcyria nutans (Bull.) Grev.
Arcyria oerstedtii Rost.
Arcyria pomiformis (Leers.) Rost.
Arcyria stipata (Schw.) A. Lister
Badhamia affinis Rost.
Badhamia capsulifera (Bull.) Pers.
Badhamia gracilis Macbr.
Badhamia lilacina (Fries) Rost.
Badhamia macrocarpa (Ces.) Rost.
Badhamia obovata (Peck) S. J. Smith
Badhamia ovispora Racib.
Badhamia panicea (Fries) Rost.
Badhamia utricularis (Bull.) Berk.
Calomyxa metallica (Berk.) Nieuwl.
Ceratiomyxa fruticulosa (Muell.) Macbr.
Cienkowskia reticulata (Alb. & Schw.) Rost.
Clastoderma debaryanum Blytt
Comatricha elegans (Racib.) Lister
Comatricha fimbriata G. Lister & Cran
Comatricha flaccida (List.) Morg.
Comatricha irregularis Rex
Comatricha laxa Rost.
Comatricha longa Peck
Comatricha nigra (Pers.) Schroet.
Comatricha nodulifera Wollman & Alexop.
Comatricha pulchella (Bab.) Rost.
Comatricha typhoides (Bull.) Rost.
Cornuvia serpula Rost.
Craterium leucocephalum (Pers.) Ditm.
Cribraria aurantiaca Schrad.
Cribraria elegans Berk. & Curt.
Cribraria intricata Schrad.
Cribraria minutissima Schw.
Cribraria tenella Schrad.
Diachea leucopodia (Bull.) Rost.
Diachea splendens Peck
Dictydiaethalium plumbeum (Schum.) Rost.
Dictydium cancellatum (Batsch) Macbr.
Diderma effusum (Schw.) Morg.
Diderma globosum Pers.
Diderma hemisphericum (Bull.) Hornem.
Diderma radiatum (L.) Morg.
Diderma testaceum (Schrad.) Pers.

Didymium clavus (Alb. & Schw.) Rabenh.
Didymium difforme (Pers.) S. F. Gray
Didymium iridis (Ditm.) Fr.
Didymium melanospermum (Pers.) Macbr.
Didymium nigripes (Link) Fr.
Didymium serpula Fr.
Didymium squamulosum (Alb. & Schw.) Fr.
Didymium trachysporum G. Lister
Echinostelium cribrarioides Alexop.
Echinostelium elachiston Alexop.
Echinostelium minutum deBary
Enerthenema papillatum (Pers.) Rost.
Erionema aureum Penzig
Fuligo cinerea (Schw.) Morg.
Fuligo septica (L.) Weber
Hemitrichia clavata (Pers.) Rost.
Hemitrichia serpula (Scop.) Rost.
Lamproderma arcyrioides (Somm.) Rost.
Lamproderma arcyrionema Rost.
Lamproderma columbinum (Pers.) Rost.
Lamproderma muscorum (Lév.) Hagelstein
Lamproderma scintillans (Berk. & Br.) Morg.
Leocarpus fragilis (Dicks.) Rost.
Lepidoderma tigrinum (Schrad.) Rost.
Licea biforis Morg.
Licea pedicellata Gilb.
Lindbladia tubulina Fries
Lycogala epidendrum (L.) Fries
Lycogala flavofuscum (Ehrenb.) Rost.
Macbrideola decapillata Gilb.
Metatrichia vesparium (Batsch) Nann.-Brem.
Mucilago crustacea Wigg.
Oligonema flavidum (Peck) Peck
Perichaena chrysosperma (Currey) Lister
Perichaena corticalis (Batsch) Rost.
Perichaena depressa Libert.
Perichaena vermicularis (Schw.) Rost.
Physarella oblonga (Berk. & Curt.) Morg.
Physarina echinospora Thind & Manocha
Physarum aeneum (Lister) R. E. Fries
Physarum albescens Macbr.
Physarum auriscalpium Cooke
Physarum bilgramii Hagelstein
Physarum bivalve Pers.
Physarum bogoriense Racib.

Table 4. Continued.

Physarum cinereum (Batsch) Pers.	*Physarum serpula* Morg.
Physarum compressum Alb. & Schw.	*Physarum straminipes* Lister
Physarum crateriforme Petch	*Physarum tenerum* Rex
Physarum didermoides (Pers.) Rost.	*Physarum virescens* Ditmar
Physarum digitatum G. Lister & Farqu.	*Physarum viride* (Bull.) Pers.
Physarum flavicomum Berk.	*Reticularia olivacea* (Eherenb.) Fries
Physarum globuliferum (Bull.) Pers.	*Reticularia splendens* (Rost.) Nann.-Brem.
Physarum gyrosum Rost.	*Stemonitis axifera* (Bull.) Macbr.
Physarum leucophaeum Fries	*Stemonitis flavogenita* Jahn
Physarum leucopus Link	*Stemonitis fusca* Roth
Physarum melleum (Berk & Br.) Massee	*Stemonitis hyperopta* Meylan
Physarum nicaraguense Macbr.	*Stemonitis splendens* Rost.
Physarum notabile Macbr.	*Trichia botrytis* (J. R. Gmel.) Pers.
Physarum nucleatum Rex	*Trichia contorta* (Ditm.) Rost.
Physarum oblatum Macbr.	*Trichia decipiens* (Pers.) Macbr.
Physarum polycephalum Schw.	*Trichia favoginea* (Batsch) Pers.
Physarum pulcherrimum Berk & Rav.	*Trichia floriformis* (Schw.) G. Lister
Physarum pusillum (Berk. & Curt.) Lister	*Trichia persimilis* Karst.
Physarum rigidum (G. Lister) G. Lister	*Trichia scabra* Rost.
Physarum roseum Berk. & Br.	*Trichia varia* (Pers.) Pers.
	Tubifera ferruginosa (Batsch) J. F. Gmel.

The question concerning the factor or factors initially responsible for spore germination remains unanswered. In view of the preponderance of evidence, there is no question but that spores germinate by one of two separate and distinct methods. However, we will never know why this difference exists until the nature of the factor or factors that initiate the process of germination is clearly understood, and until the chemical nature of the cell wall has been definitely established.

The question of longevity of spores needs reexamination using spores from a variety of species in which the fruiting structures have been developed under rigidly controlled environmental conditions. On the basis of existent reports, spores of *Hemitrichia clavata* appear to have the greatest longevity (75 years) of any myxomycete studied thus far. This may be entirely fortuitous, however, since *H. clavata* merely may have been the oldest specimen in which spore germination was observed in the herbarium to which the investigator had access. Perhaps it is true that *H. clavata* does have the greatest longevity of any myxomycete, but it is difficult to understand why this particular species should be unique in this respect. It should be borne in mind that in nearly all studies of myxomycete spore germination virtually nothing is known concerning the conditions under which the spores were formed or stored. Similarly, the problem of dormancy in spores of certain myxomycete species needs further examination, since existent reports suggest that, at least in certain species, spores will not germinate even though they are morphologically mature until after they have undergone an after-ripening period.

From the foregoing brief account it is obvious that while at this time we are in possession of a good working knowledge of myxomycete spore germination, there remain sufficient unanswered questions to occupy the time and utilize the research energies of myxomycete specialists for many years to come. Here, as well as quite frequently throughout the rest of this book, the necessity for the development of techniques for culturing many more species in pure culture on chemically defined media becomes apparent.

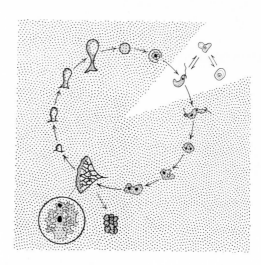

3

Myxamoebae, Swarm Cells, and Microcysts

With the germination of the spores the active, haploid phase of the life cycle of the Myxomycetes begins. This consists of myxamoebae, swarm cells, and, under certain environmental conditions, microcysts, and it ends, as we shall see in the next chapter, with the formation of the zygotes.

In heterothallic species, the haploid stage can be maintained indefinitely in the laboratory by culturing different mating types in separate containers. Thus, the haploid and diploid stages of heterothallic Myxomycetes provide exceptionally good experimental material for the study of ploidy and its effects on the developmental physiology of organisms.

NUMBER AND TYPE OF PROTOPLASTS ISSUING FROM THE SPORE

Germinating spores give rise to one to four and occasionally more myxamoebae or swarm cells. DeBary (1864) was the first to note that more than one protoplast may emerge from a spore of *Didymium squamulosum* and of *D. difforme*, but since that time this observation has been repeated with a number of species by various investigators. The most extensive study of this problem is probably that of Smith (1929b), who observed germination of the spores of 62 species. In 33 of these,

Table 5. Number of swarm cells issuing from germinating spores of Myxomycetes. (Smith, 1929b.)

Species	No. Swarm Cells	Observer	Date
Fuligo septica (L.) Gmel.	1–4	E. C. Smith	
Badhamia ovispora Racib.	1–2	E. Jahn	February 1928
Badhamia panicea (Fr.) Rost.	1–4	E. C. Smith	
Badhamia orbiculata Rex	1–8	E. C. Smith	
Badhamia magna Peck	1–4	E. C. Smith	
		F. A. Gilbert	June, 1928
Badhamia utricularis (Bull.) Berk.	1–4	E. C. Smith	
Badhamia lilacina (Fr.) Rost.	1–4	F. A. Gilbert	June, 1928
		E. C. Smith	
Badhamia rubiginosa (Chev.) Rost.	1–4	E. C. Smith	
Physarum serpula Morg.	1–2	F. A. Gilbert	June, 1928
		E. C. Smith	
Physarum cinereum (Batsch) Pers.	1–4	E. C. Smith	
Physarum virescens Ditm.	1–2	F. A. Gilbert	
		E. C. Smith	
Physarum didermoides Rost. var. *lividum* List.	1–2	E. C. Smith	
Physarum leucopus Link	1–2	F. A. Gilbert	June, 1928
Physarum notabile Macbr.	1–4	E. C. Smith	
Physarum fulvum List.	1–4	E. C. Smith	
Physarum compressum A. & S.	1–4	F. A. Gilbert	June, 1928
Craterium leucocephalum (Pers.) Ditm.	1–2	E. C. Smith	
Mucilago spongiosa (Leyss.) Morg.	1–4	F. A. Gilbert	June, 1928
		E. C. Smith	
Mucilago spongiosa var. *solida* Sturgis	1–4	E. C. Smith	
Didymium melanospermum Macbr.	1–2	E. C. Smith	
Didymium squamulosum (A. & S.) Fr.	1–2	E. C. Smith	
Didymium nigripes (Link) Fr.	1–4	W. Heitzmanowna	1922
Didymium difforme Duby	1–2	F. X. Skupienski	1927
Diderma effusum (Schw.) Morg.	1–2	E. C. Smith	
Diderma radiatum (L.) Morg.	1–2	E. C. Smith	
Lepidoderma tigrinum (Schrad.) Rost.	1–4	E. C. Smith	
Stemonitis fusca (Roth) Rost.	1–2	E. C. Smith	
Stemonitis flavogenita Jahn	1–2	E. C. Smith	
Stemonitis splendens Rost.	1–2	E. C. Smith	
Comatricha nigra Schroeter	1–4	E. J. Schwartz	1914
Enerthenema papillatum (Pers.) Rost.	1–2	E. C. Smith	
Lamproderma violaceum (Fr.) Rost.	1–4	E. C. Smith	
Hemitrichia serpula (Scop.) Rost.	1–4	E. C. Smith	
Hemitrichia vesparium (Batsch) Macbr.	1–2	E. C. Smith	
Hemitrichia clavata (Pers.) Rost.	1–4	E. C. Smith	
Trichia persimilis Karst	1–2	E. C. Smith	
Trichia favoginea (Batsch) Pers.	1–2	E. C. Smith	
Trichia botrytis Pers.	1–4	E. C. Smith	

some spores produced more than one protoplast. Table 5 is taken from Smith's paper and lists the species known, up to that time, to exhibit this phenomenon. Smith noted that the emergence of more than one protoplast from a spore is much more frequent in some species than in others. In some species four swarm cells issue from each spore regularly; in others, the overwhelming majority of the spores produce only one.

In more recent years, Ross (1957b) and Koevenig (1961a, c, 1964) are the only investigators who have paid any attention to this point. Ross states that in all 19 species he studied "all spores produced from one to four cells at germination." Koevenig's observations on *Physarum gyrosum* indicate that only a single cell usually issues from a germinating spore, but that in *Fuligo cinerea* two protoplasts may emerge. The basic reason for the multiple emergence of swarm cells from single spores is not clear. It has been postulated that myxomycete spores are uninucleate at maturity, and that a mitotic nuclear division followed by cytokinesis occurs in some spores producing two protoplasts which emerge at germination. Direct evidence for this phenomenon has been obtained recently by Koevenig (1961a), who filmed karyokinesis and cytokinesis in, and the subsequent emergence of two protoplasts from, a spore of *Fuligo cinerea*.

The number of nuclei in mature spores of Myxomycetes prior to germination, however, needs further investigation. Smith (1929b) observed two nuclei in some spores of several species of *Arcyria* and as many as eight protoplasts issuing from a spore of *Badhamia orbiculata* (now *B. affinis*). As we have already noted, Carroll (in Alexopoulos, 1966) has demonstrated that some spores of *Arcyria cinerea* contain eight nuclei. There is also good evidence (see Chapter 4) that young myxomycete spores may become quadrinucleate, and that some nuclei degenerate during the spore maturation process. Inasmuch as the number of protoplasts issuing from a spore is a function of the spore phase of the nuclear cycle, a thorough investigation of spores in many species, coupled with careful germination experiments, is necessary to give us the desired explanation.

In summary, we may say that in the endosporous species the number of cells produced by a germinating spore varies for different spores even in the same species, but that there appear to be strong tendencies in particular species for individual spores to produce either one or more than one naked cell.

Gilbert (1935) has shown that in *Ceratiomyxa*, the spore, upon germination, produces a quadrinucleate globose protoplast which cleaves into four uninucleate cells. These divide once more to form an octette of cells, each of which becomes flagellate and swims away. This development has been confirmed in part by McManus (1958) and wholly by the Sansomes (1961).

FLAGELLATION

The amoeboid cell that issues from a germinating myxomycete spore may be a swarm cell equipped with flagella, or it may be a non-flagellate myxamoeba. The important point to note here is that it appears that all such cells in all species of true Myxomycetes are potentially flagellate. The spores of enough species have been germinated to permit us to generalize on this point with a reasonable degree of certainty without precluding, of course, that some exceptions may still be found. The discovery by Aldrich (1967 and unpubl.) of basal bodies in the spores of *Didymium iridis* and *Physarum flavicomum*, as noted in Chapter 2, gives added support to the fundamental character of flagellation in the Myxomycetes, which differentiates them from the Acrasiales in which neither flagella nor basal bodies have been found.

Nevertheless, it has been reported (Alexopoulos, 1960b) that *Echinostelium minutum* is able to complete its developmental cycle from spore to spore without ever forming flagella, and that it is probable that certain other species may be able to dispense with the flagellated stage altogether. One may speculate that in no species whose general life cycle fits the pattern that Ross (1957b) has called the "briefly flagellate type" is a flagellate stage required, and that such species may possibly represent a stage in the current evolution of the Myxomycetes leading eventually to an aflagellate life cycle.

The stimulus that initiates the formation of flagella is not known. Kerr (1960), who studied the kinetics of flagellar formation in his strain of *Didymium nigripes*, believes that an aqueous medium alone may be sufficient to stimulate formation of flagella in this organism, and Aldrich (1968) states that the myxamoebae of *Physarum flavicomum* released from the spores on an agar surface undergo synchronous transformation into swarm cells when distilled water is added to the culture. Kerr (1960) obtained no evidence that light, sudden change in pH, or washing amoebae free of nutrients or of bacteria had any effect. To study the process of flagellation, Kerr spread spores of *Didymium nigripes* together with *Aerobacter aerogenes* on SMB medium consisting of 1 g yeast extract, 10 g glucose, 10 g bacto peptone, 1 g $MgSO_4 \cdot 7 H_2O$, and 0.96 g K_2HPO_4, and incubated the cultures at 23° C. The spores germinated, and the large population of myxamoebae which covered the plate in three days was harvested, suspended in distilled water, and washed three times in a refrigerated centrifuge. Optimal conditions for flagella formation were obtained by incubating myxamoebae in a 0.05 solution of $NaHCO_3$ at pH 9.1 or a 0.05 M solution of Na_2HPO_4 at pH 8.2. Under these conditions the entire population became flagellated within 60 minutes. Flagellation was prevented by $NaHCO_3$ concentration of 0.1 M or above.

In an attempt to ascertain the effect of age of myxamoebae on flagellation, myxamoebae were harvested in the logarithmic phase of growth, at the cessation of feeding, and in the stationary growth phase. Myxamoebae in the exponential phase of growth, when washed almost completely free of bacteria, developed flagella as rapidly as those harvested from plates on which the bacterial layer had just cleared (Kerr, 1965a). However, Kerr's results indicate that in the presence of a large number of living bacterial cells flagellation is inhibited. He attributes this effect to the consumption of O_2 by the living bacterial cells. Inasmuch as the same effect was produced when washed amoebae were kept under N_2, and 10^{-4} M 2,4-Dinitrophenol was tested, the conclusion was reached that the flagellation process requires oxidative phosphorylation.

Streptomycin inhibits flagellation in M/200 pH 6.2 phosphate buffer in direct proportion to its concentration. In the absence of the drug, flagella develop within an hour or two. The addition of 10–100 μg/ml of streptomycin to the medium inhibits flagellation in *Didymium nigripes* and *Physarella oblonga*. Ten μg tyrothrycin/ml, 50 μg acriflavin/ml, and 10 μg cycloheximide/ml also inhibit flagella formation in *D. nigripes* (Kerr 1961, 1965a).

Amoeba–Swarm Cell Relationship

The amoebic and swarm-cell stages of the Myxomycetes are interconvertible in many species. Whereas in the absence of free water the protoplasts remain in the myxamoebal stage, in a liquid environment they become flagellated. Nevertheless, supplying or withholding water does not necessarily control flagellation in all species. Ross (1957b) has described three types of life cycle, which he has named *briefly flagellate, flagellate,* and *completely flagellate*. In the briefly flagellate type, of which *Didymium squamulosum, Physarella oblonga,* and *Physarum oblatum* are examples, the flagellate stage lasts 24 to 30 hours. After that period, all cells are amoeboid and remain irreversibly so. In the flagellate type, exemplified by *Physarum polycephalum* and *Fuliga septica,* the protoplasts that issue from the spores are usually flagellated, and swarm cells are present in the cultures up to 100 to 130 hrs after germination. In the completely flagellate type, in which Ross has placed all species he studied in orders other than the Physarales, the spores upon germination produce flagellate cells which may still be found in the cultures several weeks later. Wollman (1966), working with a number of *Comatricha* species, reported that her cultures were never devoid of swarm cells even after plasmodia had grown to cover the entire agar surface of the Petri dish and even after sporulation had taken place. She propagated her successful cultures by transferring to new Petri dishes a few drops of the supernatant liquid in which swarm cells were always suspended. McManus (1961a) had previously reported that in her cultures of *Stemonitis fusca* swarm cells abounded even up to the time "when the plasmodium is almost ready to fruit."

The transformation of a myxamoeba into a swarm cell was followed by Schuster (1965b) in fixed and stained cells, using both the light and the electron microscopes. He described this transformation in *Didymium nigripes* as follows:

> The transformation can be summarized as a sequence of events leading to the formation of a polarized flagellate from a previously non-polarized myxamoeba. In a myxamoeba, the centrosphere (Golgi plus centrioles) located on the nuclear membrane, comes to define what is to be the anterior end of the flagellate. The nucleus appears to elongate, with the centrosphere located at the apex of the elongating nucleus. The elongation may be a function of a connection between the flagellum cone and the nucleus, which is also suggested in NH_4OH treated cells where the nucleus is found associated with the isolated kinetid. Through further stretching (and possibly migration) the nucleus becomes a comma-shaped structure, whose apex is now located beneath the plasma membrane. The cytoplasm in the region about the nucleus appears to undergo a gradual movement in a posterior direction. This continues until the anterior end of the cell is tapered and the posterior and stouter end somewhat more rounded. The contractile vacuole complex comes to lie at the posterior end of the now recognizable swarm cell. [Fig. 5.]

Schuster also noted modifications in the mitochondria during transformation of myxamoebae. In addition to typical mitochondria, he found some that were vacuolated and many that showed intratubular inclusions as shown in Table 6.

Schuster (1965a) has also found that mitochondria of *Didymium nigripes* have a central core of DNA. The same situation seems to prevail in the mitochondria of *Physarum flavicomum* (Aldrich, 1967).

When a swarm cell changes to a myxamoeba, the flagella are resorbed in one of two ways. Either they are whipped against the body of the swarm cell and fuse with its protoplast, or they are pulled into the cell as the nucleus moves inward from its peripheral position (Koevenig, 1964).

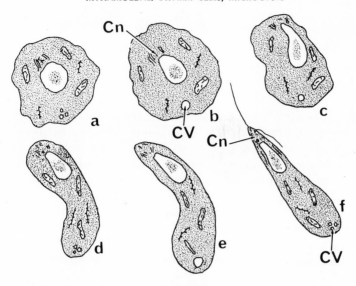

Fig. 5.   Representation of the stages in the transformation of a myxamoeba into a swarm cell. Typical myxamoeba (a) shows no polarity. The earliest recognizable stage in the transformation (b) shows an elongating nucleus with the centrosphere (Cn) at its anterior extent. The contractile vacuole complex (CV) is included to mark the posterior region of the transforming individual. The nucleus elongates still further (c), bringing it and the centrosphere in close contact with the plasma membrane. Streamlining occurs (d) with the cytoplasm coming to lie behind the nucleus. This is continued in (e). Swarm cell shown at (f) exhibits distinct polarity. Flagella form soon after centrioles make contact with the plasma membrane (stage c or d), and while the outline of the cell is still amoeboid. For simplicity, however, flagella are shown only in stage (f). (Redrawn from Schuster, 1965.)

Table 6.   *Didymium nigripes:* Percentage of mitochondria with typical and modified morphologies. (Schuster, 1965.)

	Myxamoeba (N = 128) [*]	Flagellating Myxamoebae (N = 151) [*]
Typical mitochondria	89.8	51.7
Vacuolated mitochondria	—	2.6
Mitochondria showing intratubular inclusions	10.2	45.7

[*] Denotes total number of mitochondria counted in low power micrographs.

Number of Flagella

Early students of Myxomycetes regarded the swarm cells as typically uniflagellate, faithfully recording, however, occasional biflagellate cells they had observed (deBary, 1859; Jahn, 1905; Vouk, 1911; Gilbert, 1927; Howard, 1931a; Sinoto and Yuasa, 1934). In 1935, von Stosch reported that in several species the biflagellate condition is the rule. He found the swarm cells of nine species to have two unequal anteriorly attached flagella, a long active one directed forward and a short, recurved one directed backward, which was difficult to observe because it was appressed to the body of the swarm cell. *Stemonitis* sp. and *Cribraria vulgaris* von Stosch found to be uniflagellate.

The studies of Elliott (1948, 1949) extended von Stosch's observations to 58 species, representing 30 genera. In all of these, the swarm cells were found to be typically biflagellate and heterokont, although in some species, such as *Physarella oblonga,* the flagella were reported to be almost equal in length. At the same time and without knowledge of Elliott's work, Locquin (1949a), using cinephotomicrography and phase-contrast optics, presented what he considered to be "indisputable evidence" of the presence, in all 58 species he studied, of the short, recurved, immobile flagellum that had been reported by von Stosch and was subsequently found by Elliott. Later, others continued to report a biflagellate condition in various species (McManus, 1958; Ross, 1957b), but conflicting reports on the flagellation of the swarm cells in individual species did not cease.

Although the work of Elliott and subsequent workers appeared to have more or less settled the controversy on flagellation in favor of a biflagellate condition, Cohen's communication to the Ninth International Botanical Congress reopened the question. Cohen (1959) reported that flagellation is not necessarily the same in all species. Using electron micrograph shadowcasts he supported his thesis that in some species the swarm cells were uniflagellate. Further, he stated that one of the causes of the controversy was the presence of flagellum-like protoplasmic extensions (pseudoflagella), which he adequately demonstrated and which, he believed, previous workers had possibly mistaken for flagella. The work of McManus (1961a, b) with *Stemonitis fusca* and *Clastoderma debaryanum* seemed to support Cohen's thesis. McManus found only a single flagellum in the former, but an additional short, recurved flagellum in most swarm cells of the latter.

In his attempt to resolve the question of flagellation using cinephotomicrographic techniques, as well as standard fixing and staining procedures, Koevenig (1961a) confirmed Cohen's discovery of pseudoflagella by actually filming these structures as they migrated from the front to the posterior end of the cell. He also reported the presence of true second flagella in from one per cent to 50 per cent of the swarm cells he studied, this percentage varying with the species, the age, and the condition of the swarm cells. Of further interest in this connection is Kerr's (1960) paper on flagellation of *Didymium nigripes,* in which he stated that newly flagellated cells are uniflagellate but may become biflagellate after several hours.

Recent studies of thin sections with the electron microscope tend to support the view that the swarm cells of the Myxomycetes are biflagellate, typically possessing one long, active flagellum directed forward and one short, recurved flagellum directed backward and appressed against the protoplast of the swarm cell. Schuster (1965b) has described such a situation in *Didymium nigripes,* and Aldrich (1966) observed it in *Physarum flavicomum* and *Stemonitis nigrescens.* Gottsberger (1967) also reported a long and a short flagellum on the swarmers of *Trichia varia.*

Several workers have detected two basal bodies in swarm cells or myxamoebae of different species. Sinoto and Yuasa (1934) found them in *Ceratiomyxa fruticulosa* and *Physarella oblonga;* Ellison (1945) described them in *Stemonitis axifera, S. fusca,* and *Fuligo septica;* Kerr (1960) and subsequently Schuster (1965b) in *Didymium nigripes* (Kerr's strain); Koevenig (1961c, 1964) in *Physarum gyrosum;* and Aldrich (1968) in *Physarum flavicomum.* The fact, however, that a uniflagellate condition has been repeatedly reported (Gilbert, 1927; Wilson and Cadman, 1928; Cohen, 1959; Kole, in Alexopoulos, 1962, p. 76; McManus, 1961a; Koevenig, 1961a, c; Benedict, 1962) in such species as *Reticularia lycoperdon* and *Stemonitis fusca* cannot be easily dismissed. Extensive studies with phase contrast, interference contrast, and electron microscopy are needed to give us a definitive answer to this interesting question. From the existing knowledge it appears probable at present that myxomycete swarm cells in general are potentially biflagellate but that uniflagellate cells are commonly and perhaps regularly produced by some species.

Structure of Flagella

Both Schuster (1965b) and Aldrich (1968) have demonstrated that myxomycete flagella are constructed on the expected 9 + 2 strand pattern (Fig. 6A). Because no tinsel-type flagella have been found in the Myxomycetes, both of the swarm-cell flagella have been described as whiplash (Bessey, 1950; Alexopoulos, 1962). In her discussion of fungal flagella Hawker (1965) states that "the tapering form of the whiplash results

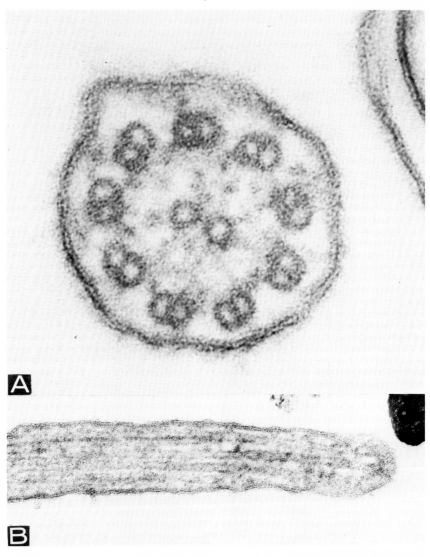

Fig. 6. *Physarum flavicomum*. Electron micrographs of long flagellum. A. Cross-section showing 9 + 2 pattern. × 480,000. B. Blunt tip. × 120,000. (Aldrich, 1968. Courtesy Henry Aldrich and Cell Research Institute, University of Texas at Austin.)

from the greater length of the two central strands and the unequal length of the peripheral ones." There is ample evidence that in the Myxomycetes blunt or knobbed flagella occur commonly. Whether these are only modifications of the whiplash type, as Ellison (1945) believes, or entirely different structures is still controversial. The few extant ultrastructural studies of myxomycete flagella (Cohen, 1959; Kole, in Alexopoulos, 1962; Schuster, 1965b; Aldrich, 1966, 1968; Gottsberger, 1967) are beginning to yield much needed information on these points. Aldrich (1966, 1968) shows the longer flagellum of *Physarum flavicomum* to be blunt (Fig. 6B) and states that he also found the shorter flagellum of *Stemonitis nigrescens* to be blunt. Gottsberger (1967), after a study of the flagella of *Trichia varia* concludes: "Der Feinbau der Geisseln lässt erkennen, das as sicht bei beiden Geisseln, der langen und der kurzen, um Fadenund nicht um Peitschengeisseln handelt." Concerning the knobbed flagella, Gottsberger's electron micrographs show that the knob consists entirely of flagellar membrane which extends beyond the fibrils and sometimes forms a knob-like swelling.

Development of Flagella

It has been pointed out previously that in *Physarum flavicomum* and *Didymium iridis*, basal bodies have been found in the spores. As stated above, these are discernible in the myxamoebae as fully developed centrioles lying below the plasma membrane (Fig. 7) and surrounded by Golgi sacs and vesicles. They give rise to the flagella during transformation of the myxamoeba into a swarm cell. In *P. flavicomum* (Aldrich, 1968) a primary flagellar vesicle, which appears to be formed by the fusion of several smaller vesicles, develops at the distal end of at least one and possibly both basal bodies. The vesicle elongates by continual fusion with secondary vesicles and, as the bud of the flagellum elongates into it, the elongating vesicle forms the sheath of the flagellum. Aldrich believes that just before the emergence of the flagella from the myxamoeba the buds of both flagella are within a common vesicle.

At the time of flagellar emergence, a double cone of microtubules attached at its apex to the basal body of the longer, active flagellum, is evident. The outer cone, consisting of about 40 microtubules, lies just under the plasma membrane, its base ending at the level of the posterior portion of the nucleus. The inner cone ends in the cytoplasm near the nuclear envelope.

CELL DIVISION

Myxamoebae divide by mitosis and cytokinesis and under optimum conditions produce large populations before the next stage in the life

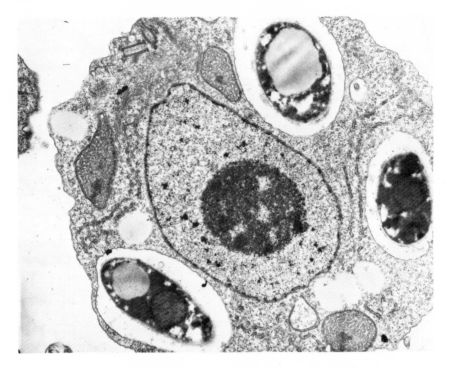

Fig. 7.   Myxamoeba of *Physarum flavicomum* showing two basal bodies.
× 17,500.   (Aldrich, 1968.   Courtesy Henry Aldrich and Cell Research Institute,
University of Texas at Austin.)

cycle is initiated. In heterothallic species, especially those in the order
Physarales, clonal cultures may be maintained indefinitely by transferring
occasionally to fresh agar slants and adding a few ml of bacterial suspension after the swarm cells or myxamoebae have been introduced.

Although cell multiplication has been noted by all who have cultured
Myxomycetes from deBary to the present time, Howard (1931a), Koevenig (1964), and Sylvia Kerr (1967) have given the most detailed description of this process, in *Physarum polycephalum*, in *P. gyrosum*, and in
Didymium nigripes (Kerr's strain) respectively. Inasmuch as it is reasonably safe to assume that this fundamental process does not differ
basically in different species, the following brief discussion will be based
on Koevenig's observations on living material recorded on film by phase-
contrast cinephotomicrography.

Cell division occurs only in the myxamoebal stage, the flagella being
resorbed before or during prophase. Prophase lasts 15–60 minutes, during which time the nucleolus becomes less distinct and eventually disap-

pears. As streaming slows down, the cell becomes more regularly spherical. The nucleus moves to the center of the cell, the nuclear membrane disappears, cell volume increases, pseudopodial activity ceases; contractile vacuoles increase in number and decrease in size; rod-shaped chromosomes become visible. During metaphase, which lasts 40–300 seconds, a definite spindle becomes visible, but centrioles are not seen. The chromosomes move to the equatorial plane. Anaphase lasts 45–320 seconds. The chromosomes move to the poles; the spindle is shortened; the fibers between the separating chromosome groups constrict and the cell becomes ovoid. Pseudopodial activity is resumed during telophase and increases during cleavage. Furrowing requires 100–320 seconds. A nuclear membrane reforms around each daughter nucleus; the nucleoli re-form from fusing granules; streaming and pseudopodial activity increase.

Koevenig's description shows that mitosis in the myxamoebae of *Physarum gyrosum* is extranuclear; i.e., the nuclear membrane disappears during the process, as had been reported by Wilson and Cadman (1928) for *Reticularia lycoperdon* and by Cadman (1931) for *Didymium iridis*. Mitotic divisions in plasmodia [Wilson and Cadman, 1928; Howard, 1932; Guttes, Guttes, and Rusch, 1961; Kessler, 1964 (cf. Koevenig and Jackson, 1966); Koevenig and Jackson, 1966; McManus and Roth, 1968] and presumed meiotic divisions in sporangia (Schuster, 1964a) and in spores (Aldrich, 1967) have been described as intranuclear. Koevenig and Jackson (1966) suggest that there may be a significant and perhaps diagnostic difference in the type of nuclear division in the haploid and diploid nuclei of the Myxomycetes. However, Sylvia Kerr's (1967) results with *Didymium nigripes* (Kerr's strain), if confirmed, would seem to indicate that, at least in some species, this difference between the nuclear divisions in the amoebae and the plasmodia is independent of ploidy.

Schuster (1964b) recorded a generation time of 14.5 hours for the myxamoebae of *Didymium nigripes* and 8.8 hours for those of *Physarum cinereum*, both in axenic culture with killed bacterial cells. Blickle (1943) has accelerated cell division by adding sulfhydryl, as 2.6×10^{-7} in parathiocresol, to the culture medium. Myxamoebal populations increased more rapidly in the sulfhydryl than in the control cultures.

FEEDING HABITS OF SWARM CELLS AND MYXAMOEBAE

Although a number of early workers (Cienkowski, 1863a; deBary, 1864; Strasburger, 1884) had sown myxomycete spores on various media and had obtained swarm cells, it appears that Lister (1890) was the first to observe that swarm cells ingested bacteria and digested them in food vacuoles. Pinoy (1903), who believed in the existence of a symbiosis between slime molds and bacteria, was the first to employ a single species of bacteria in his cultures (but without surface-sterilizing the spores he started with) and thus to approach a monoxenic culture. It was Gilbert (1928a, b) who made the first study of the feeding habits of swarm cells. Studying first *Dictydiaethalium plumbeum* and then about 20 species representing a number of families, he sowed the spores of each species together with those of the fungi to be tested and recorded the behavior of the swarm cells with reference to the fungus spores. Gilbert found that an important factor determining whether the swarm cells of Myxomycetes would ingest spores of a given fungus was the relative size of the spore and the swarm cell. If the spores were not too large, they would generally serve as food for the swarm cells. However, certain spores were preferred to others; some were ingested but not digested; and some were rejected altogether. "No myxomycete showed a special preference for spores which were not taken in . . . by other myxomycetes."

Concerning bacteria that can serve as food for myxamoebae and swarm cells, although *Aerobacter aerogenes* is now preferentially employed by investigators for monoxenic cultures of Myxomycetes, *Escherichia coli, Serratia marcescens, Flavobacterium sp.* and other bacteria have been successfully used by some. In one of the present authors' experience, spore formers such as *Bacillus subtilis* are not particularly favorable species for rearing myxomycete clonal cultures, but Kerr (1963) successfully used *B. megaterium* as well as *Aerobacter aerogenes* when he reported the axenic cultivation of myxamoebae of *Didymium nigripes* in the presence of dead bacterial cells killed with formalin. Growth was also obtained by Kerr when dead bacterial cells were shattered by sonication or by treatment in a Waring blender and the filter-sterilized supernatant liquid was used as a medium. Schuster (1964b) was also able to grow axenically the myxamoebae of *Didymium nigripes* (same isolate that Kerr used) and of *Physarum cinereum* in the presence of heat-killed bacterial cells.

Axenic culture of myxamoebae in the absence of dead bacteria was achieved by Ross (1964) with *Badhamia obovata*. Spores sown on cornmeal agar germinated and gave rise to myxamoebae which fed on the bacteria present. A drop of the bacteria-myxamoebae culture was then placed on the surface of cornmeal agar. The liquid was soon absorbed, and the myxamoebae began to migrate away from the inoculated region. Myxamoebae which had migrated away from the original source and which appeared to be free of bacteria were then placed on nutrient agar where they multiplied and produced axenic populations. The medium which supported the best growth contained chick embryo extract in addition to cornmeal extract which was indispensable. When hematin was substituted for the chick embryo extract, growth was greatly reduced.

A discussion of swarm cells would not be complete without mentioning Indira's report (1964) of the formation of swarmers from plasmodia in *Arcyria cinerea* and *Stemonitis herbatica*. According to this report, "Myxamoebae are cut off at random from the advancing fan or from the veins of the plasmodium. A pseudopod is put forward from the plasmodium and it continually changes in shape. . . . Within a short time, it develops flagella and swims away as a swarmer with the characteristic rotating movement."

Indira's observations on *A. cinerea* and *S. herbatica* were confirmed by Ross and Cummings (1967) on plasmodia of a species described as being close to *Physarum pusillum*, and these latter workers supported their observations with photographic evidence. It would now be most interesting to isolate swarm cells originating from plasmodia and to determine their ploidy and their ability, especially in heterothallic species, to carry the life cycle to completion in single swarm-cell cultures. Such a method of swarm-cell production would explain the profusion of swarm cells over a long period of time in cultures of certain species of the Stemonitaceae, as noted by McManus (1961a) and Wollman (1966).

MICROCYSTS

Under unfavorable conditions such as overcrowding, lack of food, accumulation of various metabolic products, drought in some instances and overabundance of water in others, myxamoebae round up, develop a thin wall, and form microcysts. There seems to be no significant change in cellular structure before encystment (Schuster, 1965b). Centrioles and microtubules have been found in microcysts indicating that upon excystment a fully formed myxamoeba is produced.

The process of encystment in *Physarum gyrosum* and *Fuligo cinerea* is well described by Koevenig (1964):

Encystment in *P. gyrosum* and *F. cinerea* took several hours for completion. A swarm cell resorbed its flagellum and rounded up. The refractive index of the cytoplasm (null pt. ca. 13% bovine serum albumin) gradually increased and, along with a decrease in cell volume, indicated a condensation of the cytoplasm. The nucleus occupied a central position and also decreased in volume. Mitochondria accumulated around the nucleus. The contractile vacuole ceased to pulsate and disappeared. All food vacuoles disappeared. Staining with IKI failed to show starch or glycogen granules as found in spores of *Entamoeba histolytica* (Cleveland and Sanders, 1930). A thick, refractile membrane gradually formed around the cell.

Whether all structures that have been interpreted as microcysts are actually encysted cells is questionable. Both deBary (1859) and Cienkowski (1863a) called attention to the fact that some "microcysts" are unwalled. Such structures resume their activities under favorable conditions without casting off a wall or membrane. Cadman (1931) states that in *Didymium iridis*, the so-called microcysts are unwalled and, in her opinion, represent a stage toward disintegration rather than a protective mechanism.

Germination of true microcysts was observed by Howard (1931a) in *Physarum polycephalum*. From his description it appears that a very small pore is dissolved in the microcyst membrane through which the protoplast oozes. Thus the germination of the microcyst in this species is not comparable to the germination of the spore where the wall cracks widely open. Rather it is comparable to the pore method of spore germination so frequently encountered in the Stemonitales.

The conditions that cause excystment have not been studied, but reversing those that appear to cause encystment often initiates the resumption of activity. In *Physarum pusillum* and *Physarum flavicomum*, for example, clonal myxamoebal cultures that have been stored in one of the present authors' laboratories on agar slants for a year and consist entirely of microcysts resume activity when transferred to fresh media and supplied with newly grown bacteria. The recently reported success in lyophilizing myxamoebae (Kerr, 1965b; Davis, 1965) and obtaining normal cultures from the lyophilized material is another indication that the microcysts represent a resting stage which carries the myxomycete over unfavorable conditions.

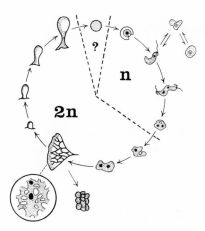

4

The Nuclear Cycle

Except under unusual circumstances, the myxamoebae or swarm cells that issue from germinating spores are uninucleate and are regarded as haploid. A general belief among students of Myxomycetes is that coalescence of amoeboid or flagellated protoplasts is a prerequisite for plasmodial formation in most species that have been investigated, and that only rarely, under unusual circumstances, may a plasmodium develop from single protoplasts that issue from the spores (Kerr, 1967; Henney, 1967). There is considerable disagreement, however, as to the behavior of the nuclei after coalescence has taken place.

In the discussion that follows, any fusion of haploid cells known to result in the formation of a diploid zygote will be regarded as sexual regardless of the morphology of the fusing cells and will be termed *syngamy*. The fusion of cells preceding nuclear fusion will be termed *plasmogamy*, and fusion of the nuclei will be termed *karyogamy*. Fusion of protoplasts without reference to subsequent fate of the nuclei will be termed *coalescence*.

PLASMOGAMY

That syngamy occurs in many species of Myxomycetes has been well established by actual observation in some and by genetic experiments in others. That sexual fusions occur in heterothallic species cannot be denied. Whether so-called homothallic species are actually so, as some investigators claim, or whether they complete their life cycles apogamously, i.e., without karyogamy or meiosis, as others insist is one of the great questions regarding these organisms.

Cienkowski (1863a, b) appears to be the first person after deBary (1854) to report coalescence of myxamoebae in the Myxomycetes before plasmodium formation. He reported that in *Didymium difforme* and *Physarum leucopus* two or three myxamoebae come in contact and fuse. Other myxamoebae are then attracted to the plasmodial initial so formed and coalesce with it, thus adding to its mass.

In 1911, Jahn published his paper *Der Sexualakt* in which he concluded that myxamoebae fuse in pairs and form a uninucleate, diploid structure which he regarded as the first stage of the plasmodium. Subsequent fusions of amoebae with plasmodia Jahn considered to be phagocytic. Skupienski (1926, 1927) working with *Didymium difforme* reached the conclusion that cell coalescence was a prerequisite to plasmodium formation and agreed with Cienkowski that two to many myxamoebae may fuse initially to form the plasmodium. Wilson and Cadman (1928) recorded plasmogamy in *Reticularia lycoperdon*. They, too, observed multiple fusion of swarm cells, but believed that only two cells fuse initially and that the others coalesce subsequently with the zygote and are digested. Cayley (1929) reported fusion of paired swarm cells of *Didymium difforme*. She does not mention multiple fusions. Schünemann (1930) observed fusion of myxamoebae in *Didymium nigripes*, and Cadman (1931) in its variety *xanthopus* (*D. iridis*). Howard (1931a) stated that in *Physarum polycephalum* swarm cells fuse to form zygotes. Von Stosch (1935) reported that fusion in *Didymium nigripes* was between swarm cells, not between myxamoebae. Ross (1957b), studying 19 species of Myxomycetes, found syngamy to occur in all. In the briefly flagellate type of life cycle (see page 33) he found plasmogamy to occur between myxamoebae; in the other two types, between flagellated cells. Although he noted some exceptions he believed that, in general, individual species conformed to one of the two patterns. Koevenig (1961c, 1964), on the other hand, reported having observed plasmogamy in both *Stemonitis flavogenita* and *Physarum gyrosum* occurring by fusion of both flagellated cells and of myxamoebae. His observations indicate that in *Didymium iridis* and *Fuligo cinerea* plasmogamy occurs between myxamoebae and in *Reticularia lycoperdon* only between swarm cells. Kerr (1961) at about the same time reported both types of plasmogamy in *Didymium nigripes* (Kerr's strain), and McManus (1961b) described fusion of swarm cells in *Clastoderma debaryanum*.

In none of the publications cited above have the fusing swarm cells or myxamoebae been reported to be morphologically different. Abe (1934), attempting to distinguish between fusing cells of five species, stated that she found a difference in oxidation-reduction potential and electrical charge. Kambly (1939b), working with *Reticularia lycoperdon*, which Abe had not studied, was unable to confirm her results. McManus (1961a) and Benedict (1962), both working with *Stemonitis fusca*, claim that in this species fusion takes place between a myxamoeba and a swarm cell. McManus observed what she supposed to be plasmogamy in stained material and only suggested that such fusions may take place. Benedict, on the other hand, observed living material and described plasmogamy as follows:

Two swarm cells were seen with posterior ends attracted to each other but were never seen fusing to form a zygote. Also two or three myxamoebae were seen in contact with each other but could not be found fusing. All such contacts always resulted in separation again of the swarm cells and myxamoebae. However a myxamoeba and a swarm cell would fuse. Syngamy actually occurred only in the following way in the microcultures and required less than one minute for completion. A not quite round, non-flagellate, granular-appearing myxamoeba lay in contact with a rounded, just quiescent but still flagellate, translucent-appearing swarm cell. The protoplast making up the myxamoeba flowed into and thoroughly mixed with the protoplast of the swarm cell or was engulfed by it and made one large swarm cell.

Although Benedict does not describe nuclear fusion, his drawings indicate that he believed it to take place. It is interesting that Ross (1957b), who had included *S. fusca* in the 19 species in which he studied syngamy, recorded copulation of swarm cells.

Although many of the above papers are convincing in their claims that myxamoebae or swarm cells fuse in pairs to form single cells, the ultimate proof of such occurrence was offered by Koevenig (1961a), who recorded on motion-picture film fusion of swarm cells and of myxamoebae in *Physarum gyrosum*.

Indirect but unquestionable evidence that syngamy takes place in at least some species of Myxomycetes has been obtained by von Stosch (1935), Dee (1960, 1962, 1966a, b), Collins (1961), Henney (1967), and Wollman (1966), who showed that unless compatible clones in certain isolates of *Didymium nigripes, Physarum polycephalum, Didymium iridis, Physarum flavicomum,* and *Comatricha laxa* respectively are mixed plasmodia are not generally formed. Some of these results will be discussed more extensively under "Compatibility."

It may thus be considered as proved that syngamy does take place in several species of Myxomycetes. There are, however, several questions that remain unanswered at this time.

The question of multiple fusions and of fusions of swarm cells or myxamoebae with plasmodia, for example, was revived recently by Wollman (1966) who, in several species of *Comatricha*, repeatedly noticed clumping of swarm cells among themselves and around microscopic plasmodia (Fig. 8). Without actually observing plasmogamy, she believed that these plasmodia originated in the center of such clumps. In *Licea biforis* Wollman and Alexopoulos (1967) reported what appeared to be coalescence of swarm cells with protoplasmodia, although they did not follow the fate of the nuclei in such apparent fusions. Such clumping behavior of swarm cells Wollman (unpublished results) found to be symptomatic of sexual maturity in clones of different mating type in *Comatricha laxa*. When she mixed compatible clones, after rather than before clumping had occurred, mating (as manifested by plasmodial formation) was much more rapid. That gametes must probably attain physiological maturity before syngamy takes place was also suggested by Cayley (1929) for *Didymium difforme*.

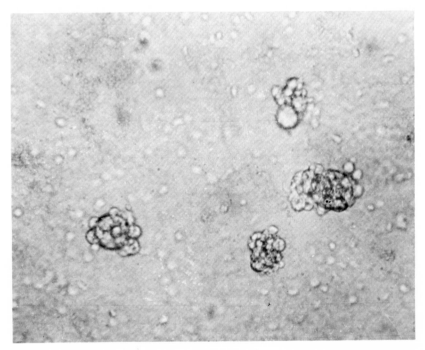

Fig. 8. *Comatricha typhoides.* Aggregations of swarm cells around young spherical plasmodia. × 180. (Wollman, 1966. Courtesy Constance Wollman.)

In a detailed study of syngamy in *Didymium iridis*, in which he brought together cells of opposite mating types and watched them with phase-contrast optics, Ross (1967a) again substantiated previous observations by many investigators on this point. He found that syngamy did not occur immediately but that "close proximity for several hours was required before the amoebae became capable of fusing." He suggested that this may indicate the existence of substances, produced by one or both mating types, that induce syngamy, and that amoebae may require a period of physiological maturation before they are able to respond to such substances.

Of the three exosporous species known, only in *Ceratiomyxa fruticulosa* has plasmogamy been investigated. Gilbert (1935) reported fusion of swarm cells in pairs and coalescence of unpaired swarm cells with pairs resulting in groups of three to seven "all fused at their posterior ends." Both McManus (1958) and the Sansomes (1961) seem to disagree with Gilbert on the occurrence of multiple fusion, the former stating that it is very rare and the latter denying its occurrence.

From all the above it may be concluded that in spite of some contradictory statements in the literature it appears that the general pattern of plasmogamy, in Myxomycetes in which sexuality is operative, calls for fusion of swarm cells or myxamoebae in pairs, some species favoring one method, some another, but many employing either according to circumstances. Multiple plasmogamy is still a possibility, but it is probable that where such a condition seemingly prevails individual cells are added to already fused pairs of swarm cells or myxamoebae, and very probably digested. Multiple fusions of myxamoebae, without karyogamy, may be expected to occur in apogamic forms. We shall return to the question of multiple fusions in our discussions of karyogamy and heterokaryosis.

KARYOGAMY

Cienkowski (1863a, b), who first described plasmogamy in the Myxomycetes in some detail could find no nuclei in the young plasmodium and believed that the nuclei of the fused cells disintegrated. Nuclei in the plasmodium were first demonstrated by Schmitz (1879) and subsequently by Strasburger (1884), Lister (1893), and others. Lister (1893) at first believed that when the swarm cells fuse "the nuclei remain distinct and do not coalesce." Jahn (1911) is usually credited with the discovery of karyogamy in the Myxomycetes.

Nuclear fusion in the Myxomycetes has been reported to occur in the fusion cell, shortly after plasmogamy, or to take place somewhere in the plasmodium, at an early stage according to some, at a later stage according to others. The majority of investigators favor the first of these three views. Jahn (1911) working with *Physarum didermoides* stated that the amoebae copulate and become young uninucleate plasmodia, thus placing karyogamy in the fusion cell. The same view is shared by Wilson and Cadman (1928) for *Reticularia lycoperdon,* Cadman (1931) for *Didymium iridis,* Howard (1931a) for *Physarum polycephalum,* von Stosch (1935) for *D. nigripes,* and Ross (1957b) for 19 species. All of the above based their conclusions on stained preparations in which nuclei were found in close proximity or in contact and presumably in the act of fusing. Ross observed living cells and fixed them when noting interesting stages. Fusion of nucleoli was also reported in most of the above papers. Koevenig (1961a, c), using phase-contrast cinephoto-micrography, actually observed and filmed karyogamy in living fusion cells of *Physarum gyrosum.* Therrien (1966b), using spectrophotometric analysis of nuclear DNA, showed that there were two kinds of uninucleate amoebae in five-day-old cultures of *Didymium nigripes* (Kerr's strain). The amount of DNA in the nuclei of the recognizably larger amoebae was about double that in the nuclei of the smaller. He concluded that the larger amoebae were zygotes in which karyogamy had taken place (Fig. 9). Finally, Ross (1967a) published a fine series of phase-contrast photomicrographs which show fusion of nuclei in the zygotes of *Didymium iridis* (Fig. 10). Of great interest, however, is Ross's assertion that some fusion cells coalesce with multinucleate plasmodia before karyogamy has taken place, and his photomicrographs show what he believes to be the haploid nuclei remaining unfused in the plasmodial cytoplasm (Fig. 11). At this stage the plasmodium depicted in Fig. 11 would be hetero-karyotic containing diploid, haploid (+), and haploid (−) nuclei. Whether the haploid nuclei multiply and become distributed in the plasmodium as do the nuclei in a heterokaryotic mycelium would be interesting to discover. There is no evidence at the present time to sup-port such a conclusion.

The opposite view—that of karyogamy occurring in the plasmodium—has been held by Prowazek (1904), who found what he believed to be nuclei fusing in pairs in the plasmodium of *Physarum psittacinum;* by Kranzlin (1907) for *Arcyria cinerea;* by Skupienski (1926, 1927, 1928), who placed nuclear fusion of *Didymium difforme* in the mature plas-modium just before spore formation; and by Schünemann (1930) for *Didymium nigripes.* The only modern research that suggests that nuclear fusion may occur in the plasmodium is that of Dee (1960) who found the nuclei of the amoebae and the plasmodium of *Physarum polycephalum* to have the same amount of DNA, measured by a microdensitometer. Nevertheless, she was careful to point out the limitations of the instru-ment she was using and the relatively large probable error in her meas-urements.

Turning to *Ceratiomyxa* we find the same controversy. The early papers reported nuclear fusion late in the life cycle, but the more recent papers state that it follows plasmogamy in the fusion cell. Olive (1907b)

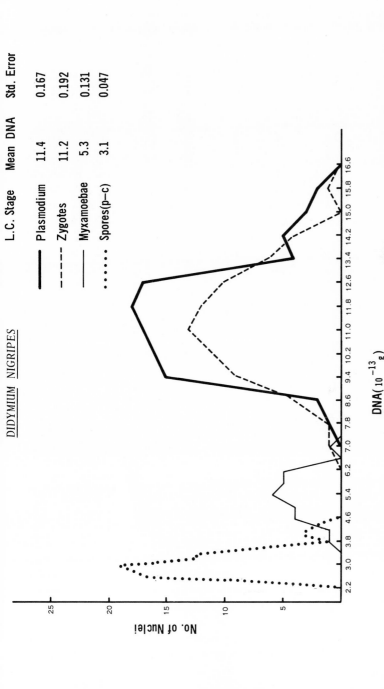

Fig. 9. DNA content of nuclei in four stages of the life cycle of *Didymium nigripes* (Kerr's strain). (Therrien, 1966b. Courtesy C. D. Therrien. Reproduced by permission of the National Research Council of Canada from the Canadian Journal of Botany 44:1667–1675, 1966.)

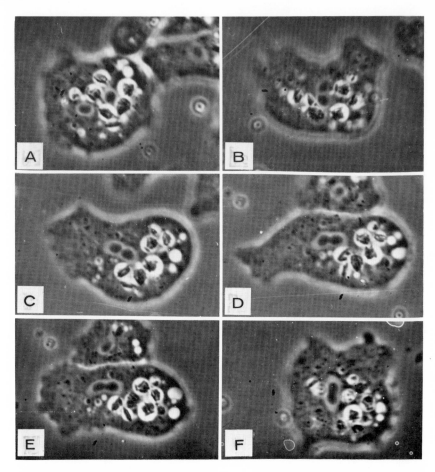

Fig. 10. Karyogamy in *Didymium iridis*. A. 1 second after plasmogamy. B. 4 minutes later. C. 1 minute later. D. 2 minutes later. E. 30 seconds later. F. 14 minutes later. All × 1400. (Ross, 1967. Courtesy Ian Ross.)

believed that plasmogamy established a dikaryotic condition which ended with nuclear fusion in the fructification just before protospore formation. Jahn (1908) also believed that karyogamy was delayed and that it took place in the plasmodium but prior to fruiting. Gilbert (1935) in his detailed study of *Ceratiomyxa* showed that karyogamy takes place soon after two or possibly more swarm cells fuse. When two cells fuse, one of the nuclei is always active, the other passive. The former migrates toward the passive and fuses with it. When several swarm cells fuse into one protoplasmic mass, the nuclei again fuse in pairs, one of each

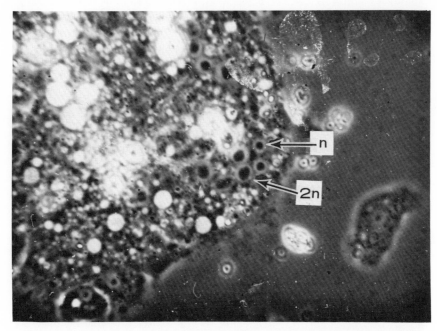

Fig. 11. *Didymium iridis.* Haploid (small) and diploid (large) nuclei (arrows) in a young plasmodium. × 1400. (Ross, 1967. Courtesy Ian Ross.)

pair migrating toward the other. Gilbert does not mention what becomes of the extra nucleus when odd numbers of swarm cells fuse.

The Sansomes (1961) agree that karyogamy follows plasmogamy in the fusion cell of *Ceratiomyxa* but, as stated before, deny the occurrence of multiple fusions.

It should be clear from the above summary that the literature is overwhelmingly in favor of karyogamy occurring soon after the fusion of swarm cells or myxamoebae in all species in which karyogamy has been well established, but that indisputable proof of its position in the life cycle, obtained through observation of living material, is indeed rare.

COMPATIBILITY

Heterothallism

The first report that an incompatibility mechanism, similar to that discovered in the Zygomycetes by Blakeslee, also exists in the Myxomycetes was that of Pinoy (1908), who stated that his cultures of *Didymium nigripes* produced two kinds of plasmodia, (+) and (−), the former yellow, the latter black. If segregated, these plasmodia sclerotized but never sporulated. Portions of the sclerotia placed in water gave rise to myxamoebae. When Pinoy mixed myxamoebae derived from the two types of plasmodia, his cultures sporulated in ten days. Although the existence of heterothallism in the Myxomycetes is now definitely established, Pinoy's concept of the incompatibility mechanism in these organisms is not in accordance with the facts as they are now known.

To Jahn (1911) must be given credit for obtaining the first results with undoubted monosporous cultures. Working with *D. squamulosum,* Jahn isolated single spores, recorded that a single amoeba issued from each, that an amoebal population resulted, and that plasmodia were formed. Skupienski (1926, 1927, 1928), working with monosporous cultures of *Didymium difforme,* concluded that the organism was heterothallic. He obtained plasmodia only when he mixed (+) and (−) myxamoebal clones and maintained that the spores of this organism were "unisexual." Cayley (1929), investigating the same organism, obtained plasmodia in monosporous cultures and concluded that "sex segregation" must take place during spore germination. Apparently she did not consider the possibility of homothallism or apogamy. Schünemann (1930) worked with *Physarum leucopus, Didymium difforme, D. squamulosum,* and *D. nigripes* (*D. iridis* according to von Stosch). Isolating over 200 spores of the last species, he obtained plasmodia in every case. More than 100 of his monosporous cultures fruited. Obtaining the same results with the other species, even when he used Skupienski's isolate of *D. difforme,* he decided there was no genotypic differentiation of "sex" in any.

Von Stosch (1935) worked with *Didymium nigripes, D. iridis, D. difforme, D. squamulosum, Physarum cinereum,* and *Diderma* sp. He established 14 monosporous cultures of *D. nigripes* which produced myxamoebal populations that eventually encysted without forming plasmodia. When he mixed the cysts in all possible combinations two at a time, he obtained plasmodia from certain matings and showed that 9 of the cultures were of one mating type and 5 of another. By establishing 47 monosporous F_1 cultures and mating them to the parent strains, he obtained the expected results and stated that *D. nigripes* is heterothallic. Monosporous cultures of the other species resulted in plasmodia, and since he was unable to demonstrate meiosis in his cytological preparations, he concluded that they were apogamic.

Kerr and Sussman (1958) investigated an isolate they believed to be *Didymium nigripes.* They plated a small number of spores together with *Aerobacter aerogenes* and obtained plaques of myxamoebae which soon developed plasmodia. They assumed that the myxamoebal population in each plaque originated from the germination of a single spore.

Kerr (1961), continuing work with this organism, reported plasmogamy. Von Stosch and coworkers (1964) studied Kerr's strain cytologically and decided it was apogamic.

Dee (1960, 1962) proved without question that the strain of *Physarum polycephalum* she used in her experiments, and which she had obtained from Rusch (McArdle Laboratory, University of Wisconsin), is heterothallic. Not only did she show it consisted of two mating types, but she obtained all expected combinations when she crossed an emetine resistant (−) clone with a wild type (+) clone and analyzed the progeny for mating type and resistance. At the same time, Collins (1961) had studied the mating type systems of *Fuligo cinerea* and *Didymium iridis*. He labelled the former homothallic, assuming that syngamy was necessary for plasmodial formation, and showed the latter to be heterothallic. His results are of considerable interest. Of 256 isolated spores of *D. iridis*, 101 germinated, 79 yielded myxamoebal clones which developed no further, and 22 produced plasmodia (Table 7). Mating 18 of his clones

Table 7. *Didymium iridis.* Original single-spore isolations from thirteen sporangia. (Collins, 1961.)

Sporangium No.	No. of Spores Isolated per Sporangium	No. of Spores Germinated	No. of Spores Yielding Plasmodia	Per Cent Germinated	Per Cent Yielding Plasmodia
1	12	12	5	100.0	41.6
2	15	12	4	80.0	33.3
3	23	18	3	78.2	16.6
4	19	14	2	73.1	14.2
5	25	1	0	4.0	0.0
6	30	0	0	0.0	0.0
7	15	3	0	20.0	0.0
8	25	0	0	0.0	0.0
9	12	5	0	41.6	0.0
10	9	4	2	44.4	50.0
11	19	10	2	52.6	20.0
12	18	7	2	38.8	28.5
13	34	15	2	44.1	13.3
Totals	256	101	22	39.4	21.7

in all combinations two at a time, he obtained a pattern of plasmodial formation that strongly suggested bipolar heterothallism. This was further confirmed by taking 25 F_1 clones, mating 14 of them among themselves, and crossing all 25 to two tester clones of opposite mating type. The results were as expected (Fig. 12).

Especially intriguing were the results Collins obtained when he studied the F_1 generation from the ca. 22 per cent of his original monosporous cultures which behaved as if homothallic. When he germinated 72

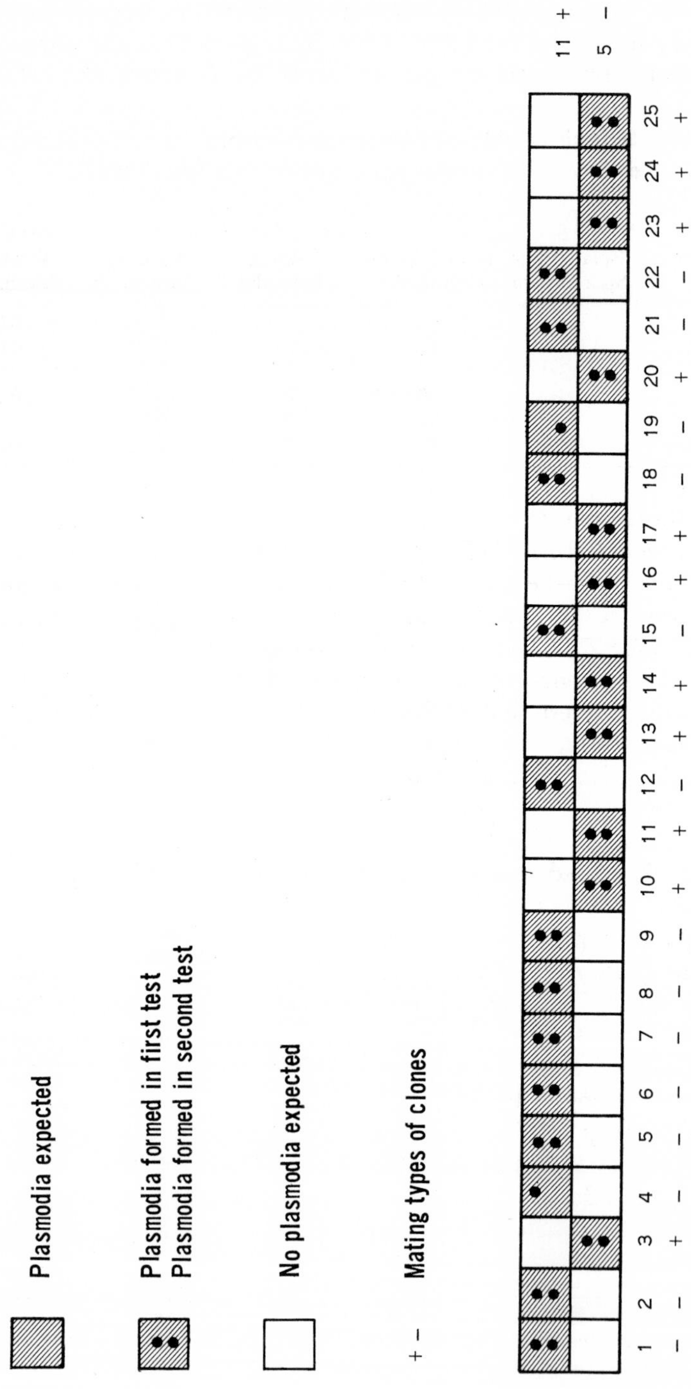

Fig. 12. *Didymium iridis.* Results obtained from backcrossing 25 F₁ clones to two parental clones of opposite mating types. (Redrawn from Collins, 1961.)

spores from sporangia obtained in single spore culture, none of the clones produced plasmodia (Table 8). When he crossed 20 of the clones in all combinations, no consistent pattern could be detected, but when he

Table 8. *Didymium iridis.* Single-spore isolations from five sporangia derived from single-spore culture. (Collins, 1961.)

Sporangium No.	No. of Spores Isolated per Sporangium	No. of Spores Germinated	No. of Spores Yielding Plasmodia	Per Cent Germinated	Per Cent Yielding Plasmodia
1	18	14	0	72.2	0.0
2	17	13	0	76.4	0.0
3	12	7	0	58.3	0.0
4	6	6	0	100.0	0.0
5	35	32	0	91.4	0.0
Totals	88	72	0	81.8	0.0

crossed the 20 clones to tester clones of known mating type, a typical two allele–one locus mating type pattern was obtained. There are obviously other factors besides mating type that govern plasmodial production, at least in this species. Continuing his work alone (Collins, 1963) and with Ling (1963) he crossed his isolate with two other races and showed the existence of multiple alleles in *Didymium iridis*. It is of considerable interest that Mukherjee and Zabka (1964), working with three isolates of the same organism,[1] obtained a somewhat different pattern which did not conform to the single locus–multiple allele theory of Collins. Instead, they proposed that two closely linked loci control incompatibility of *D. iridis*. Unfortunately, because of the small number of clones they used and the fact that intraracial sterility developed in their clones, which prevented them from continuing their experiments, their data are not nearly as convincing as one would hope.

Collins (1963) and Collins, *et al.* (1964) have secured evidence for multiple allelism in *Physarum pusillum*. Dee (1966b) also reported the same situation with *P. polycephalum*. Of particular interest are the questions raised by Henney and Henney (1968) with *P. flavicomum* and *P. rigidum*. Working with 9 isolates, all believed at first to be *P. flavicomum* (Henney, 1967), some from widely separated geographical areas, Henney and Henney found them all to be heterothallic. In crossing clones from different isolates, it became evident that some of these would cross in all combinations and others would not. Genetic barriers

[1] These were labelled HH, BB, and TT. HH was the original strain that Collins had used and was also one of the two strains that Alexopoulos and Zabka (1962) had worked with; BB was the second strain employed by Alexopoulos and Zabka; and TT was a new isolate.

separated the isolates into three groups with what appeared to be a multiple allele series in each group (Fig. 13). Isolates within each group were compatible in any combination of alleles, but intergroup isolates were incompatible in all combinations. These results prompted Henney and Henney to compare both the morphology of the sporangia and the behavior of the plasmodia of the 3 groups with the thought that they may represent three distinct species. Detailed studies revealed that the nine isolates fell into three groups not only on the basis of sporophore

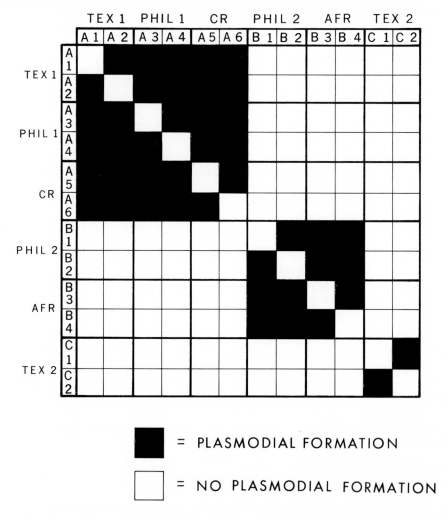

Fig. 13. *Physarum rigidum flavicomum.* Three series of multiple alleles in all combinations. (Courtesy Mary Henney.) For explanation see text.

morphology but also on the physiology of their plasmodia. These groups paralleled the incompatibility groups. Morphological differences between group 1 and the other two groups were much more pronounced, however, and on that basis it was decided that group 1 was not *P. flavicomum* but *P. rigidum,* a closely related species. Because of overlapping morphological characters groups 2 and 3 were tentatively retained in *P. flavicomum.* Additional complexities were revealed when Henney (1967) undertook an analysis of the F_1 generation of the six isolates with which she had originally worked. F_1 spores produced by intraisolate crosses gave the expected results, whether crossed among themselves or with selected tester clones of opposite mating types (Table 9), but F_1 spores from interisolate, intragroup crosses failed to germinate except in a very few instances. Of over 1000 spores isolated only 3 germinated. Each of these cultures gave rise to a plasmodium, but without first producing a myxamoebal population. One of these plasmodia fruited. From a single sporangium of this fruiting Henney isolated 40 spores, 15 of which germinated and again gave rise to plasmodia directly, bypassing the myxamoebal population stage of the life cycle.

Even assuming that the 3 groups of isolates represented 3 distinct species, the failure to germinate of spores produced by interisolate crosses within the same group cannot be due to the sterility often displayed by interspecific hybrids, for the isolates within a single group are morphologically indistinguishable. It should be emphasized, too, that both the sporangia and spores produced by such interisolate crosses were perfectly formed and in all ways typical.

An explanation of the unexpected behavior of the few interisolate F_1 spores that germinated may be sought in a recent paper by Aldrich (1967). In an ultrastructural study of meiosis in 3 species of *Physarum,* including *P. flavicomum,* Aldrich concluded that meiosis takes place in the young spores after cleavage and wall formation. If, for some unknown reason, meiosis is inhibited in spores produced by interisolate, intragroup crosses, a spore, upon germination, would liberate a diploid protoplast which would develop into a plasmodium and sporulate producing diploid spores again. A diploid strain might thus be established which would reproduce apogamously without ever forming haploid myxamoebae. Interesting as this hypothesis may be, it would not explain the failure to germinate of most spores formed by interisolate crosses.

Heterothallic isolates are now known in 5 species of Myxomycetes, namely *Didymium iridis, Physarum flavicomum, P. polycephalum, P. pusillum,* and *Comatricha laxa.* In addition, there are strong indications from unpublished results obtained at the University of Texas that at least two other species (*Fuligo septica* and *Physarum globuliferum*) may include heterothallic strains.

Table 9. Ten clones of the F$_1$ generation of *Physarum flavicomum* Texas I (A)* crossed in duplicate to tester clones of opposite mating types of each of the six isolates. (Henney, 1967.)

Clone Numbers	Tex I *		Phil I *		C R *		Phil II		AFR		Tex II	
	A1	A2	A3	A4	A5	A6	B1	B2	B3	B4	C1	C2
AF$_1$S1	OO	XX	XX	XX	XX	XX	OO	OO	OO	OO	OO	OO
AF$_1$S3	OO	XX	XX	XX	XX	XX	OO	OO	OX	OO	OO	OO
AF$_1$S6	OO	XX	XX	XX	XX	XX	OO	OO	OO	OO	OO	OO
AF$_1$S7	OO	XX	XX	XX	XX	XX	OO	OO	OO	OO	OO	OO
AF$_1$S8	OO	XX	XX	XX	XX	XX	OO	OO	OO	OO	OO	OO
AF$_1$S2	XX	OO	XX	XX	XX	XX	OO	OO	OO	OO	OO	OO
AF$_1$S4	XX	OO	XX	XX	XX	XX	OO	OO	OO	OO	OO	OO
AF$_1$S5	XX	OO	XX	XX	XX	XX	OO	OO	OO	OO	OO	OO
AF$_1$S9	XX	OO	XX	XX	XX	XX	OO	OO	OO	OO	OO	OO
AF$_1$S10	XX	OO	XX	XX	XX	XX	OO	OO	OO	OO	OO	OO

X = Plasmodial formation.
O = No plasmodial formation.
* See Henney and Henney (1968) for designation of these isolates as *Physarum rigidum*.

Illegitimate Matings

It will be remembered that in Collins' first experiments with *Didymium iridis*, 22 per cent of the clones produced plasmodia even though that particular isolate was proved to be heterothallic. Such selfing has been reported in virtually all papers which deal with heterothallic Myxomycetes (Collins, 1961; Dee, 1966; Henney, 1967). Several explanations have been offered for this phenomenon among which are: (1) contamination with a clone of opposite mating type; (2) diploid spores producing clones during the development of which meiosis takes place giving rise to two mating types; (3) mutation of one or more amoebae in a clone from one mating type to another; and (4) illegitimate mating between cells of the same mating type.

Collins and Ling (1968) in an attempt to resolve this problem in *Didymium iridis* propose that, in their material, the clonally produced plasmodia were the result of illegitimate matings between amoebae of the same mating type. They reached this conclusion by genetically analyzing the spores from sporangia developed by clonally produced plasmodia and by appropriate crosses showing that they were all of one mating type. Nevertheless they presented no proof that zygotes were actually formed and that the plasmodia did not result from the coalescence of myxamoebae without karyogamy ever taking place! Their results, certainly, eliminated possibilities 1, 2, and 3 above. The plasmodia in question appear to have originated either through illegitimate matings, as the authors state, or apogamically.

Homothallism and Apogamy

Another important question which has not been resolved to everyone's satisfaction is the question of apogamy in the Myxomycetes.

A number of species or strains have been induced to complete their life cycles in single spore culture on agar media. Among them are:

Comatricha typhoides (Wollman, 1966)
Didymium difforme (Schünemann, 1930)
Didymium iridis (Collins, 1965)
Didymium nigripes (Kerr's strain) (Kerr and Sussman, 1958)
Didymium squamulosum (von Stosch, 1935)
Echinostelium minutum (Olive, 1960)
Fuligo cinerea (Tahiti strain) (Collins, 1961)
Licea biforis (Wollman and Alexopoulos, 1967)
Perichaena depressa (Wollman and Alexopoulos, 1964)
Physarella oblonga (Gehenio and Luyet, 1950)
Physarum cinereum (von Stosch, 1935)

Physarum leucopus (Schünemann, 1930)
Physarum nicaraguense (Solis, 1962)
Physarum pusillum (Alexopoulos and Henney, unpublished)

It will be noticed that *D. iridis* and *P. pusillum* are also listed under the heterothallic species (see page 59). Some isolates are heterothallic and some complete their life cycles in monosporous cultures. Preliminary results in one of the writers' laboratories indicate the same may be true of *Fuligo septica*. Whether the strains or species which complete their life cycles in monosporous cultures are homothallic or apogamic is the big question.

It is impossible to prove, of course, that without syngamy no plasmodia are ever formed, except in heterothallic species in which the vast majority of isolated clones do not develop beyond a swarm cell/myxamoebal population. The two main proponents of apogamy in the Myxomycetes are von Stosch (1935, 1937, 1964, 1965) and Luyet (1950). Luyet based his argument on Gehenio and Luyet's (1950) results with *Physarella oblonga* which completes its development in monosporous or mono-myxamoebal cultures. He interpreted these results as indicating that no sexual fusions are necessary. This, of course, does not take into consideration that the organism may be homothallic. Indeed, Ross (1957b) reported syngamy in this species and has also presented evidence that syngamy does take place in *Didymium squamulosum*. His photographs of karyogamy are rather convincing.

Von Stosch's (von Stosch, *et al.*, 1964) claim of apogamy for one strain of *Physarum polycephalum* and for Kerr's strain of *Didymium nigripes* is based on "comparative chromosome counts in amoebae, presporal mitoses and meioses and from the comparative morphology of these three kinds of nuclear divisions." These workers state that "up to now no Myxomycetes simultaneously sexual and homothallic have been found. . . ." As Martin (1940) writes: "Von Stosch's report of apogamy and suggestion that this phenomenon is possibly of widespread occurrence in the group, if confirmed, will be of help in the interpretation of many of the discrepancies in the literature."

While the manuscript of the present volume was in the final stages of preparation, Kerr (1967) published his observations on plasmodial formation on a minute mutant (S3) of his strain of *Didymium nigripes*. In this isolate when spores were spread on agar media, very tiny clones of myxamoebae developed around the spores and minute plasmodia appeared within 48 hours. Through time-lapse and intermittent photography it was determined that the amoebae continue dividing for 24 hours or longer and that some of them at least become differentiated into plasmodia subsequently, without fusing with other cells. Such plasmodia developed through karyokinesis without cytokinesis and were followed to the 4-nucleate stage. It is of particular interest to note here Kerr's report that "There were obvious major differences between these nuclear divisions and those where the amoebae divided into two. Metaphase was greatly prolonged. Shortly after anaphase began the nuclei became indistinguishable. Sometime later two daughter nuclei appeared." Kerr further states that he saw binucleate cells fuse to form quadrinucleate cells and, on one occasion, a binucleate cell fuse with a uninucleate cell to form one with three nuclei. Inasmuch as he had also observed phagocytosis of uninucleate cells (presumably myxamoebae) by binucleate cells, he interpreted the uninucleate cell that fused with the binucleate as an already differentiated plasmodium, the nucleus of which had not as yet divided.

At about the same time, Sylvia Kerr (1967), working in the same laboratory, studied the wild type, in which Kerr (1961) had reported fusion of amoebae, and two mutant strains of the same organism. Spores of the wild type were plated out and began to germinate in about 16 hours. The amoebae began to divide 2–4 hours later and in another 15 hours plasmodia began to differentiate. She writes: "Plasmodia first appeared as large uninucleate cells which could be distinguished readily from amoebae by cytoplasmic characteristics." Later on she states, "I have never observed the origin of uninucleate plasmodia from the fusion of 2 amoebae." It is not clear, however, whether any one myxamoeba, observed to have arisen by division from another, was actually seen to differentiate into a plasmodium.

Sylvia Kerr also described the difference in nuclear division between amoebae and "uninucleate plasmodia." As other workers had for different species (see page 41), she also found the mitotic divisions in the amoebae to be extranuclear but those in the plasmodia to be intranuclear. It is difficult at this time to understand why the nucleus of a cell would divide one way when cytokinesis is to follow but in a different manner when cytokinesis is precluded unless we assume a doubling of DNA at the time of "differentiation." The implications of such "differentiation" are vast and call for a series of investigations on various "homothallic" species to discover whether these are not in reality apogamic as von Stosch (1935) believes. It is important to repeat here that von Stosch, et al. (1964) were unable to find any indication of meiosis in Kerr's strain of *Didymium nigripes* and concluded it is apogamic. Sylvia Kerr's results tend to support von Stosch on this point. Unfortunately, no other laboratory has produced evidence in support of apogamic development in any species of Myxomycetes up to now, but neither is solid proof of homothallism in any species to be found in the literature.

MEIOSIS

The place of meiosis in the life cycle of the Myxomycetes is even more controversial. Only about *Ceratiomyxa fruticulosa* is there perfect agreement. Gilbert (1935), Wilson and Ross (1955), and Sansome and Dixon (1965) all reported meiosis taking place in the spore, and all found the chromosome number to be $n = 8$.

Evidence for Meiosis

The only absolute criterion for the occurrence of meiosis in the life cycle of an organism is the reduction of the chromosome number by one-half after two closely successive nuclear divisions have been completed. In the Myxomycetes, such direct evidence is not easily obtainable because the chromosomes are minute and because in many species their number is very large and accurate counts are difficult to make. Nevertheless, a number of workers have presented chromosome counts in support of their conclusions. Foremost among these are Jahn (1908), Wilson and Cadman (1928), Cadman (1931), von Stosch (1935), Guttes, Guttes, and Rusch (1961), and Ross (1967c). Because of the difficulty in obtaining comparative chromosome counts other investigators have cited indirect evidence for meiosis. Wilson and Ross (1955) and Ross (1961), for example, based their conclusions on the occurrence of two nuclear divisions, the first of which provided certain fairly reliable cytological indicators of meiosis, such as chromosome bridges and rings. Therrien (1966a, b) measured DNA spectrophotometrically at various stages of the life cycle. This is a relatively new technique, the results of which must be interpreted with great care because they are related to the stage at which nuclei are fixed and stained. Nuclei stained before DNA replication, i.e., at the 1C stage, will have only half the amount of DNA present in nuclei that have attained the 2C stage. Proper timing is important here inasmuch as division figures are not sought, and conclusions are based solely on comparative amounts of DNA.

The presence of synaptinemal complexes during nuclear division has been presented as evidence of meiosis by Carroll and Dykstra (1966) and by Aldrich (1967). The significance of these structures as indicators of meiosis is discussed on page 74.

Results Obtained by Various Investigators

The results obtained by various investigators on the occurrence of meiosis in the Myxomycetes has been recently summarized by Aldrich (1967) as shown in Table 10 (pages 66–71), modified from his paper.

An examination of this table shows that the conclusions reached by various researchers can be grouped into four main categories:

1. Meiosis is accomplished in one division prior to cleavage.
2. Meiosis I takes place in the sporangium before cleavage and meiosis II in the spores at germination.
3. Meiosis I and II occur in the sporangium prior to spore cleavage.
4. Meiosis takes place in the spores after cleavage.

There is also a group of investigators who found only a single nuclear division before cleavage, but who did not commit themselves as to the nature of the division or the place of meiosis in the life cycle.

Jahn (1908, 1911, 1933) and Guttes, Guttes, and Rusch (1961) are the only workers who claim meiosis is accomplished in one division.

Kranzlin (1907), working with various species of *Arcyria, Trichia,* and *Oligonema,* was of the opinion that the first meiotic division occurs in the sporangium, immediately after karyogamy and before spore cleavage, and that the second division takes place in the spores at germination.

From the behavior of her monosporous cultures of *Didymium difforme* Cayley (1929) concluded that the first meiotic division must take place before spore formation and the second at spore germination. The assumptions on which her conclusions were based, however, were not valid. Kranzlin's scheme is not impossible. The cleaved spores would, accordingly, contain the first products of meiosis and the second division would be delayed. Modern research, however, does not seem to have brought support to this theory.

Two Divisions Before Spore Cleavage. We come now to the third theory which is supported by several investigators. Four techniques have been used by this group (sections, squashes, spectrophotometric analysis of DNA, and electron microscopy) to study 18 organisms. Each worker concluded that, in the organism(s) he studied, meiosis takes place before cleavage. Of particular interest in this connection are the results obtained with *Didymium iridis.* Both Schünemann (1930) and Cadman (1931), the first studying sectioned material, the second both sections and squashes, found two divisions in the sporangia before cleavage. As Aldrich (1967) states, Schünemann's meiosis I figures are not convincing. Cadman counted 8 chromosomes in plasmodial nuclei undergoing division and 4 chromosomes at the second meiotic division during cleavage. She also counted 4 chromosomes in the swarm-cell nuclei and 8 in the zygotes. Therrien (1966a, b) measured DNA spectrophotometrically in the nuclei of the myxamoebae, the plasmodia, and the mature spores of a heterothallic isolate. He found the mean DNA content of the plasmodial nuclei to be approximately double that of the myxamoebal and spore nuclei (Fig. 14). Carroll and Dykstra (1966) examined thin sec-

Table 10. Summary of results obtained by various investigators on the occurrence of meiosis in the class Myxomycetes. (Modified from Aldrich, 1967.)

Species, Listed Alphabetically*	Worker and Date	Technique Used	Stages Observed	Conclusions
Arcyria cinerea	Kranzlin, 1907	Sections	Developing sporangia	Nuclear fusion in young sporangium, followed by Meiosis I. Meiosis II as spore germinates.
Arcyria incarnata	Lister, 1893	Squashes	Developing sporangia	A single division within the hour preceding cleavage.
Badhamia utricularis	Lister, 1893	Squashes	Developing sporangia	A single division within the hour preceding cleavage.
Badhamia utricularis	Jahn, 1933	Sections	Developing sporangia	A single meiotic division preceding cleavage.
Ceratiomyxa fruticulosa	Olive, 1907	Sections	Developing sporophores and spores	Meiosis I and II in young spore.
Ceratiomyxa fruticulosa	Jahn, 1908	Sections	Developing sporophores and spores	A single meiotic division before spore formation.
Ceratiomyxa fruticulosa	Gilbert, 1935	Sections and whole spores	Developing sporophores and spores	Two divisions in spore. Presumed meiotic. Nuclei in second division smaller.
Ceratiomyxa fruticulosa	Wilson and Ross, 1955	Squashes	Developing sporophores and spores	Meiosis I and II occur in spore.
Ceratiomyxa fruticulosa	Sansome and Dixon, 1965	Squashes	Mature spores	Meiosis I and II occur in the spore.
Comatricha nigra	Lister, 1893	Sections	Developing sporophores and spores	A single division preceding cleavage.
Comatricha nigra	von Stosch, 1937	Sections	Developing sporangia and spores	Meiosis I and II in the spore about 12 hours after cleavage.

* All names according to Martin and Alexopoulos (1968).

Table 10. Continued.

Species, Listed Alphabetically	Worker and Date	Technique Used	Stages Observed	Conclusions
Comatricha typhoides	Wilson and Ross, 1955	Squashes	Developing sporangia	Meiosis I and II precede cleavage.
Dictydium cancellatum	Jahn, 1901	Sections	Developing sporangia	No division figures found.
Dictydium cancellatum	Ross, 1961	Squashes	Developing sporangia	Meiosis I and II before cleavage.
Didymium clavus	Dangeard, 1947	Sections	Developing sporangia and spores	Meiosis I and II in spores.
Didymium difforme	Cayley, 1929		Developing sporangia	Meiosis I before cleavage. Meiosis II at germination.
Didymium (nigripes var. *xanthopus) iridis*	Schünemann, 1930	Sections	Developing sporangia	Meiosis I and II precede cleavage. Meiosis I figures not convincing.
Didymium (nigripes var. *xanthopus) iridis* (but different from Schünemann's according to Schure, 1949)	Cadman, 1931	Squashes	Developing sporangia	Meiosis I and II precede cleavage.
Didymium (nigripes) iridis (same as Schünemann)	von Stosch, 1935	Sections	Developing sporangia and spores	Meiosis not seen in spore. Division figures observed prior to cleavage.
Didymium iridis	Therrien, 1966 a, b	Microspectrophotometry	Myxamoebae, plasmodium, mature spores	Meiosis I and II before cleavage.
Didymium iridis	Carroll and Dykstra, 1966	Electron microscopy	Developing sporangia	Synaptinemal complexes and division figures preceding cleavage. Meiosis occurs before cleavage.
Didymium melanospermum	Harper, 1914	Sections	Developing sporangia and mature spores	One synchronous division precedes cleavage. No division seen in spores.

Table 10. Continued.

Species, Listed Alphabetically	Worker and Date	Technique Used	Stages Observed	Conclusions
Didymium nigripes	von Stosch, 1935	Sections	Developing sporangia	A single mitotic division precedes cleavage. Meiosis I and II follow in twelve-hour-old spore.
Didymium nigripes (Kerr's strain)	Schuster, 1964 a	Electron microscopy	Developing sporangia	Division figures in the sporangium prior to cleavage. No synaptinemal complexes shown. Division figures were "presumed to be meiotic."
Didymium nigripes (Kerr's strain)	Therrien, 1966 a, b	Microspectrophotometry	Amoebae, plasmodium, post-cleavage spores	Meiosis I and II precede cleavage.
Didymium squamulosum	von Stosch, 1937	Sections	Sporangia and spores	Division figures before cleavage. Only one atypical division seen in the spore. This probably not meiotic.
Enteridium sp. (*Reticularia*)	Harper, 1914	Sections	Developing sporangia	One synchronous division preceding cleavage.
Fuligo septica	Rosen, 1893	Sections	Developing sporangia (aethalia)	Saw division in sporangium before cleavage.
Fuligo septica	Harper, 1900	Sections	Developing sporangia (aethalia)	A single division at cleavage.
Fuligo septica	Ross, 1961	Acetoorcein squashes	Developing sporangia (aethalia)	Meiosis I and II in sporangium before cleavage.
Hemitrichia clavata	Harper and Dodge, 1914	Sections	Developing sporangia	Division figures as cleavage begins.
Lamproderma arcyrioides	Ross, 1960	Squashes	Developing sporangia	Meiosis I and II preceding cleavage.
Lamproderma arcyrionema	Wilson and Ross, 1955	Squashes	Developing sporangia	Meiosis I and II preceding cleavage.

Table 10. Continued.

Species, Listed Alphabetically	Worker and Date	Technique Used	Stages Observed	Conclusions
Lycogala epidendrum	Harper, 1914	Sections	Developing sporangia and mature spores	One division precedes cleavage. No divisions seen in spores.
Lycogala epidendrum	Wilson and Ross, 1955	Squashes	Developing sporangia	Meiosis I and II precede cleavage.
Lycogala exiguum	Conrad, 1910	Sections	Developing sporangia	A single division at cleavage.
Metatrichia vesparium	Wilson and Ross, 1955	Squashes	Developing sporangia	Meiosis I and II preceding cleavage.
Mucilago crustacea	Schure, 1949	Squashes	Developing sporangia	Meiosis I and II during cleavage.
Perichaena vermicularis	Ross, 1967 c	Squashes	Myxamoebae, cleaving plasmodiocarps, young spores	Meiosis just before cleavage or in young spore depending on conditions at fruiting.
Physarella oblonga	Bisby, 1914	Sections	Cleaving sporangium	Nuclei divide just before cleavage.
Physarella oblonga	Ross, 1961	Squashes	Developing sporangia	Meiosis I and II just before cleavage.
Physarum cinereum	von Stosch, 1935	Sections	Developing sporangia	Division in cleaving sporangia. No meiotic figures found in spores.
Physarum didermoides	Jahn, 1911	Sections	Developing sporangia	One division, believed to be meiotic, before spore formation.
Physarum didermoides	Schure, 1949	Squashes	Developing sporangia	One mitotic division before cleavage.
Physarum flavicomum	Therrien, 1966 a	Microspectro-photometry	Myxamoebae, plasmodium, post-cleavage spores, mature spores.	Meiosis I and II precede cleavage.

Table 10. Continued.

Species, Listed Alphabetically	Worker and Date	Technique Used	Stages Observed	Conclusions
Physarum flavicomum	Aldrich, 1967	Electron microscopy	Young spores	Synaptinemal complexes; intranuclear divisions; disintegrating nuclei; meiosis I and II in young spores.
Physarum globuliferum	Aldrich, 1967	Electron microscopy	Young spores	Synaptinemal complexes; meiosis occurs in young spores.
Physarum gyrosum	Koevenig, 1964	Squashes	Developing sporangia	Division figures just before spores are delimited. Not determined whether one or two divisions.
Physarum leucophaeum	Lister, 1893	Squashes	Developing sporangia	A single division within the hour preceding cleavage.
Physarum polycephalum	Howard, 1931 a	Sections	Developing sporangia	A single mitotic division preceding cleavage.
Physarum polycephalum	Dalleux, 1940	Stained squashes	Developing sporangia	A single division preceding cleavage.
Physarum polycephalum	Ross, 1961	Squashes	Developing sporangia	Meiosis I and II preceding cleavage.
Physarum polycephalum	Guttes, Guttes, and Rusch, 1961	Chromosome counts; sections	Developing sporangia	One meiotic division prior to cleavage.
Physarum polycephalum (sexual isolates)	von Stosch, *et al.* 1964	Sections	Sporangia and spores	Meiosis in day-old spores.
Physarum polycephalum	Aldrich, 1967	Electron microscopy	Young spores	Synaptinemal complexes; meiosis occurs in young spores.
Physarum pusillum	Therrien, 1966 a	Microspectrophotometry	Myxamoebae, plasmodium, mature spores	Meiosis I and II preceding cleavage.
Reticularia lycoperdon	Wilson and Cadman, 1928	Squashes	Developing sporangia	Meiosis I and II just prior to spore cleavage.

Table 10. Continued.

Species, Listed Alphabetically	Worker and Date	Technique Used	Stages Observed	Conclusions
Stemonitis axifera	Wilson and Ross, 1955	Squashes	Developing sporangia	Meiosis I and II precede cleavage.
Stemonitis fusca	Bisby, 1914	Sections	Developing sporangia	Saw dividing nuclei just before spores were delimited. No comment on meiosis.
Stemonitis fusca	Koevenig, 1964	Squashes	Developing sporangia	Meiosis I and II in developing sporangium.
Stemonitis pallida	Wilson and Ross, 1955	Squashes	Developing sporangia	Meiosis I and II just before spore delimitation.
Trichia (fragilis) botrytis	Lister, 1893	Sections	Developing sporangia	A single division preceding cleavage.
Trichia persimilis	Kranzlin, 1907	Sections	Developing sporangia	Nuclear fusion in young sporangium, followed by meiosis I. Meiosis II occurs as spores germinate.
Trichia persimilis	Wilson and Ross, 1955	Squashes	Developing sporangia	Meiosis I and II precede cleavage.
Trichia (fallax) decipiens	Strasburger, 1884	Sections	Developing sporangia	One synchronous division just before spore cleavage.
Trichia (fallax) decipiens	Lister, 1893	Squashes	Developing sporangia	A single division within the hour preceding cleavage.
Trichia (fallax) decipiens	Kranzlin, 1907	Sections	Developing sporangia	Nuclear fusion in young sporangium, followed by meiosis I. Meiosis II occurs as spores germinate.
Trichia varia	Jahn, 1933	Sections	Developing sporangia	One division before cleavage.
Tubifera microsperma	Ross, 1961	Squashes	Developing sporangia	Meiosis I and II in sporangium preceding cleavage.

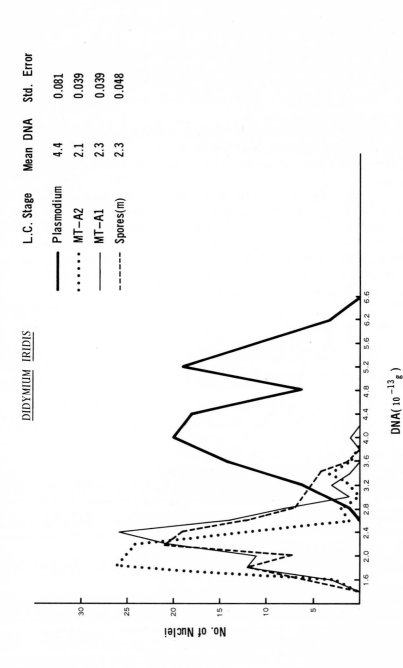

Fig. 14. DNA content of nuclei in three stages of the life cycle of *Didymium iridis*. (Courtesy C. D. Therrien. Redrawn from Therrien, 1966b, and reproduced by permission of the National Research Council of Canada from the Canadian Journal of Botany 44:1667–1675, 1966.)

tions of young, uncleaved sporangia in which the nuclei were dividing synchronously and which clearly demonstrated the presence of synaptinemal complexes therein.

Thus, in this one species, we have abundant evidence, obtained by varying techniques, supporting the occurrence of meiosis in the sporangium prior to spore delimitation. The only discordant note is the one sounded by von Stosch (1935) who studied Schünemann's strains of *D. iridis* and found it to be apogamic.

We know that the strain of *D. iridis* studied by Therrien and by Carroll and Dykstra is heterothallic and that there can be no question of apogamy there. Schünemann's strain, which von Stosch also studied, was not heterothallic. We now have evidence (Collins, 1965) that some strains of *D. iridis* complete their life cycles in monosporous cultures. These strains have been termed homothallic by Collins but without proof that syngamy takes place. If we assume that von Stosch, *et al.* (1964) are correct when they write, ". . . no Myxomycetes simultaneously sexual and homothallic have been found . . . ," then von Stosch's earlier results stand in contradiction with those of Schünemann but not necessarily with those of the other investigators.

Meiosis After Cleavage. Let us now examine the case for meiosis occurring in the spores after cleavage has taken place.

We have already seen that here is perfect agreement that this is true in *Ceratiomyxa fruticulosa*. For the endosporous species, von Stosch (1935, 1937, 1964, 1965), Dangeard (1947), and Aldrich (1967) are the workers that support this theory. Dangeard, working with *Didymium clavus,* found 2 or 4 nuclei in some maturing spores; in others he observed 2 resting nuclei side by side with a metaphase plate of 8 chromosomes. He believed this to be evidence for meiosis in the spore. Von Stosch's arguments in support of his contention that meiosis occurs in the spore are much more convincing. Von Stosch studied a heterothallic isolate of *Didymium nigripes* and the same isolate of *Didymium iridis* which Schünemann had used and which both Schünemann and von Stosch found able to complete its life cycle in single spore culture. In the heterothallic *D. nigripes* he found meiosis to occur in the maturing spore with one nucleus disintegrating after each division, leaving the spore uninucleate and haploid. He counted 24–25 chromosomes in meiotic metaphase, 27 during the division of the myxamoebae, and 59 in the plasmodial divisions. In *D. iridis,* in which he could not demonstrate meiosis, he counted 81 chromosomes in myxamoebal divisions and considered this organism to be triploid and apogamic. Later, working with *Comatricha nigra,* he reported finding two divisions in the maturing spores, supporting his previous conclusions. In his 1965 review article von Stosch includes a generalized life cycle diagram in which meiosis in the Endosporeae is shown to occur in the young spores.

Aldrich (1967) worked with heterothallic isolates of *Physarum flavicomum, P. globuliferum,* and *P. polycephalum.* Using the electron microscope he searched for synaptinemal complexes. He found them in all three species occurring in the spores at the beginning of a nuclear division he interpreted as meiosis I (Fig. 15). He also presented evidence for a second division in the spores of *P. flavicomum* and found quadrinucleate spores with evidence of nuclear degeneration following meiosis (Fig. 16).

In 1964 Moses and Coleman stated, "Neither the complex nor anything resembling it has ever been seen in somatic chromosomes." Since that statement was printed, however, Sotelo and Wettstein (1964), Schin (1965a, b), and Wolstenholme and Meyer (1966) have found similar structures in the nuclei of spermatids of *Gryllus,* and Menzel and Price (1966) have also found them to occur occasionally in anthers of tomato haploids where meiosis would normally take place in diploid plants. All these observations might be interpreted to mean that the mere presence of synaptinemal complexes is not an absolute criterion of the position of meiosis in the nuclear cycle (Ross, 1967c). It must be emphasized, however, that in his study of *P. flavicomum* Aldrich (1967) found (1) a normal mitotic prophase during pre-cleavage division with no synaptinemal complexes; (2) a gradual appearance of synaptinemal complexes in dividing spore nuclei 18 hours after cleavage, reaching nearly 100 per cent occurrence 20 hours after cleavage; and (3) nuclei in metaphase, anaphase, and telophase inside the spores about 24 hours after cleavage. Significantly, perhaps, Aldrich also found that the mitotic spindles in the nuclear divisions within the maturing spores were intranuclear (Fig. 17), a strong indication that these nuclei were diploid (see page 41), supporting his contention that meiosis had not taken place prior to spore formation.

No one up to this time had searched for meiotic divisions in *P. flavicomum* or *P. globuliferum,* but several people had investigated *P. polycephalum.* It will be remembered (Table 10) that Howard (1931a) found only one division prior to spore delimitation in the sporangium of this species. We have already mentioned Guttes, Guttes, and Rusch's conclusion that this division is meiotic. Aldrich's thesis of meiosis taking place in the maturing spore agrees in general with von Stosch's findings for several species including heterothallic strains of *P. polycephalum* (von Stosch, *et al.,* 1964) but is in direct contradiction with those of Ross (1961) who found two divisions (interpreted as meiosis I and II) before spore formation and "no evidence of any nuclear division . . . in the spores at any stage of development."

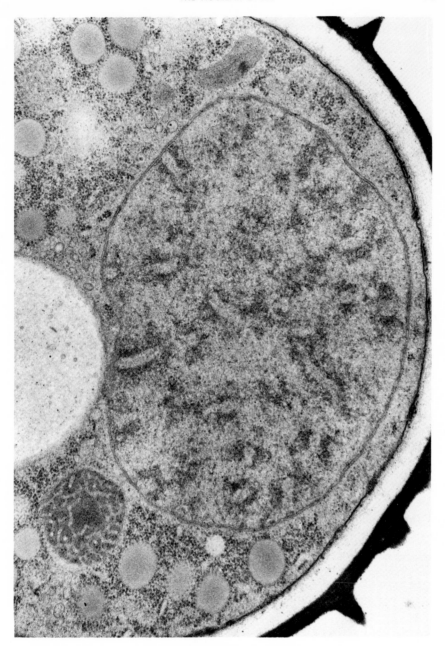

Fig. 15. *Physarum flavicomum.* Synaptinemal complexes in nucleus of young spore. × 34,500. (Aldrich, 1967. Courtesy Henry Aldrich and Cell Research Institute, University of Texas at Austin.)

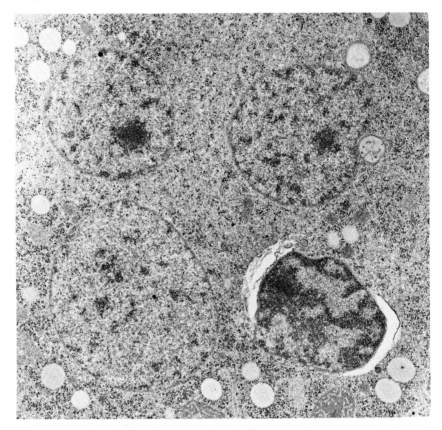

Fig. 16. *Physarum flavicomum.* Four nuclei in a young spore; one enclosed in a vacuole and degenerating. × 13,600. (Aldrich, 1967. Courtesy Henry Aldrich and Cell Research Institute, University of Texas at Austin.)

Ross based his conclusions on squashes made in rapid succession during sporangial development in culture. He was unable to count chromosomes during the first division, but counted $n = 90 \pm 3$ in what he interpreted to be the second division.

It must be emphasized here that it is possible that all isolates of a myxomycete species do not necessarily behave in the same way. Indeed, as was mentioned above, it has been shown by Collins (1965) for *Didymium iridis,* and by Alexopoulos and Henney (unpublished, 1966) for *Physarum pusillum* and *Fuligo septica* that some isolates are heterothallic and others complete their life cycles in monosporous cultures. Similarly, it is conceivable that in the isolate of *P. polycephalum* studied by Ross meiosis takes place just before the spores are delimited, while in

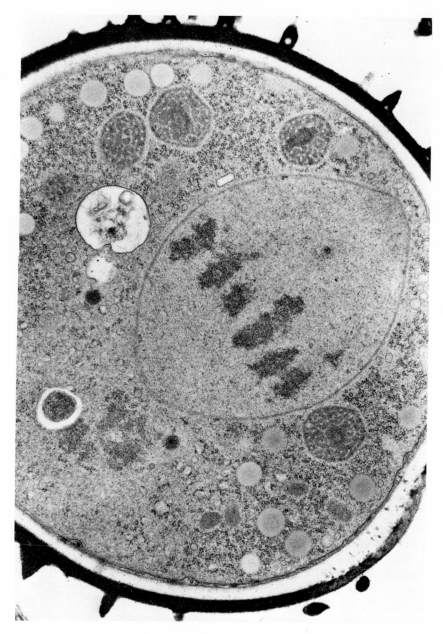

Fig. 17. *Physarum flavicomum.* Nucleus in young spore dividing by intranuclear division. Meiosis I (?). × 17,850. (Aldrich, 1967. Courtesy Henry Aldrich and Cell Research Institute, University of Texas at Austin.)

the one Aldrich studied it may be delayed until after the spores are formed.

More difficult to reconcile are the results of Aldrich with those of Therrien (1966a) on *Physarum flavicomum*, because they were based on studies of the same isolate. Therrien measured spectrophotometrically the DNA in the nuclei of myxamoebae, plasmodia, post-cleavage spores, and mature spores of *P. flavicomum* and found the same amount of DNA in all stages except in the plasmodial nuclei which had twice that amount. He concluded that meiosis takes place before cleavage. To explain such contradictory results one would have to assume that the place of meiosis in the myxomycete life cycle is not precisely fixed and may take place at cleavage or after spore wall formation in the same isolate. And indeed this is exactly the hypothesis that Ross (1967c) proposes in a very recent paper. Working with *Perichaena vermicularis*, which he grew on agar media in incubators programmed for 14 hours light and 10 hours darkness corresponding to the normal day–night cycle, he made comparative chromosome counts and reported 25 ± 2 in the amoebae and 50 ± 4 in the plasmodia. During nuclear divisions which occurred 4 to 5 hours after fruiting had begun "all countable nuclei possessed 25 ± 2 chromosomes." Cleavage and spore formation followed. About 2 per cent of the cleaved sections were binucleate, the majority being uninucleate. One of the nuclei in the binucleate segments appeared to be in the process of disintegration. No sign of nuclear division was found in the spores. Ross then reprogrammed the incubators shifting the light–dark cycle so that the dark period was from 10:00 A.M. to 8:00 P.M. Not until the seventh generation after recycling did the organism adjust to the new conditions. In the intervening generations, cultures fruited at irregular times and division synchrony was disrupted; only 40–50 per cent of the nuclei actively divided at a particular time. In these, the chromosome count was uniformly 50 ± 4, indicating meiosis was not occurring at this time. Examination of young spores revealed that nuclear division was taking place, and that some spores contained 1, 2, or 4 nuclei. All mature spores examined were uninucleate.

From these results, Ross concluded that meiosis is not necessarily linked to the morphological cycle, and that it may occur before or after cleavage depending on the conditions under which sporulation takes place. It is of considerable interest to note that all investigators who studied more than one species always found meiosis to occur at the same place in the nuclear cycle (Kranzlin, 1907; von Stosch, 1935; Ross, 1957b; Therrien, 1966a, b; Aldrich, 1967). Each used the same technique for all species he investigated.

Obviously what is needed is intensive investigation of many isolates of many species, using various approaches with the same isolate grown under the same and under different conditions, before the meiotic picture in the Myxomycetes will begin to clear. Nevertheless, it now appears very probable that in some species or strains meiosis does take place in the maturing spores as von Stosch first suggested. Although experimental manipulation may disrupt the nuclear cycle, as Ross's recent results with *Perichaena vermicularis* seem to indicate, the idea that the place of meiosis in that cycle may not be stable under the usual conditions prevalent in natural habitats cannot at the moment be accepted unequivocally.

HYBRIDIZATION AND HETEROKARYOSIS

Taxonomists of Myxomycetes are very well aware of the intermediate forms that exist between a number of common, widespread species. Such forms are responsible for statements like the following by Hagelstein (1944, pp. 158–159), under *Comatricha laxa:* "This is hardly more than a variety of *C. nigra,* but a useful center for forms with a more open capillitium . . . *C. ellissii* is merely one of the numerous phases grouped together under *C. laxa* as a center."

Three closely related species in the genus *Trichia* are separated on the basis of diameter of elaters and markings of the spore walls. The elaters of *T. favoginea* are 6–8 microns in diameter; those of *T. persimillis* are 4–6 microns. The reticulations of *T. favoginea* are complete in the form of narrow bands; those of *T. persimillis* are incomplete pitted bands. In *T. affinis* the elaters are 4–6 microns in diameter and the reticulations complete, or nearly complete, pitted bands. Hagelstein (1944, p. 227) writes of *T. affinis,* "The form is intermediate between *T. favoginea* and *T. persimillis.*" Farr (1958), after a thorough study of a large number of collections of the three species, decided there was complete intergradation of characters and united the three species under the oldest name, *T. favoginea.*

Intermediate forms such as the above, when they occur in plants, are usually suspected of being hybrids and are often proved to be just that (Alston and Turner, 1963). Alexopoulos (1963), discussing this situation, pointed out that "there does not appear to be a single report in the literature of proved interspecific hybridization in the Myxomycetes." It may be added to this that, in the laboratory of one of the writers, several attempts have been made to hybridize closely related species without success. Indeed, even different forms of what is undoubtedly the same species do not hybridize easily, as shown by Alexopoulos' (1964b) futile attempts to cross the yellow and white forms of *Physarella oblonga* and by Henney's experiments with *Physarum flavicomum.* As Henney (1967) and Henney and Henney (1968) have shown, only morphologically identical isolates of this species are sexually compatible. However, three clear cases of hybridization between co-specific isolates with genetic markers other than mating type are now known. The first two include the successful hybridization of an emetine-resistant strain of *Physarum polycephalum* with the wild type (Dee, 1962) and of an actidione-resistant strain with the wild type (Dee, 1966a). The third is the mating of two isolates of *Didymium iridis* with plasmodia of different colors (Collins and Clark, 1966a).

It has often been assumed that since plasmodia supposedly originate only from single zygotes by nuclear division they are unquestionably homokaryotic. Reports by Skupienski (1934, 1939), Torrend (1909), Gray (1945), Alexopoulos and Zabka (1962), and Alexopoulos (1964b) prompted Alexopoulos (1963) [2] to write in his recent review article:

> The inability of the plasmodia of various races of the same species to fuse one with another again raises the question of the existence of heterokaryosis in a plasmodium. Inconceivable as it may be that all the nuclei in a large plasmodium are and always must be genetically identical, the fact remains that up to now no evidence of heterokaryosis has been obtained in any myxomycete and all attempts to produce a heterokaryon in the laboratory have, to my knowledge, failed.

Three papers published since then have dealt in part with this question. Kerr (1965c) working with two strains of *Didymium nigripes*, one (C6) giving rise to plaques surrounded by large plasmodia, the second (A20) to plaques containing only amoebae, was able to induce fusion between the plasmodia of the two strains. He then broke up the fused plasmodia mechanically and plated out the resulting minute fragments (microplasmodia) which he allowed to fruit. Analysis of the plaques resulting from spore germination revealed that both strains could be recovered from the fragmented fusion plasmodium. These results would normally be interpreted as proof of synthesis of a heterokaryon, except for the fact that the A20 genetic markers were lost when plaques from spores obtained from unfragmented fusion plasmodia were scored. Kerr explained his results by assuming the A20 characters are controlled by non-chromosomal factors.

Collins (1966), studying *Didymium iridis,* suggested the existence of an incompatibility mechanism for plasmodial coalescence. He attempted to fuse plasmodia of known parentage and showed that only plasmodia with common parents would coalesce except in two instances where the fusing plasmodia had one parent in common. These last two fusions,

[2] The results in the 1964 article had been communicated to the Mycological Society of America at its 1958 Annual Meeting.

Collins believed, "probably brought about the creation of heterokaryotic plasmodia."

In a later paper, Collins and Clark (1968) reported the creation of two types of heterokaryons in *D. iridis* through the coalescence of plasmodia (1) of two different colors, brown (Bb) and cream (bb), and (2) with two sets of mating type alleles, A^1A^2 and A^2A^4.

In view of these results it is now reasonable to assume that since heterokaryosis has been induced in the laboratory it may also occur in nature under certain conditions.

Carlile and Dee (1967) reported that in *Physarum polycephalum* only plasmodia with identical genotype at the fusion locus "f" would coalesce. With certain combinations of strains, however, fusion is followed by a lethal reaction which destroys one or both of the fused plasmodia. No explanation was offered for this reaction.

CHROMOSOME NUMBERS

Early investigators who counted chromosomes in the endosporous species always reported small numbers (Harper, 1900; Jahn, 1911; Wilson and Cadman, 1928; Schünemann, 1930; Cadman, 1931). Von Stosch (1935, 1937) was the first one to make much larger counts. His results were confirmed in a general way by Wilson and Ross (1955), and subsequently by Ross (1960, 1961, 1966, 1967b, c) who also reported large numbers.

Contrary to the disagreements mentioned above, all four researchers who have counted chromosomes in *Ceratiomyxa fruticulosa* agree that the correct number is $n = 8$. Table 11 summarizes the counts that have been reported in the literature for various species of Myxomycetes.

A great variation in chromosome number was found by Ross (1966) in different microplasmodia of his strain 51c of *Physarum polycephalum* growing in axenic culture in liquid media. All nuclei in the same microplasmodium had the same chromosome number, but the number varied greatly in different plasmodia in the same culture. The variation suggested a polyploid series within the same strain. The same situation was found to prevail in the myxamoebae of *Badhamia obovata*. Growing Myxomycetes in liquid media axenically subjects them, of course, to most unnatural conditions, and great caution should be exercised in accepting conclusions drawn from such experiments as validly applying to the developmental history of the Myxomycetes in nature. Nevertheless, it is interesting, but not surprising, to know that the number of chromosomes does not seem to affect the ability of the plasmodia to grow and that of their nuclei to divide. Polyploidy is not uncommon in more complex

Table 11.

Species	Haploid Number	Investigator
Ceratiomyxa fruticulosa	8	Jahn (1908)
	6–8	Gilbert (1935)
	8	Wilson and Ross (1955)
	8	Sansome and Dixon (1965)
Badhamia utricularis	8	Jahn (1933)
Comatricha nigra	30	von Stosch (1937)
Dictydium cancellatum	25 ± 3	Ross (1961)
Didymium iridis	8 ± 1	Schünemann (1930)
	4	Cadman (1931)
	81	von Stosch (1935)
Didymium nigripes	8	Schünemann (1930)
	27	von Stosch (1935)
Didymium squamulosum	8	Jahn (1911)
Fuligo septica	12	Harper (1900)
Lamproderma arcyrionema	53 ± 2	Ross (1960)
Metatrichia vesparium	90 ± 3–4	Wilson and Ross (1955)
Perichaena vermicularis	25 ± 2	Ross (1967b, c)
Physarella oblonga	50 ± 3	Ross (1961)
Physarum flavicomum	35 ± 2	Ross (1966)
Physarum polycephalum	90 ± 3	Ross (1961)
	no more than 8	Guttes, et al. (1961)
Reticularia lycoperdon	4	Wilson and Cadman (1928)

organisms, and polyploids seem to have no difficulty surviving in nature. It would be very interesting, indeed, in view of the coalescence experiments reported in the previous section, to determine whether plasmodia with different chromosome numbers would coalesce. Of even greater interest is the existence, and the apparent ability to grow and divide, of myxamoebae representing a polyploid series, as Ross points out, and the possibility that diploid amoebae, for example, may proceed to form plasmodia without sexual fusions and possibly to sporulate without meiosis.

In connection with differences in chromosome numbers and their possible effects on fusion of protoplasts, it is important to mention that in heterothallic strains of Didymium iridis the amoebae of the two mating types have been reported to have different amounts of DNA in their nuclei (Therrien, 1966b). It would be interesting to investigate the chromosome situation in these strains and to see if the difference in DNA content is reflected in different counts.

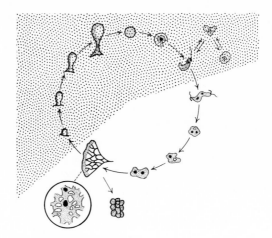

5

Plasmodial Formation

There are two general aspects to the question of plasmodial formation. The first is developmental and deals with the mechanism involved; the second is environmental and examines the conditions under which the developmental mechanism operates.

DEVELOPMENT

Plasmodial formation, as we have seen, was believed by Cienkowski (1863a, b) to be the result of the coalescence of several swarm cells. Since that time, it has been well established that in many species or strains syngamy is an integral part of the life cycle and a prerequisite to plasmodial formation. There are two questions to which we must now direct our attention: (1) How is the plasmodium formed in species in which gametic unions occur? (2) How is it formed in strains that, if von Stosch (1935, 1937, 1964, 1965) is correct, complete their life cycles apogamously?

We have seen that all those who believed that karyogamy was delayed until a late stage in plasmodial development agreed that the initial plasmodial stage was a result of fusion of two to several cells, as Cienkowski (1863a, b) has written. This viewpoint was defended by Skupienski (1926, 1927, 1928) and by Schünemann (1930) in later years. However, once the position of karyogamy was firmly established in the fusion cell of many species the question remained: Does the zygote develop into a plasmodium by growth and nuclear division or is there an aggregation and multiple fusion of zygotes that result in plasmodial formation?

Nuclear Division versus Multiple Fusion of Zygotes

Jahn (1911) illustrated his discussion of plasmodial formation in *Physarum didermoides* with drawings of mitosis in a zygote and in a 6-nucleate plasmodium. These drawings were made from stained preparations. Jahn admitted that it is often not easy to distinguish an uninucleate plasmodium (zygote) from a myxamoeba, but he stated, "Zwar ist der Kern eines jungen Plasmodiums, wenn er kurz vor der Teilung steht, viel grösser als ein Amöben kern."

Lister (1925), in his introduction to the Monograph of Mycetozoa, presents drawings made from stained material Jahn had sent him. It is of interest that the nuclei in the 5-nucleate plasmodium shown (see Fig. 18f) are about the same size as the nucleus of the myxamoeba (Fig. 18a). Size of nuclei is not always a good criterion for distinguishing between a myxamoeba and a zygote. It cannot be denied, however, that the differ-

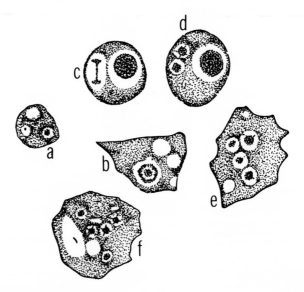

Fig. 18. *Didymium squamulosum* Fries. All the same magnification. a. Myxamoeba. b. Zygote with a single large diploid nucleus and several vacuoles. c. Zygote or young plasmodium with a single nucleus undergoing mitotic division, and a large digestive vacuole containing the remains of a myxamoeba. d. Young plasmodium with two resting nuclei, and a digestive vacuole containing a myxamoeba. e, f. Young plasmodia with four or five nuclei respectively. [Redrawn from Lister, 1925. By permission of the Trustees of the British Museum (Natural History).]

ence in size between haploid and diploid nuclei is often substantial, as shown in Ross's (1967a) recent phase-contrast photomicrographs (Fig. 11, page 53). Wilson and Cadman (1928) studied the formation of the plasmodium in *Reticularia lycoperdon,* and their drawings show divisions of the fusion nucleus and of two nuclei side by side in a binucleate plasmodium. Cadman reported the growth of zygotes into plasmodia for *Didymium iridis.* Her drawings indicate a considerable difference in size between the haploid nucleus in the myxamoeba and the diploid nucleus in a zygote. In one drawing she shows two nuclei dividing and one resting in the same cell. Howard (1931a) was of the opinion that the zygote undergoes nuclear division and becomes converted into a plasmodium in *Physarum polycephalum.* He made camera-lucida drawings which illustrate various steps in this process, but was careful to state, "A complete series of steps showing the origin of the plasmodium from the zygote is lacking." Obviously, he did not regard drawings made from stained preparations as absolute proof of development.

In his 1957b paper, in which he described three life-cycle patterns in the Myxomycetes, Ross correlated method of plasmodial formation with swarm cell or myxamoebal fusions. He proposed that species in which swarm cells copulate produce plasmodia from single zygotes whereas in those in which fusion of myxamoebae takes place "zygotes come together in large numbers and coalesce into multinucleate plasmodia."

It is not clear from his paper whether in the flagellate and completely flagellate types Ross actually watched individual known zygotes become multinucleate. His photographs are of killed, fixed, and stained preparations. Also, he presents no proof that in the briefly flagellate type the large number of aggregated cells shown (Ross, 1957b, Fig. 7) are indeed zygotes. Kerr (1961) isolated fusing pairs of swarm cells of *Didymium nigripes* (Kerr's strain) in separate chambers and noted that plasmodia developed in 67 per cent of these cultures (Table 12) and fruited.

Next to actually watching the development of a plasmodium from a zygote, Kerr's method is probably the best, but Kerr failed to prove that karyogamy took place in the "fusing" cells he isolated, and his method, therefore, did not rule out apogamic development of the plasmodia. Indeed, Sylvia Kerr's work (1967) from the same laboratory would, if confirmed, indicate apogamy in this species. Koevenig's (1961a) well-known film shows a uninucleate amoeboid cell of *Physarum gyrosum,* in which two successive mitoses take place and render it quadrinucleate. This cell Koevenig believed to be a zygote, basing his conclusion on (1) the observations, filmed in an earlier sequence, that in the amoebae cytokinesis follows karyokinesis; (2) his observations that syngamy does take place in *P. gyrosum;* and (3) the difference in type of division between haploid and presumed diploid nuclei (see page 41). Koevenig (1964) also states that he has seen fusion "between zygotes, a zygote and

Table 12.   Isolation of fusing pairs of myxamoebae by micromanipulation.
(Kerr, 1961.   Reproduced by permission of Academic Press, Inc.)

Number isolated	52
Examined after 8 hours, still fusing,	
or fused (plated after 20 hours)	31
Of those plated:	
Number with amoebae	0
Number with plasmodia only	21
Summary	
Isolated, formed plasmodia	39 per cent
Isolated, survived as fusing pairs,	
formed plasmodia when plated	67 per cent

a two-nucleate plasmodium, and a zygote and six-nucleate plasmodium."
Again, he did not see the formation of the zygotes he observed fusing
but determined their nature from their size, the size of their nuclei, their
granular nature, and the vigor of the streaming they exhibited.

Nevertheless, Koevenig (1961a, b, 1964) made no mention of an
aggregation of zygotes, whereas Ross's photomicrograph, referred to
earlier, clearly shows a large number of cells (presumed to be zygotes)
in close proximity to a minute plasmodium which could have been formed
by the coalescence of several zygotes. Such a phenomenon is commonly
seen in cultures of certain species of Physarales. It remained to be determined (1) whether the aggregated stage is due to a food stimulus, as
Ross (1957b) was inclined to believe, or (2) whether a chemotactic or
other aggregation mechanism was operating.

In a recent excellent paper, Ross (1967a) clearly shows that in
Didymium iridis a plasmodium may develop from a single zygote or
from the successive coalescence of several zygotes, thus confirming Koevenig's results with *Physarum gyrosum*, which showed that either method
may be used by a particular species in developing its plasmodia. It is of
interest to record that Ross believes that the pathway a developing
plasmodium takes depends on spatial relationships between zygotes in a
culture. If a zygote is spatially isolated, it develops by itself; if other
zygotes are nearby, coalescence takes place. Active movement of zygotes
toward one another was not seen and the coalescence of zygotes in the
microcultures appeared to be fortuitous.

FACTORS AFFECTING PLASMODIAL FORMATION

The chief difficulty in growing many species of Myxomycetes in artificial culture is encountered at the point of plasmodial formation. In
many species spores germinate, and a myxamoebal or swarm cell popula-

tion is easily obtained. Plasmodial formation, however, does not take place, and the myxamoebae eventually round up, often encyst, and, in any case, develop no further. Whether this is due to a failure of gametic fusion to take place or to the failure of zygotes to develop into plasmodia is not known.

Very few studies have been directed toward discovering the environmental factors that favor or prevent plasmodial formation. Early workers (Strasburger, 1884; Stahl, 1884; Čelakovský, 1893; Lister, 1901; and Miller, 1898) grew plasmodia from spores on various natural substrata such as tan bark, hay infusion, plant stems, mushroom sporophores, etc., in various containers. Agar, used to solidify Vicia-infusions, was first employed by Klebs (1900) for the culture of Myxomycetes, but it was Constantineanu (1907) who made the first extensive study of their artificial cultures. Constantineanu worked with a number of species, mostly in the Physarales, and studied the influence of media, temperature, and moisture on the development of various phases. He found Knop's solution with dextrin or dextrin and glucose to be the most favorable medium. *Fuligo septica* formed plasmodia between 14° and 35° C, *Physarum didermoides* between 7° and 30° C, and *Didymium squamulosum* between 5° and 30° C. Constantineanu claims to have obtained plasmodia of the following species both on solid and in liquid media: *Fuligo septica, Physarum didermoides, Didymium squamulosum, Amaurochaete fuliginosa, Perichaena depressa, Badhamia macrocarpa, Leocarpus fragilis, Stemonitis fusca, Dictydium cancellatum, Diderma effusum,* and *Ceratiomyxa fruticulosa.* Inasmuch as he mentions obtaining fructifications of only a few of these, there is no way of knowing whether the plasmodia of the others belonged indeed to the species he started with.

There seems to be a gap of 50 years in the literature dealing with conditions that influence the formation of plasmodia in culture.

Kerr and Sussman (1958) inhibited plasmodial formation in *Didymium nigripes* (Kerr's strain) by adding 2 per cent glucose or 0.2 per cent brucine to the medium. The addition of 0.1 per cent sulphanilamide delayed plasmodium formation for 24 hours. No attempt was made to discover whether the inhibition was due to the prevention of gametic copulation or the growth of the zygotes. Therrien (1966b), using the same strain, inhibited plasmodial formation by adding 2 per cent glucose to the medium, following Kerr and Sussman's method, but he found two types of amoeboid cells in his cultures, one type with twice as much DNA as the other. He concluded that the presence of glucose did not prevent formation of zygotes but rather their development into plasmodia.

Kerr (1961), studying the factors that favor plasmodial formation in his strain of *Didymium nigripes,* found that the optimal concentration of amoebae for plasmodial formation was 2.5×10^5/ml. He based his conclusion on the number of "small clonal plasmodia free from myx-amoebae" without, however, providing proof that the plasmodia were indeed clonal, i.e., that each was derived from a single zygote. He also found that the addition of $SrCl_2$ at 0 time to suspensions of $1 \times 10^5/m$ myxamoebae in phosphate buffer stimulated plasmodial formation. This effect was apparently due to a stimulation of zygote formation, for in the presence of $SrCl_2$, Kerr observed fusing pairs of swarm cells which were rarely found in the control cultures.

The effect of temperature and light on plasmodial formation in *Physarum nicaraguense* was studied by Solis (1962). She inoculated 48 plates, each containing 20 ml CM/2 agar [1] with the same quantity of spores and added a suspension of *E. coli*. Twelve cultures were grown in continuous light, and 12 in continuous darkness in each of four temperatures: 15°, 20°, 25°, and 30° C. Table 13, taken from Solis, shows

Table 13. Relation of light and temperature to plasmodium formation in *Physarum nicaraguense*. Duration of experiment: 47 days. (Solis, 1962.)

Temperature of Incubator	Number of Cultures		Time Required for Plasmodium Formation		Number of Cultures Which Formed Plasmodia	
	Light	Dark	Light	Dark	Light	Dark
15° C	12	12	27 days	27 days	9	10
20° C	12	12	5 days	5 days	12	12
25° C	12	12	3 days	3 days	12	12
30° C	12	12	—	—	—	—

that light had no effect. Whether the very pronounced effect of temperature was actually exerted on plasmodial formation alone, however, is very debatable. Spore germination was very probably delayed at the lower temperatures and at 30° C, and accelerated at 20° and even more at 25° C. If zygote formation is prerequisite to plasmodial formation in this species, temperature probably exerted an influence on this pre-plasmodial stage also.

Although carefully controlled experiments other than those already mentioned have not been performed to determine the influence of various environmental factors on plasmodial formation, certain statements in the literature indicate that the environment is of considerable importance in determining whether plasmodia are formed in a given culture. Thus, Alexopoulos (1960a) states that aphanoplasmodia require a film of water for growth, and Wollman and Alexopoulos (1964) emphasize that "In the absence of such a film the plasmodia of the Stemonitales will usually

[1] See Appendix.

sclerotize." Indira and Kalyanasundaram (1963), however, reported that they were able to grow *Stemonitis herbatica* and *Arcyria cinerea* on agar surface as well as under water. Indira (1965) later reported she had grown *Diachea splendens* on agar, and since she did not mention keeping the cultures flooded, it is assumed the agar surface was relatively dry.

Wollman (1966), in an extensive study of stemonitaceous and trichiaceous species in agar culture, reports that the plasmodium of *Calomyxa metallica* develops only under water and that withholding water from the cultures of *Perichaena depressa* at their initial stages sharply reduces plasmodial formation. According to Wollman, "There appears to be a very delicate water balance necessary for the successful culture of *C. [Comatricha] laxa*. For example, water must be present in abundance for the swarm cells to swim efficiently, and then a good covering for the early developmental phases of the plasmodia. . . ." *Comatricha typhoides*, on the contrary, has a remarkable tolerance for a wide range of conditions during its early developmental phases. Even when the agar surface is relatively dry, swarm cells persist and crawl on the agar still retaining their flagella. Whether plasmodia are formed under these conditions is not stated. In summary, Wollman, referring to her experience with members of the Stemonitales and Trichiales, states that such species "thrive best in dark incubators set at a temperature of 20° C with free water present during germination of the spores and early plasmodial development."

In the present authors' experience, the presence of free water in a culture is not necessary for and may, in some instances, be inhibitory to plasmodial formation in the Physarales.

It should be obvious from the above review of the literature that although considerable progress has been made in recent years on the problem of plasmodial formation, much remains to be done. It appears fairly certain that in species in which gametic fusion is prerequisite to plasmodial formation a plasmodium may be formed either by the growth of a single zygote or by the successive coalescence of many zygotes, but the question of zygote aggregation requires further investigation. Sufficient data are not available to support either theory—that zygote fusion is fortuitous or that an active aggregation occurs. The question of the existence of apogamy in the Myxomycetes is, as has been emphasized, still highly controversial. Finally, the physiology of plasmodial formation is all but unknown. Until the factors that induce plasmodial formation in the Myxomycetes are discovered and such knowledge can be effectively applied, no progress can be made in culturing the majority of species. Without spore-to-spore culture under controlled conditions, our knowledge of the life history of these organisms must of necessity remain incomplete.

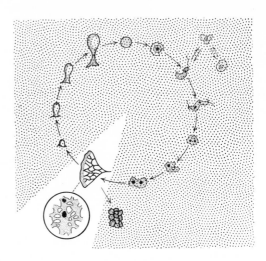

6
The Plasmodium

The most characteristic stage of a myxomycete is the assimilative structure, the plasmodium, a naked, free-living, multinucleate, motile mass of protoplasm which varies in size and morphological details with age and type, with species, and to a certain extent with the nature of the substrate on which it is growing. The more general recognition of the existence of a *slimy* plasmodial stage in the life history of these organisms is reflected in Fries's (1829) application of the name *Myxogastres* to the group and Link's (1833) initial use of the name *Myxomycetes*. The careful studies of the myxomycete life cycle published by deBary (1858) definitely established the position and importance of the plasmodium in the life cycle, but today—over one hundred years later—critical studies of the plasmodia of most species of Myxomycetes have yet to be made.

Earlier investigators understandably confined their observations of plasmodia to the larger and more obvious types, and hence there arose the rather general concept that all myxomycete plasmodia are fundamentally alike, although a few of the earlier workers suggested that this might not be correct (e.g., deBary, 1887; Zukal, 1893). Thus, Cienkowski (1863b), deBary (1887), and Strasburger (1884), who made detailed studies of myxomycete plasmodia, concerned themselves almost entirely with the usually large and conspicuous plasmodia of various species of the order Physarales. This emphasis on the physaraceous plasmodium was further strengthened when Howard (1931b) demonstrated the ease with which *Physarum polycephalum* can be cultured on agar medium, and Camp's (1936) subsequent development of a moist-chamber method of culturing this species provided a method of supplying almost unlimited quantities of relatively clean (though not uncontaminated) plasmodia. Since 1931, a large proportion of the many studies involving plasmodia have been conducted with *P. polycephalum*, and, as Alexopoulos (1960a) has pointed out, for those investigators who are not interested in the Myxomycetes *per se* but only in their usefulness as tools in cytological, biochemical, and biophysical research, there is only one plasmodium—that of *Physarum polycephalum*. This situation had a remarkable parallel in the early stages of development of the field of filamentous fungus physiology, where a beginning student might soon arrive at the belief that there was only one important filamentous fungus —*Aspergillus niger*.

With the major emphasis for about a century on one type of plasmodium, all examples of which were quite similar in virtually every respect except color, it is not surprising that Martin (1940) stated: "At the present time, it seems unlikely that study of the plasmodia will throw much light on this subject [systems of classification], although that, of course, is not impossible. . . ." Lister (1925) listed plasmodial color for each species where known, apparently as a possible aid to species identification.

With respect to color, the great majority of species of Myxomycetes have plasmodia that are either colorless or some shade of yellow. Furthermore, when growing in their natural habitats, plasmodia may change color by the ingestion of colored food particles. For example, Pinoy (1903, 1915), Skupienski (1920), and Kambly (1939a) have described color changes in plasmodia due to the ingestion of bacterial associates. Seifriz and Zetzmann (1935) have demonstrated that the color of *P. polycephalum* varies with pH. On the basis of his own observations and those of others, Kambly (1939a) concluded that color of plasmodium is neither a good taxonomic character nor a dependable factor in the delimitation of strains or races. This conclusion may be correct in many instances; however, Gray (1948) was able to distinguish between plasmodia of *Didymium nigripes* and *D. iridis* by culturing them on similar media at a time when there was considerable uncertainty as to whether the latter was a species or merely a variety of the former.

If plasmodial color is ever to become a useful characteristic in taxonomic studies, it will be so only if plasmodia are cultured under a standard set of conditions and color changes are duly noted. A case in point is provided by the very common species, *Metatrichia vesparium*. Lister (1925) described the plasmodium as purple-red, Gray (1938) as white, Carr (1939b) as yellow, and Mangenot (1933) and Nauss (1943) as black. Wollman (1966) has recently shown that the young plasmodium of this species is colorless, becoming black gradually as it becomes more mature, and McManus (1962) showed that the color changes with pH: the color ranges from bright lemon-yellow at pH 1.0 to dark brick-red at pH 13.0; in the pH range of 5.0–8.0 the color is black. The recent study of Collins and Clark (1966a) of the inheritance of plasmodial color in *Didymium iridis* is of interest in this connection (see page 80).

Although deBary had commented earlier that plasmodia of *Stemonitis fusca* (as well as several other species of Myxomycetes) are inconspicuous bodies which are not visible to the naked eye until they come to the surface of their substrates just prior to sporulation (Fig. 19), the first

Fig. 19. Heaped plasmodium of *Stemonitis fusca* just prior to the beginning of sporulation. × 1. (Gray, 1938.)

critical observations on *Stemonitis* plasmodia were made by Čelakovský (1893) on *S. fusca*. Čelakovský noted a lack of differentiation of the outer and inner plasma layers of the plasmodial strands as well as an unusual transparency of the strands—a transparency recorded a few years later by Miller (1898) for three unidentified species of *Stemonitis*. Thom and Raper (1930) also saw *Stemonitis* plasmodia, but for the most part earlier workers have seen this type of plasmodium only when it became heaped up preparatory to sporulation.

Zukal (1893) cultured *Licea parasitica* on willow bark and observed that its plasmodium was minute, nearly immobile, and without either vein-like structures or rhythmic, reversible protoplasmic streaming. The plasmodium described by Zukal was so different from all other plasmodia that had been described up to that time that Lister (1925) considered the species an exceptional one. Santesson (1948) has objected to Zukal's description of the plasmodium of *L. parasitica*, claiming that Zukal thought that the parasitic imperfect fungus *Illosporium roseum* was the plasmodium of the myxomycete he named. However, evidence has slowly accumulated to the effect that all plasmodia are not morphologically alike, a view expressed by both Watanabe (1932) and Nauss (1947), and it seems probable that Zukal may have been correct. Unfortunately, neither Watanabe nor Nauss attempted to describe the major differences between plasmodia. However, Alexopoulos (1960a) described three general types of plasmodium which he named protoplasmodium, aphanoplasmodium, and phaneroplasmodium.

TYPES OF PLASMODIA

Protoplasmodium

The protoplasmodium (Fig. 20) is the characteristic type of plasmodium formed by such minute species as *Echinostelium minutum, E. elachiston, Licea parasitica,* and *Clastoderma debaryanum.* Zukal (1893)

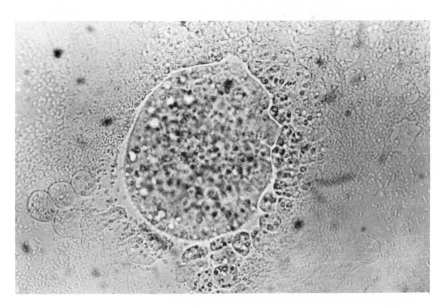

Fig. 20.   Protoplasmodium of an undescribed myxomycete.   × 500.

appears to have been the first to observe this type of plasmodium, which remains microscopic throughout its entire existence and is more or less homogenous. Such a plasmodium forms no veins and has a very slow, irregular streaming in contrast to the rapid, rhythmical, reversible streaming so characteristic of other larger types of plasmodia. On the basis of his observations on bark cultures of *E. minutum*, Peterson (1952) expressed the belief that a plasmodium of this species gives rise to only a single sporangium, a belief that was substantiated by the work of Alexopoulos (1960b). This belief was further substantiated by the work of McManus (1961b) on *C. debaryanum*, and thus it appears likely that the sporangia of many minute species are each formed from a single plasmodium.

The plasmodia of *E. minutum* are recognizable when they attain a diameter of 20–30 microns, at which time they resemble large myxamoebae which are flat, more or less round in outline, and have at least one contractile vacuole. The plasmodium is colorless, and many short pseudopodia are extended along the periphery. It migrates very slowly over the substrate, and streaming is very slow and without discernible pattern. Just prior to forming the fructification, the plasmodium is homogenous in structure with a granular ground substance containing conspicuous food and contractile vacuoles. Although the plasmodium may sometimes have an irregular outline, it does not differentiate an advancing fan-shaped region and does not at any time exhibit a reticulation. Because of its resemblance at maturity to the very young plasmodia of species with other plasmodial types, Alexopoulos (1960a, 1962) expressed the belief that the protoplasmodium represents the most primitive type of myxomycete plasmodium.

Aphanoplasmodium

The second type of plasmodium, the aphanoplasmodium, is exemplified by the plasmodia of *Stemonitis fusca, S. flavogenita, Comatricha laxa, C. nodulifera, C. typhoides,* and *Lamproderma scintillans.* These plasmodia usually are not seen during their early stages because of their flat, transparent nature, and they are obvious to the naked eye only when they become clumps of plasmodia which soon begin to take the shapes of sporangia characteristic for the species. This has led to the suggestion that such plasmodia live within the woody substratum on which fruitings are commonly found and emerge only for sporulation. There is no evidence either to support or to deny this idea, but it seems possible that during its early stages an aphanoplasmodium could be *on the surface* of a woody substratum and still not be detected.

As noted above, Čelakovský, Miller, and Thom and Raper apparently had observed plasmodia of *Stemonitis* before they had advanced to the obvious clumped stage just prior to sporulation, but it was not until 1959, when Alexopoulos was able to follow the complete development of a *Stemonitis* plasmodium from spores in culture, that the "stemonitoid" plasmodium was fully described. The observations of Alexopoulos on *S. flavogenita* were soon followed by those of McManus and Richmond (1961) on *S. fusca* and Indira and Kalyanasundaram (1963) on *S. herbatica,* and these yield definite proof that the "stemonitoid" plasmodium is a distinct type. Benedict (1965) has also studied *S. fusca* and has observed that after syngamy the zygote grows and forms a stellate plasmodium which ultimately becomes the aphanoplasmodium.

The first recognizable stage of the aphanoplasmodium (as described for *S. flavogenita* and *S. fusca*) may be a rounded mass of protoplasm, and hence may closely resemble a protoplasmodium or a very young phaneroplasmodium; however, in many instances the plasmodium may be elongated and exhibit the tendency to extend pointed pseudopodia (Fig. 21A), which gives it an irregular outline. At this stage it may form a long hypha-like strand which leads to another irregular mass, or it may produce a few branches which will begin to anastomose and form a reticulum (Fig. 21B–G). The plasmodium at this stage may be 400 microns or more in length and is greatly flattened and highly transparent. The confining membrane is very thin, and inside this membrane the entire protoplast exhibits a rhythmic, reversible streaming which may be quite rapid or so slow as to be almost imperceptible. Even after a well-developed reticulum is formed, the plasmodium may have no definite margin and no differentiated advancing fan (Fig. 22). Strands protrude in every direction ending abruptly or terminating in vesiculose, irregular swellings which often spread out giving the impression of bursting bubbles which allow the jelly-like contents to flow out and form puddles. Puddles from adjacent vesicles sometimes coalesce and form protoplasmic sheets resembling small fans of a phaneroplasmodium. The plasmodium now grows rapidly and may assume a variety of shapes. Sometimes strands grow for a considerable distance without branching, but eventually branches are produced and a large, often symmetrical, reticulum with large meshes (100–200 microns or more) is formed (Fig. 23). The strands are nearly isodiametric and bear such a resemblance to hyphae that they could quite justifiably be used to support Martin's (1959, 1966) arguments for the fungal affinities of the Myxomycetes. At other times, many branches are formed at short intervals; they may rebranch and anastomose either forming networks with small meshes (20–80 microns) or ending abruptly. A third variation is that in which the main strand is quite large (18–35 microns in diameter) and is surrounded by a thin network of fine strands which issue as branches of the main strand (Fig.

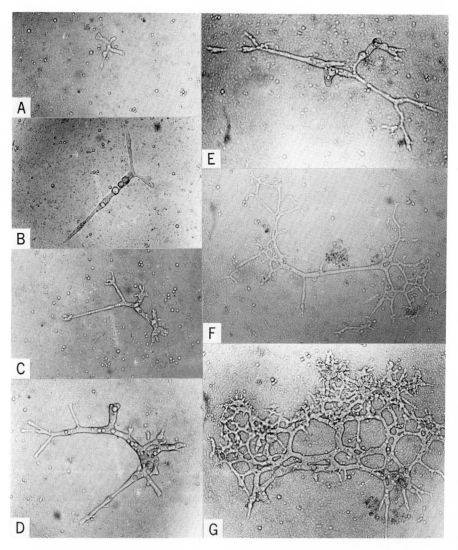

Fig. 21. *Stemonitis hyperopta.* Aphanoplasmodium. Seven plasmodia (A–G) at different stages of development in the same culture dish on Difco Noble's agar. × 200.

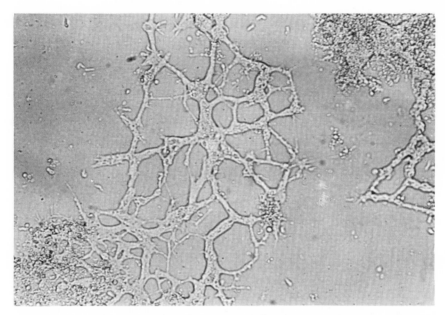

Fig. 22. Aphanoplasmodium of *Comatricha laxa*. Early stages showing reticulum formation. × 200. (Wollman and Alexopoulos, 1964.)

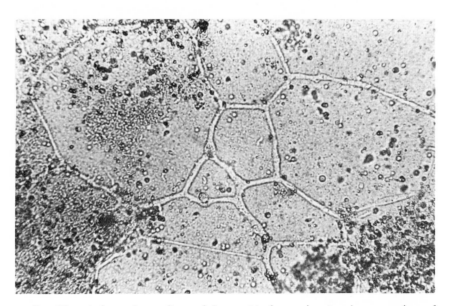

Fig. 23. Aphanoplasmodium of *Stemonitis fusca* showing large meshes of the plasmodial reticulum. × 200.

24); the protoplast is often differentiated into a non-motile outer region and a streaming central region.

As the aphanoplasmodium grows older it forms one or more fans with definite margins, and at this stage it begins to resemble the better known plasmodium of the Physarales. Even at an advanced age, however, the plasmodia are so flat and transparent that they are nearly invisible to the naked eye. Alexopoulos (1960a) suggests that the apparent failures in the past to grow *Stemonitis* in culture from spores were not so much failures to obtain plasmodia as failures to recognize them. He considers the "invisibility" of the immature plasmodium as one of its principal characteristics. It is only when the plasmodium is about to sporulate that its strands thicken and become coralloid (Fig. 25).

Phaneroplasmodium

The third type of plasmodium, the phaneroplasmodium, is the best known type and has been reported in all species of Physarales whose plasmodia have been studied. In view of their ubiquity and the fact that over one-third of all the known species are in this order, it is not surprising that Physarales plasmodia came to be considered the prototype of myxomycete plasmodia (Fig. 26). This type is larger, more obvious, and hence more frequently encountered, and as a result the great preponderance of plasmodial studies have been conducted with phaneroplasmodia. Although most phaneroplasmodia usually cover an area of only a few square centimeters, sometimes they may be larger, and plasmodia of *Fuligo septica* with areas of 0.5–1.0 square foot are not uncommon. An extreme case is described by Poteat (1937) in which, if the "fairy ring" fruiting of *Physarum cinereum* which he had described arose from a single plasmodium, the plasmodium encircled an area of about ten square feet immediately prior to sporulation.

Apparently by a succession of nuclear divisions (see Chapter 5), the zygote grows into a minute plasmodium (Fig. 27A) in which streaming is detectable with a magnification of × 400 by the time it is 30–40 microns in diameter; however, streaming is confined to the central part. Stewart and Stewart (1959) state that plasmodia of *Physarum polycephalum* in this stage show no definite channel structure; reversal-like changes occur occasionally but not regularly. On the basis of his observations, Alexopoulos (1960a) states that this is also true of at least ten other species of Physarales and notes that in this early stage the phaneroplasmodium is hardly distinguishable from a protoplasmodium in the same stage of development. The phaneroplasmodium soon elongates, however, and develops a definite channel in which the protoplasm begins a rhythmic, reversible streaming. One end of the elongated structure becomes wider,

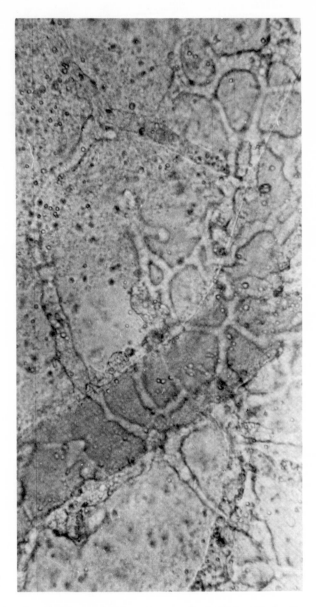

Fig. 24. *Comatricha typhoides*. Large plasmodial strand surrounded by a network of finer strands which issue as branches of the main strand. × 180. (Wollman, 1966. Courtesy Constance Wollman.)

Fig. 25.   Plasmodium of *Stemonitis* sp. just before fruiting, showing coral-loid structure.   × 5.   (Alexopoulos, 1960a.)

and the plasmodium moves in the direction of the wider end (Fig. 27B). The wider anterior portion begins to take the shape of a fan (Fig. 27C), and, in contrast to the aphanoplasmodium, the differentiation between an outer, jellified, non-streaming region and an inner, more fluid, streaming region is quite definite.

As the phaneroplasmodium grows further, the anterior fan thickens and becomes a sheet of protoplasm in which streaming channels originate. The more prominent channels are oriented from front to back with shorter connecting channels oriented at right angles and/or diagonally to the main channels. Farther back the plasmodium is reticulated (Fig. 26, page 102), but the plasmodial strands are irregularly wide instead of being regular and hypha-like as in the aphanoplasmodium. Camp (1937b) states that the reticula of *P. polycephalum* may develop either by branching at the plasmodial margin followed by anastomoses of branches coming into contact, or by the development of perforations in continuous plasmodial sheets with the subsequent withdrawal of protoplasm away from the perforations and into the vein-like strands. A distinct characteristic of the phaneroplasmodium is its three-dimensional appearance in contrast with the marked flatness of the aphanoplasmodium. As a result, the plasmodium is visible to the unaided eye even when it is only about 1 mm long. In older plasmodia the strands may appear quite swollen, and the protoplasm appears much denser than in the aphanoplasmodium (Fig. 26). Generally speaking, the phaneroplasmodium is larger and spreads over a greater substrate area than either the protoplasmodium or the aphanoplasmodium. However, there are exceptional cases among aphanoplasmodia, since occasional large fruitings of *Stemonitis* in nature indicate that on occasion rather large aphanoplasmodia may occur. Alexopoulos (1960a) suggests that phaneroplasmodia differ from aphano-plasmodia in physiology as well as in morphology, since in his culture work he never observed the development of aphanoplasmodia on agar surfaces that had been permitted to dry, while the development of phaneroplasmodia is usually favored by dryer conditions. On the other hand, Indira and Kalyanasundaram (1963) state that they cultured the aphanoplasmodium of *Stemonitis herbatica* successfully on a dry agar surface as well as on glass under water.

While protoplasmodia, aphanoplasmodia, and phaneroplasmodia unquestionably represent three distinct types, it is quite possible that, as a greater number of species are critically studied (again this will await the development of suitable culture methods), it may be found that all plasmodia cannot be neatly placed into one or another of these three well-defined categories. Thus, Alexopoulos (1960a) reported his observations on plasmodia of *Arcyria cinerea* which developed from spores grown on cornmeal agar and indicated that they were intermediate between the aphanoplasmodium and the phaneroplasmodium. This intermediate position of the *A. cinerea* plasmodium was confirmed by Indira and Kalyanasundaram (1963). More recently McManus (1962) has studied two other species of the Trichiales—*Metatrichia vesparium* and *Hemitrichia serpula*—and notes that these plasmodia have some characteristics in common with all three of the presently named plasmodial types. The plasmodium of *Perichaena vermicularis* also belongs to this intermediate group (Ross, 1967c). The decision as to whether or not a fourth type of plasmodium is represented here will have to be deferred until critical studies have been made on additional species of the order Trichiales.

Nauss (1949) has described the plasmodium of a new genus and species of organism which she named *Reticulomyxa filosa*, which, if proved to be a myxomycete, would add still another distinct plasmodial type to the list. This investigator expresses the opinion that *R. filosa* may belong to some group intermediate between the Myxomycetes and the Foraminifera, but since it has never been observed to fruit, no decision may be made regarding its position.

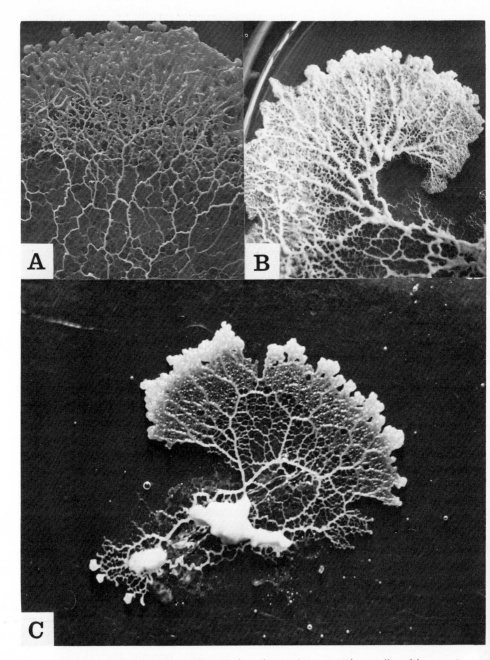

Fig. 26.   Phaneroplasmodia of the Physarales.   A. *Physarella oblonga*; B.
Physarum gyrosum; C. *P. polycephalum*.   [B. Alexopoulos, in *The Fungi* (Ains-
worth and Sussman, eds.) Chap. 8, p. 218, 1966; by permission of Academic
Press, Inc.   C. Courtesy Ian A. Staff.]   A × 2, B × 1.62, C × 3.

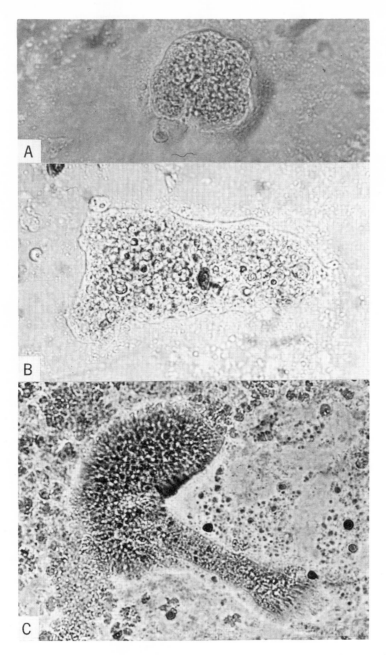

Fig. 27. *Physarella oblonga* forma *alba*. Development of the phaneroplasmodium. A. Very young plasmodium (54 microns in diameter) which at this
stage resembles a protoplasmodium. B. Older plasmodium (114 microns long)
in which polarity has been established, moving toward the left. C. Plasmodium
in a later stage of development (265 microns long) showing development of the
anterior fan. A and B × 570, C × 400. (Alexopoulos, 1960a.)

REGENERATIVE CAPABILITIES OF PLASMODIA

It has been the common experience of many investigators working with large phaneroplasmodia in agar culture or in moist chambers that subcultures can be made easily by transferring bits of plasmodium to a fresh substrate. When such transfers are made the plasmodium is injured, but with reasonable care many separate plasmodia can be obtained, and under suitable conditions each of these will grow to large size and can in turn be subdivided. The size of these artificially prepared propagules may be quite small, but they remain alive and they grow and thus provide evidence that, in general, the plasmodium appears to have remarkable regenerative powers.

Although slight contact of a plasmodial strand with some object that does not break the strand will cause an immediate cessation of streaming on either side of the point of contact, when a large strand is cut or punctured quickly, there is an immediate outflow of endoplasm. Protoplasmic streaming immediately stops on either side of the injured part, and both the plasmodium in the strand and the protoplasm that flowed out soon gelate. The phenomenon of stoppage of streaming due to injury or to slight mechanical shock has long been known (Winer and Moore, 1941; Seifriz and Epstein, 1941; Seifriz, 1943) and is referred to by Seifriz and Epstein as "shock anesthesia." Apparently the duration of the period of "anesthesia" varies with the degree of the shock force.

Skupienski (1953) described the macroscopic changes that occur when plasmodia of *Didymium squamulosum* are injured, but Rakoczy (1961) attempted to examine the microscopic changes that follow injury to plasmodia of *D. iridis* as well as the changes that occur during regeneration. She classified plasmodial regeneration into three types, the type apparently being determined by whether the cutting injury is applied to large strands, strands of "average" size, the advancing frontal part of a plasmodium, or small anastomosing strands. Thus, when a large strand is cut there is an outflow of protoplasm which joins the severed ends of the strand; protoplasmic streaming is later restored and the effused protoplasm is resorbed. No effusion of protoplasm occurs when average size strands or a plasmodial front is cut. The protoplasm contracts on either side of the cut, and after a time streaming is restored and plasma expansion leads to fusion at the cut, the plasmodium now being restored to its former state. When small, anastomosing strands are cut, there is contraction on either side of the cut, and with restoration of streaming the two parts of the severed strand are resorbed by the larger strands that it connected. Isolated fragments of plasmodium as small as 0.01 mg or less were found capable of forming new plasmodia. The regenerative capability depended less on size of the fragment than on age of plasmodium, and fragments taken from cultures during the period of optimal growth (eight-day-old cultures on oat agar) exhibited the most regular growth and migration rates.

Since calcium ions are known to be necessary for the regeneration of injured protoplasm, Rakoczy attempted to remove calcium from the plasmodial environment by addition of 0.1 M potassium oxalate. She found that immersion of a whole plasmodium in such a calcium-binding solution caused complete degeneration of protoplasm in a very short time. Apparently, she attributes this to the non-availability of calcium in such an environment, but the possibility of oxalate being toxic must also be considered.

The fact that severed plasmodial strands will "heal" and new plasmodia can be reconstituted from small fragments of injured plasmodia is indicative of two remarkable properties of myxomycete protoplasm: (1) the capability of the plasmasol to gelate quickly, and (2) the rapidity with which plasmodial protoplasm can form new bounding membranes. Stewart and Stewart (1960b) have suggested that new plasma membrane may have its origin in the limiting membranes of the many vesicles, which they have observed in plasmodia of *P. polycephalum*. The fact that plasmodia can be reconstituted from very small fragments also indicates that the two properties referred to above are resident throughout the entire plasmodium.

GROSS STRUCTURE

Since the phaneroplasmodium is the largest, most obvious, and generally most readily available plasmodium, the bulk of the work that has been done on plasmodial structure has been done with this plasmodial type. The species most commonly used, of course, is *Physarum polycephalum*. However, in recent years, due to the development of better culture techniques and recognition of the existence of other types of plasmodia, an increasing amount of work has been done on protoplasmodia and aphanoplasmodia. Nonetheless, because of the existence of more complete information concerning the phaneroplasmodium, the bulk of the present discussion will be concerned with this plasmodial type.

Ideally a single phaneroplasmodium assumes a fan-like shape in which the wider part (anterior) of the fan is a continuous sheet (varying in width and thickness) of protoplasm, which merges into a posterior reticulum of plasmodial strands (Fig. 26, page 102). Typically, the anterior solid sheet is lobed along the advancing margin, and often a lobe may advance much more rapidly than adjoining lobes and thus form a branch. Several such branches may anastomose if they come into contact, thus leading to reticulum formation. Camp (1937b) has pointed out that a plasmodial reticulum may also be formed by the gradual removal of protoplasm into larger veins in the continuous protoplasmic sheet, thus leading to thinning out in certain areas; these thinned-out areas then form the meshes of the plasmodial reticulum.

Plasmodial Sheath

The plasmodium is generally described as being acellular and naked. There is no question regarding its acellularity, except in a plasmodium in the process of sclerotization, but whether or not it is naked is a matter of interpretation. Certainly it is naked in the sense of not being enclosed by a rigid cell wall, but in reality there are at least two retaining structures surrounding the less viscous protoplasm of the plasmodium. The outermost structure is a hyaline sheath which surrounds the protoplasm and which apparently is not a part of the living protoplasm or, at most, is only transiently so. This sheath is most obvious on the thicker strands in the posterior reticulate portion of a typical plasmodium and least obvious on the anterior advancing portion. As a plasmodium moves forward the sheath is left behind, new sheath material apparently being continuously formed as the plasmodium grows and moves over the substrate. As the living protoplasm moves out of the sheath this structure, now a fragile tube, collapses and often appears as two low ridges on either side of the former position of the whole plasmodial strand (Fig. 28B). The "slime track" that a plasmodium leaves on its substrate is the discarded sheath, and it is generally believed to be formed by the excretion of refuse material by the plasmodium. Recent work on the ultrastructure of the plasmodium (Rhea, 1966; McManus, 1965) indicates that

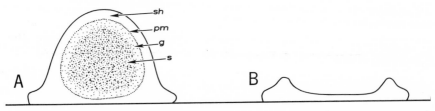

Fig. 28. A. Schematic representation of cross-section of plasmodial strand of a phaneroplasmodium: *sh*—sheath, *pm*—plasma membrane, *g*—plasmagel, *s*—plasmasol. B. Collapsed sheath after protoplasm has moved out.

the sheath has structure since it was determined to be fibrillar in nature, and Rhea suggests that the fibrillar coat might be considered a type of "exoskeleton." While Rhea did not determine whether the slime and sheath were the same, he did find that the slime track contains a fibrillar sheath. Whether or not the sheath is an "exoskeleton," it is an efficient retaining structure, since Jahn, *et al.* (1964) have shown that when expanded two or three diameters by forcing air into the plasmasol, the sheath will return to almost normal size.

Plasmodial Protoplasm

Immediately inside the sheath is a more or less circular (in cross-section) area of living protoplasm, the peripheral portion of which is usually considered to be more viscous than the innermost protoplasm. This outer hyaline protoplasm has been variously termed the plasmagel, channel wall, cortical gel, or ectoplasm and the inner, granular, more liquid protoplasm the plasmasol, streaming channel, or endoplasm. In view of the rapidity with which the plasmodial protoplasm gelates or solates, it is improbable that the plasmagel and plasmasol are of constant thickness. However, Rhea (1966) states that the cortical gel is 2 microns thick.

It has been assumed that the outermost thin layer of the plasmagel is the plasma membrane or plasmalemma, and McManus (1965) found that this membrane is three-layered—two dense outer layers with a middle transparent layer. A diagrammatic representation of a cross-section of a typical plasmodial strand showing these various parts and their spatial relationships one to the other is shown in Fig. 28A. That the plasmagel (with plasma membrane) is more viscous than the plasmasol can be easily demonstrated by puncturing the outer layer of a plasmodial strand with a fine needle and noting that there is an immediate flow of the more liquid inner protoplasm through the puncture wound. The flow is not of long duration, however, since the more liquid plasmasol soon gelates. Kar (1962) attempted to elucidate the chemical nature of the membrane but was unsuccessful. In contrast to these long-held ideas regarding the outer plasmagel, Rhea (1966) has advanced the suggestion that the gel nature of the peripheral protoplasm may be an illusion because he observed that, at the electron microscope level, the wall "gel" and channel "sol" show no structural differentiations—an observation that agrees with the findings of Stewart and Stewart (1959) and Terada (1962). The protoplasm may be considered as a non-granular "groundplasm" containing about 30 per cent by volume of inclusions (Andresen and Pollock, 1952), with the peripheral areas being relatively inclusion-free and often termed hyaloplasm.

The earliest critical observations of the structure and activities of plasmodia were those reported by deBary (1859, 1864, 1887) and Cien-kowski (1863a). These early workers described the ingestion of solid food particles by plasmodia and also noted the occurrence of vacuoles. The presence of many nuclei was established by Schmitz (1879) and Strasburger (1880) and has been observed by many workers since. F. A. Gilbert (1928c), Wilson and Cadman (1928), Howard (1931a), and H. C. Gilbert (1935) studied spore germination, fusion of swarm cells, and the early stages of plasmodial development, but the most thorough study of the structure of myxomycete plasmodia until recent times was that of Camp (1937b) on *Physarum polycephalum*.

NUCLEAR DIVISION

While all investigators who look specifically for nuclei have no dif-ficulty in finding them, the manner in which plasmodial nuclei increase in numbers was undecided for many years. Although nuclear division had been observed by Strasburger (1884) in the developing sporangia of *Trichia decipiens*, nuclear division in plasmodia was apparently first ob-served in *Badhamia utricularis* by A. Lister (1893), who concluded that nuclei increased their numbers by constriction or simple division. How-ever, in an unusual footnote to A. Lister's paper, J. J. Lister described mitotic figures in plasmodia of the same species studied by A. Lister. Subsequently, A. Lister made many observations on other species and in 1906 reaffirmed his earlier statement that plasmodial nuclei divide prin-cipally by amitosis. Later, J. J. Lister (1909) seems to have modified his earlier views slightly, since he stated that nuclei increase both by simultaneous mitotic division and by simple division, but more commonly by the latter method. Jahn (1911) reported having observed nuclear division twice in growing plasmodia of *B. utricularis*, and Schünemann (1930) found mitosis in *Didymium nigripes* by fixing small pieces of large plasmodia at hourly intervals. Division figures were not all in the same stage even in small pieces of plasmodium, and Schünemann noted that nuclear membranes were present in prophase and metaphase figures. Cadman (1931) also observed and figured mitosis in *D. iridis*.

Until the appearance of Howard's (1932) work on nuclear division in *Physarum polycephalum*, mitosis had been observed by few investigators, and this fact lent credence to the view that nuclei might also divide amitotically. By fixing small pieces of plasmodia at intervals as frequent as five minutes, Howard observed mitosis but obtained no evidence that nuclei could divide amitotically. Mitosis occurred almost simultaneously throughout a plasmodium, required only 20 to 40 minutes for completion, and did not recur with definite periodicity. The achromatic figures lacked asters and centrosomes, and division was entirely intranuclear. Koevenig and Jackson (1966) recently have published excellent mitotic figures in *P. polycephalum*, in which the nuclei are shown dividing simultaneously and the nuclear membrane is quite distinct (Fig. 29). Guttes, *et al.* (1959, 1961) have obtained very precise synchronization of nuclear division in *P. polycephalum* grown axenically in liquid medium under controlled conditions. Contrary to Howard's failure to find periodic recurrence of nuclear division, these workers reported synchronized nuclear division as occurring every 15.4 hours (as measured by doubling of DNA). Nuclear divisions in separate plasmodia in the same liquid culture were not synchronized, but when plasmodia were allowed to coalesce, nuclear divisions became synchronized in six to seven hours. The onset of mitosis could be delayed or advanced by the proper timing of nutrient additions. Nygaard, *et al.* (1960) found that there is a great increase in DNA synthesis during a one- to two-hour period starting immediately after nuclear division but that RNA synthesis is continuous. Although many years were required to establish the fact, it is now apparent that the plasmodial nuclei divide mitotically, and that the failure of some of the earlier investigators to detect mitosis was due to the fact that all nuclei in a plasmodium divide simultaneously and the process is completed in a very short period of time. The only recent report suggesting the possible occurrence of amitosis is that of McManus (1965) who figured a deeply lobed nucleus of *Metatrichia vesparium* which she suggests may be dividing amitotically.

In their description of nuclear division in *P. polycephalum*, Guttes, *et al.* (1961) state that about an hour prior to division the chromosomes move away from the periphery, and that at the beginning of prophase the nucleolus moves toward the periphery, becomes crescent-shaped, and slowly disintegrates. During this time the chromosomes begin to elongate and fill the nuclear space. No particulate centrioles were observed.

With the discovery that nuclear division can be precisely synchronized in plasmodia of *P. polycephalum*, in recent years this species has become a very popular organism for the study of mitosis *per se*. Thus, Rusch and his associates at the McArdle Laboratory of the University of Wisconsin have attempted to gain a better understanding of the nature of cancer cells by studying the biochemistry of the steps leading to mitosis (Braun, *et al.*, 1965, 1966; Brewer and Rusch, 1965; Cummins, *et al.*, 1965; Mittermayer, *et al.*, 1964, 1965, 1966a, 1966b; Rusch and Sachsenmaier, 1964; Sachsenmaier and Rusch, 1964). Considerable information has been gained, especially with regard to DNA and RNA synthesis in relation to mitosis. However, since much of this important research has implications far beyond the scope of the present work it will not be discussed here; the interested student should consult the original research communications.

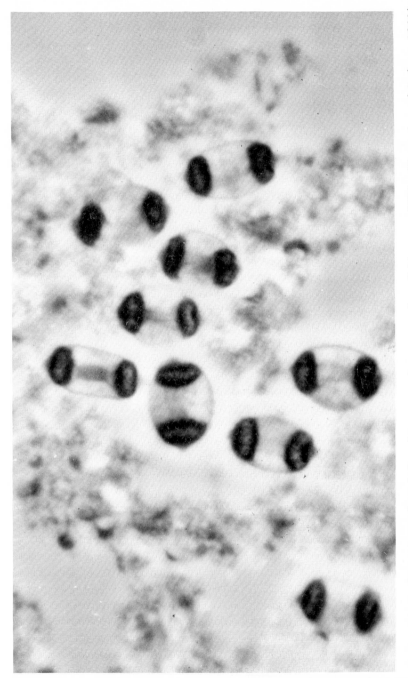

Fig. 29.   Plasmodium of *P. polycephalum* showing simultaneous nuclear divisions.   × 2700.   (Koevenig and Jackson, 1966.)

CYTOLOGY AND FINE STRUCTURE

Nuclear Size, Consistency, and Structure

Nuclei are randomly distributed throughout the plasmodium in the plasmasol and plasmagel, but both Andresen and Pollock (1952) and McManus (1965) have noted that they are not found immediately adjacent to the plasma membrane. Some difference of opinion exists regarding the size of nuclei—even in the same species. Thus, Howard (1931a) found that resting nuclei of *P. polycephalum* were globose to elliptical and 2.5–3.5 microns in diameter, Dalleux describes them as spherical with a diameter of 3.0–4.5 microns, and Andresen and Pollock state that they are spherical with a diameter of 4–7 microns. Lewis (1942) merely describes them as round, each with a large, gray nucleolus. Whether or not these variously reported size differences are real or whether they are merely reflections of different techniques employed by the various investigators remains to be determined. In his study of nuclear division in *P. polycephalum*, Howard (1932) attempted to detect evidence in living plasmodia that nuclei were in the process of dividing but was unsuccessful. It is not uncommon, especially when viewing an actively streaming plasmodium with an ordinary light microscope, to experience extreme uncertainty in identifying nuclei. The measurements made by Guttes, *et al.* (1961), which were made on plasmodia of *P. polycephalum* grown axenically in liquid medium, revealed that nuclei of this species were uniformly 4–5 microns in diameter and that each contained a single nucleolus. Rhea's (1966) measurements of nuclei were the same as those of Guttes, *et al.*, but he reported one or two nucleoli rather than one.

That plasmodial nuclear size would vary from species to species might reasonably be expected, and this is borne out by the measurements reported by Wilson and Ross (1955): *Metatrichia vesparium*—8.3 × 6.2 microns; *Stemonitis axifera*—3.1 × 2.8 microns; *Lamproderma arcyrioides*, *Lycogala epidendrum*, and *Comatricha typhoides* have nuclei that range between the sizes of *M. vesparium* and *S. axifera*.

Dalleux (1940) reported a certain degree of plasticity of nuclei (based on the finding of elongated forms) in *P. polycephalum* and *F. septica*, and Locquin (1949b) concluded from his phase-contrast cinephotomicrographic study of the protoplasmodium of *Licea biforis* that nuclei are extremely plastic and that there is a relatively rigid connection uniting a nucleus with its surrounding cytoplasm. In her electron microscopy investigations of protoplasmodia, aphanoplasmodia, and phaneroplasmodia, McManus (1965) found that nuclei were plastic and that they assume a variety of shapes when they are appressed to other organelles. In view of the earlier observations of Moore (1933, 1934, 1935) it is not at all surprising to find that more recent investigations contain reports to the effect that nuclei are plastic. In a series of observations directed primarily toward establishment of the fact that the cytoplasm of *P. polycephalum* has definite structure, Moore found that plasmodia were killed if forced through sieves of too-small pore size, but if they were left alone would pass through the sieves uninjured. Thus, plasmodia moved through hard filter paper with average pore size of one micron—too small to permit passage of nuclei even of the smallest diameter reported by Howard (2.5 microns), unless the nuclei were quite plastic and could change shape.

The multinucleate condition of the plasmodium has long been recognized, and it has been generally agreed that the number of nuclei in a large plasmodium is very great, but apparently Andresen and Pollock (1952) have made the only attempt to make actual counts of nuclear numbers. Counts were made on both smears and sections of fixed plasmodia, and from such counts it was estimated that there are about 800,000 nuclei per mm^3 of *P. polycephalum* plasmodium. Assuming the nucleus to be a sphere of average radius 2.25 microns, it was calculated that 7 per cent of the protoplasm consists of nuclei. Similar calculations made on the giant amoeba *Chaos chaos*, led to the estimate that 6 per cent of the total volume consisted of nuclei.

Reports regarding the number of nucleoli per nucleus of *P. polycephalum* are also conflicting. In the original study of this species, Howard (1931a) stated that nuclei contain one large, or two or three smaller nucleoli, but Lewis (1942) described each nucleus as containing one large, gray nucleolus. Andresen and Pollock (1952) are in agreement with Howard, since they noted one to five nucleoli per nucleus—the size varying inversely with the number of nucleoli—and Stewart and Stewart's (1960a) electron micrograph, which shows a nucleus of *P. polycephalum* with two well-defined nucleoli, supports the description of Howard. In her studies on plasmodia of *Didymium clavus, Stemonitis fusca, Clastoderma debaryanum, Metatrichia vesparium*, and an unidentified yellow phaneroplasmodium, McManus (1965) apparently found only one prominent nucleolus per nucleus in all species studied. The nucleolus is denser than the karyoplasm and often has the appearance of a loosely coiled nucleonema. According to McManus, the nucleolus has no obvious membrane. From these varying reports it is apparent that there is no fixed number of nucleoli per nucleus (Fig. 30).

As noted earlier, various investigators have observed that the nuclear membrane remains intact during mitosis, and in general the nuclear membrane seems a well-defined structure. In her ultrastructure studies, McManus observed that the nuclear membranes of all species she studied

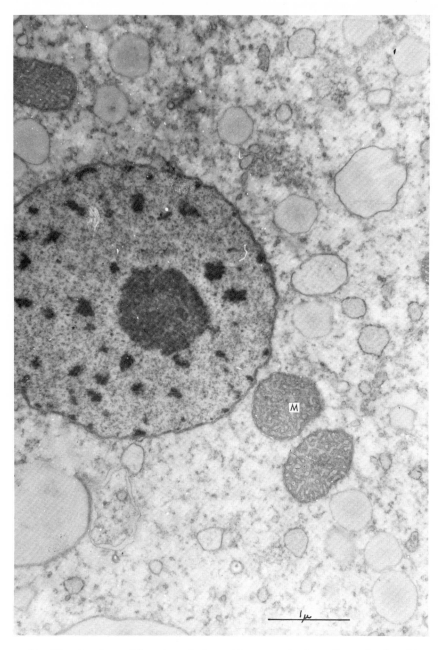

Fig. 30.   Nucleus of *P. polycephalum* with one nucleolus.   M = mitochondria.
(Photograph by P. A. Stewart.)

are about 15 mμ thick and consist of three layers: two electron-dense layers separated by a less dense layer. Interconnecting extensions from the dense layers sometimes pass through the inner layer. She observed some discontinuities in membranes and noted that sometimes there were short extensions of the nuclear membrane into the cytoplasm. There is no evidence of centrioles. However, in their ultrastructural study of mitosis in the plasmodium of *Clastoderma debaryanum*, McManus and Roth (1968) found that small groups of spindle microtubules terminate in specialized regions of the nuclear envelope at the poles. They suggest that these may be evolutionary forerunners of centrioles. Dugas and Bath (1962) found that the nuclear membrane of *P. polycephalum* was double and 300–400 Å thick. Aldrich's (1966) observations on the nuclear membrane of *P. flavicomum* confirm those of Dugas and Bath on *P. polycephalum* that it is two-layered; Aldrich also noted finding nucleopores as did Rhea (1966). Rhea also reported that in addition to nucleolus and chromatin material, some nuclei contained small bodies with dark borders, each with a core of small electron-dense granules.

As a result of their investigations of the life history and cytology of *Reticularia lycoperdon*, Wilson and Cadman (1928) reported that during mitosis in plasmodia, the nuclear membrane remains intact but during mitosis in myxamoebae the nuclear membrane disappears. This was confirmed by Koevenig (1961a, 1964) with *Physarum gyrosum*, using as evidence changes in cytoplasmic and nuclear refractive indices as revealed in time-lapse phase cinephotomicrographic films of mitosis. As was noted previously, Koevenig and Jackson (1966) have recently made the interesting suggestion that differences between myxamoebal and plasmodial mitoses may exist because of differences in ploidy. If this is proved to be true, it might be possible to distinguish between haploid and diploid nuclei on the basis of the presence or absence of a nuclear membrane during mitosis. (See also Sylvia Kerr, 1967.)

Although the question of ploidy in Myxomycetes is discussed in the section on the nuclear cycle, it should be noted here that in spite of the tremendous amount of research conducted with *Physarum polycephalum*, the question of chromosome number in this much-studied species has still not been answered. Howard (1932) first studied nuclear division in this species, but he was unable to count chromosomes in his preparations; however, Ross (1961) reported a diploid number of 90 ± 3. Guttes, *et al.* (1961) reported a diploid number of about 20 and a haploid number of 8. Koevenig and Jackson (1966) reported a number of 56 ± 2, but noted that there were some large nuclei that contained over 100 chromosomes. In a more recent paper Ross (1966) has reported that certain strains of Myxomycetes, when grown in pure culture, exhibit widely varying chromosome numbers, while *P. polycephalum* Strain 51D showed remarkable uniformity, the count in metaphase nuclei being 50 ± 2 without gross variation from this number.

Mitochondria and Other Small Inclusions

Mitochondria (Fig. 30, page 113) have been observed in Myxomycetes for many years, the first extensive report of their occurrence being that of Cowdry (1918). Cowdry examined plasmodia of young undifferentiated sporophores of ten species of Myxomycetes and found small inclusions which ranged in size from 0.25 to 0.5 micron. These inclusions stained with Janus green and were mostly spherical, although some were rod-shaped forms. They were most abundant around nuclei and vacuoles, and Cowdry stated that they were identical in morphology to the mitochondria of higher plants and animals.

Since firm establishment of the fact that mitochondria are the sites of various respiratory enzymes and, hence, the possible sites of synthesis of ATP, the immediate source of energy for protoplasmic streaming, renewed interest in plasmodial mitochondria has been evident in recent years. On the basis of their studies of succinic dehydrogenase activities of plasmodia stratified by centrifugation, Holter and Pollock (1952) suggested that this enzyme was localized in mitochondria, and Johnson and Moos (1956) found that when fractions of *P. polycephalum* plasmodium homogenate were separated in a refrigerated centrifuge, succinoxidase activity was concentrated in the mitochondrial fraction.

From the reports now existent in the literature there is no question that a variety of small inclusions are to be found in plasmodial cytoplasm, but it is not always clear as to exactly which of the structures observed with light microscopy are mitochondria. Dalleux (1940), working with *P. polycephalum* and *F. septica,* found structures which she termed chondriosomes that were punctiform bodies varying in diameter from 0.3 to 1 micron. These small inclusions were identical in growing plasmodia, sporulating plasmodia, and mature spores. Lewis (1942) observed numerous granules in both the gel layer and endoplasm of *P. polycephalum* and believed them to be mitochondria. Dangeard (1947) observed quite numerous granules in *Didymium clavus* plasmodia in all stages of sporangial formation. These accumulated in great numbers in young sporangia and eventually in the spores, and Dangeard assumed that they were chondriosomes.

Andresen and Pollock (1952) found both pigment granules and colorless granules in the plasmodium of *P. polycephalum*. The former were 1–4 microns in diameter, and the latter, which stained red in acid fuchsin and were 1 micron in diameter, were considered to be mitochondria. Applying the same type of calculations they had used earlier on nuclei, they calculated that mitochondria make up 1–2 per cent of the total volume of protoplasm. Guttes, *et al.* (1961) also found both mitochondria and pigmented granules in *P. polycephalum,* and their measurements of mitochondrial size agree with those of Andresen and Pollock. However, they report a size range of 0.2 to 2 microns for pigmented granules, and found a third type of granule which measured about 0.5 micron in diameter which they assumed to be polyphosphate.

Sponsler and Bath (1953, 1954) found submicroscopic particles of a wide range of sizes in the plasmodium of *P. polycephalum,* but noted that very minute particles seem more numerous in quantity than larger ones at the microscopic-micellar borderline. They described four different types of particles of which one type was ellipsoidal (0.6 to 1.25 microns) and contained heavily scattering particles in a lighter matrix. The methods by which Sponsler and Bath prepared their material for study are open to criticism, since they merely allowed small amounts of plasmodial material to dry on electron microscope grids. Niklowitz (1957) studied ultra-thin sections of *B. utricularis* with the electron microscope and found double-contoured membranes around the mitochondria. The interior region was finely granular, but there were also saccate granules which had double membranes and in some sections appeared to have open connections with the surrounding cytoplasm. The granules may be identical to one of the types described by Sponsler and Bath, and Niklowitz thinks that they are probably condensed phosphates. Terada (1962) also reported that the inner matrix of *P. polycephalum* mitochondria is connected with the cytoplasmic matrix through pore-like structures. Dugas and Bath (1962) have described the mitochondria of *P. polycephalum* as resembling those of most protozoa and other simple organisms: double-membraned with inward finger-like projections instead of lamellar cristae. They also noted dense angular granules and rod-shaped bodies which they did not identify. However, they suggested that the former may be nucleic acid containing particulates or glycogen reserve granules, and the latter may be microbodies such as those found in liver cells. Aldrich (1966) merely described the typical mitochondria of *P. flavicomum* as having cylindrical cores of DNA as had Schuster (1965a) for those of *D. nigripes,* but Stewart and Stewart (1961b) state that mitochondria of *P. polycephalum* are pleomorphic and contain a dense assortment of irregularly shaped cristae.

Although she did not attempt to make actual counts, McManus (1965) observed that mitochondria were rare in *Stemonitis* aphanoplasmodia numerous in protoplasmodia and phaneroplasmodia, and most numerous in the plasmodium of *M. vesparium.* Mitochondria were of the tubular type in all species studied, and McManus described them as being bounded by a membrane which consists of two dense layers separated by a transparent layer. This investigator lists no size ranges, but the structure shown in her Figure 3, which is presented as typical, measures about 0.3 × 1.0 micron.

As noted earlier, pigment granules have been reported in *P. poly-cephalum,* and Lieth and Meyer (1957) reported that in *Didymium nigripes* there were 1–2-micron oval structures which were surrounded by an osmiophilic membrane, and each contained a strongly scattering kernel. They interpreted these as pigment granules. McManus (1965) reported that the unidentified yellow phaneroplasmodium with which she worked has structures tentatively identified as pigment granules (Fig. 31), but that structures that might be pigment granules were not found in the most highly pigmented type, *Metatrichia vesparium.* This is rather surprising in view of Mangenot's (1933) detailed description of pigment granules in the plasmodium of that species. According to Mangenot, these granules are not over one micron in largest dimension, oval or circular in profile, more or less umbilicate, and appear to be entirely amorphous, judging by the fact that they are not birefringent. DeBary (1887) noted that the dark blue or violet-brown plasmodia of the Cribrariae contain large, brown granules, but he recorded no sizes for these granules and stated that they had been insufficiently examined. Although de-Bary, Guttes, *et al.,* McManus, and Andresen and Pollock all reported pigment granules, only Andresen and Pollock attempted to quantify them on a volumetric basis, and they estimated that about 5 per cent of the total volume of *P. polycephalum* consists of such granules. This must be accepted as a very rough estimate, since it has been the experience of most investigators working with yellow-pigmented plasmodia that the intensity of the color varies, and, of course, in colorless plasmodia one would not expect pigment granules at all. Allman (1955) proposed that plasmodia be quantified by determining the optical density of methyl alcohol extracts of plasmodia of *P. polycephalum,* since he found a linear relationship between optical density of such extracts and mass of plasmodium or sclerotium extracted. The accuracy of this method would undoubtedly depend on the precision with which a plasmodium was cultured and also on the age of the culture, since Guttes, *et al.* (1961) reported that pigment increases with age.

In his early observations of the colored plasmodia of the Physarales, deBary (1864, 1884) stated that pigment was associated with lime. However, Mangenot (1932) studied the plasmodium of *Fuligo septica* and found that pigment granules, while of about the same size as lime globules, were distinct from the latter and appeared different in polarized light. During sclerotization, pigment granules were retained in the macrocysts, while lime globules were regularly expelled from the protoplasm. During sporulation both pigment granules and lime globules were

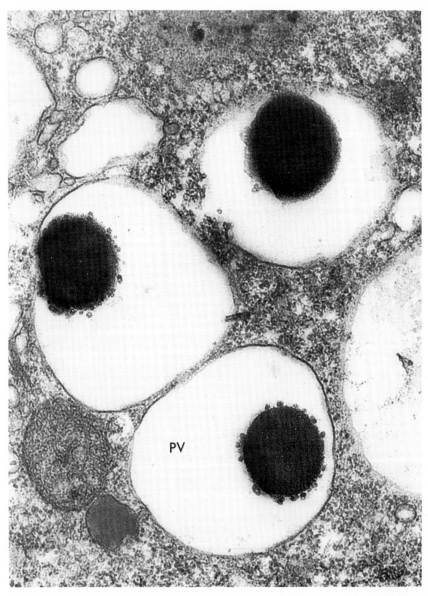

Fig. 31. Electron micrograph of portion of unidentified yellow phanero-plasmodium. PV = possible pigment granules. × 49,000. (McManus, 1965.)

expelled from the protoplasm, the outer cortical part of the aethalium containing both amorphous and crystalline lime. In a later paper, Mangenot (1934) studied a plasmodium which he refers to as *Fuligo f.* in which the lime globules were pigmented, but in two yellow-pigmented species of *Physarum*, lime globules and pigment granules were again described as separate types of inclusions.

Vacuoles

Vacuoles (Fig. 32) have long been known to occur in myxomycete structures, and it has often been stated that two types of vacuoles occur in plasmodia—food vacuoles and contractile (or pulsating) vacuoles. However, Skupienski (1929) made preparations of plasmodia, swarm cells, and myxamoebae of *Didymium nigripes* with vital stains and concluded that there are three types of vacuoles: digestive (food?) vacuoles, pulsating vacuoles, and *"vacuoles élémentaires,"* which were similar to the vacuoles of plant cells. Cadman (1931) studied *D. iridis* and agreed with Skupienski that there were three types of vacuoles. She stated, however, that these structures are often more obvious in the living organism than in stained preparations. Cadman did not find pulsating vacuoles to be obvious in plasmodia, but she noted that other investigators had reported their presence in large numbers.

Early investigators apparently had some difficulty in distinguishing between myxamoebae and uninucleate plasmodia (see Chapter 5). Skupienski (1917) stated that this could be accomplished by observing the vacuoles, a uninucleate plasmodium having more than a myxamoeba. Cadman, however, did not consider this to be a valid method of distinguishing between these structures, since she found 1 to 3 vacuoles in both myxamoebae and uninucleate plasmodia.

When Camp (1937b) made the first extensive morphological and cytological study of the plasmodium of *Physarum polycephalum*, he noted only two types of vacuoles—food and contractile. The boundaries of the contractile vacuoles were not sharply defined but were surrounded by a discontinuous layer which is optically differentiated from the hyaloplasm. This layer exhibits a reticular pattern which seems to merge with the surrounding hyaloplasm. Camp noted that there is a lack of Brownian movement in the protoplasm immediately surrounding contractile vacuoles, and for this reason he suggested that the substance immediately surrounding the fluid vacuolar contents is in the gel state. The contractile vacuoles are moved about in the streaming protoplasm, ultimately come into contact with the surface membrane, and there force their contents through small openings in the surface membrane. At systole the vacuoles flatten, lending weight to Camp's view that the sur-

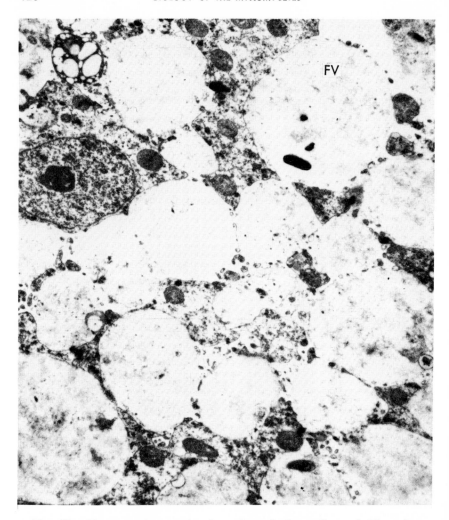

Fig. 32. Electron micrograph of portion of plasmodium of *Clastoderma debaryanum* showing food vacuoles (FV). × 9000. (McManus, 1965.)

rounding material is a gel, although he was definitely of the opinion that there is no distinct morphological membrane. Terada (1962) reported having seen contractile vacuoles with the electron microscope, but Rhea (1966), who observed large, empty vacuoles near the surface in his ultrastructure studies, stated that they might be contractile but that he had no supporting evidence.

There seems to be no doubt that food vacuoles are enclosed in definite membranes, and, from deBary's (1864) and Camp's (1937b) descriptions of the ingestion of a solid food particle with the resultant formation of a food vacuole, it is evident that the vacuolar membrane has its origin in the plasma membrane. When the advancing edge of a plasmodium comes into contact with a solid food particle, that portion in contact ceases advancing and the plasmodium on either side continues to advance; the particle then rests in a shallow depression, which becomes smaller and is finally closed. The food vacuole thus formed is attached to the external surface by a thin strand of membrane which then breaks (Fig. 33). In

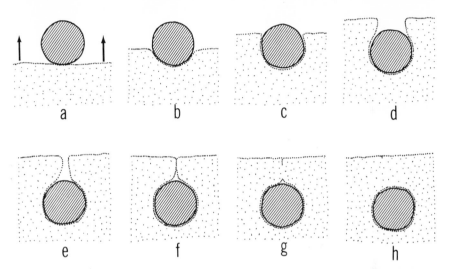

Fig. 33. Diagrammatic representation of the stages (a–h) in the ingestion of a solid food particle with resultant formation of a food vacuole. In a, the arrows indicate the direction of movement of the advancing plasmodial front.

egestion this process is reversed, the vacuole coming into contact with the plasma membrane, both membranes opening at the point of contact, and the contents being ejected. Using the more recently developed techniques of electron microscopy, food vacuoles delimited by membranes have been observed by Dugas and Bath (1962), Wohlfarth-Bottermann (1962), McManus (1965), and Rhea (1966).

Andresen and Pollock (1952) have described four rather than two or three types of vacuoles in the plasmodium of *P. polycephalum:* (1) food vacuoles, (2) vacuoles with contents of debris, (3) contractile vacuoles, and (4) empty but non-contractile vacuoles. These workers confirmed Camp's observations that there are distinct vacuolar membranes around food particles, but made no comment about the presence or absence of membranes around "debris vacuoles." They did note, however, that the contents were fluffy but not in the sense of being fibrillar. Whether or not such vacuoles behave in the same manner as food vacuoles in egestion is not known, but if they do, and the contents are fibrillar in nature, it is not beyond the realm of possibility that the fibrillar (Rhea, 1966) and felt-like (McManus, 1965) sheath material of plasmodia might have its origin in vacuoles of this type.

Contrary to Cadman's report that "pulsating" vacuoles were not obvious in plasmodia of *Didymium iridis*, Andresen and Pollock described them as numerous in *P. polycephalum*. They ranged in size up to 10 microns and contracted at intervals of about 2 minutes. On contraction they do not empty completely but remain up to 2 microns in size, gradually increasing in size and coalescing with other small vacuoles until they reach a maximum of 10 microns before again contracting. The fourth type of vacuole observed was large (up to 50 microns), empty, never observed to contract, and thought to be comparable with a similar type of vacuole described in the amoeba *Chaos chaos* by Andresen (1942). It is possible that "vacuoles élémentaires" of Skupienski are the large, spherical, empty vacuoles often observed easily in white phaneroplasmodia of the Physarales.

As described by Camp (1937b), the ingestion and egestion of solid particles result in the formation and disappearance respectively of food vacuoles, and presumably portions of the plasma membrane alternate between being plasma membrane and vacuolar membrane. Rhea (1966) has described very numerous invaginations in the plasmodia of *P. polycephalum* which, superficially at least, are reminiscent of the formation of food vacuoles described by Camp.

In view of the obvious differences of opinion that exist regarding even the number of different types of vacuoles, the difficulty of estimating the volume of a plasmodium that is made up of vacuoles is understandable. Such estimates are rendered even more difficult since apparently in an actively feeding plasmodium food vacuoles are continuously forming and disappearing, and contractile vacuoles are continuously increasing and decreasing in size. Nonetheless, Andresen and Pollock (1952) commendably attempted such an estimation and calculated that about 18 per cent of the total volume of the plasmodium consisted of vacuoles.

Fibrils

Because of their possible significance in explaining the mechanism of protoplasmic streaming a considerable amount of recent research has been directed toward proving the existence of fibrils in plasmodia. Results of such investigations (Sponsler and Bath, 1953; Kishimoto, 1958; Wohlfarth-Bottermann, 1962; Nakajima, 1964; Nakajima and

Allen, 1965; McManus, 1965; Rhea, 1966) have definitely established the existence of fibrillar structures in plasmodia. Wohlfarth-Bottermann (1962) found that the gel layer is groundplasm containing thread-like structures identical with those of amoebae. Furthermore, he found that these structures which he terms plasma filaments can form compact fibrils which he believes are merely differentiations of the groundplasm. In a later paper (1964), this investigator stated that the number of fibrils depends upon the physiological state and is very different in different areas of the plasmodium. Although fibrils are briefly referred to here in connection with the discussion of plasmodial structure, they will be discussed in greater detail in the section devoted to protoplasmic streaming and locomotion, since at this time their greatest significance appears to be in connection with these phenomena.

Other Inclusions and Organelles

Although an increasing amount of research is being conducted on the ultrastructure of plasmodia, there is as yet insufficient information to describe with certainty the complete details regarding the fine structure of this material. Rhea (1966) detected small (175 Å) dark granules some of which he presumed to be ribosomes in the cortical cytoplasm of spherules of P. polycephalum, and McManus (1965) saw bodies similar to polyribosomes (Fig. 34) described for single-celled organisms in plasmodia of D. clavus, C. debaryanum, M. vesparium, S. fusca, and a yellow phaneroplasmodium. McManus described polyribosomes as "linear arrays of electron-dense structures about 23 mμ in diameter (ribosomes) linked by strands 1.0–1.5 mμ across (messenger RNA)."

McManus (1965) found membranes arranged in lamellae resembling the Golgi apparatus of animal cells. These were not always associated with nuclei. She also noted scattered vesicles with membranes similar to the lamellae throughout the protoplasm, especially in the plasmodium of M. vesparium. In plasmodia of P. flavicomum, Aldrich (1966) found dictyosomes and gray globules which he did not identify. On the basis of her fine-structure studies, McManus (1965) concluded that most of the plasmodial components she observed have much in common with those of animal and lower plant species.

Terada (1962) described the ground cytoplasm of the plasmodium of P. polycephalum as consisting of a reticular string of vesicles or convoluted tubular strands (30–60 microns in diameter) which form a smooth-surfaced endoplasmic reticulum. He believes that sol-gel transformations are produced by small changes in the force that holds the vesicles and tubules together in a delicate network. McManus (1965) also found structures that resembled a smooth-surfaced endoplasmic

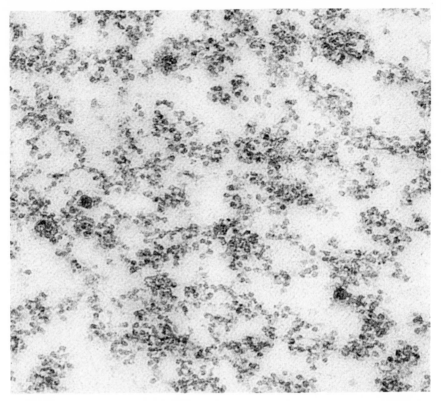

Fig. 34. Electron micrograph of portion of plasmodium of *Clastoderma debaryanum* showing polyribosomes and ground substance. × 92,500. (Mc-Manus, 1965.)

reticulum in the five plasmodia she studied, but noted that in some instances it was externally studded with electron-dense bodies. In contrast to the smooth endoplasmic reticulum reported by Terada and also by McManus, Aldrich (1966) reported a rough endoplasmic reticulum in *P. flavicomum*. However, Wohlfarth-Bottermann (1964, p. 109) has expressed the opinion that it is not endoplasmic reticulum but vacuoles that are found in plasmodia.

Vesicular structures seem to be commonly found in electron microscope studies of plasmodia. For example, McManus (1965) reported their presence in all the plasmodia she studied and stated that many have the appearance of structures such as lysosomes and microbodies in animal cells, and Rhea (1966) found both large and small vesicles in spherules of *P. polycephalum*. Stewart and Stewart (1960a) found that numerous empty-appearing vesicles of various sizes and shapes were prominent in plasmodia of *P. polycephalum* and (1960b) suggested that vesicle membranes may play a role in the rapid formation of new plasma membranes so characteristic of injured plasmodia.

Guttes and Guttes (1960) observed living plasmodia of *P. polycephalum* and found that droplets of medium were taken up by pinocytosis. Their illustrations of this process (Fig. 35) are very similar to the

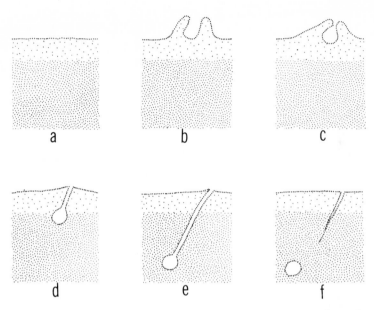

Fig. 35. Stages in the engulfment of a droplet of liquid medium by pinocytosis. (Redrawn from Guttes and Guttes, 1960, by permission of Academic Press, Inc.)

process of particulate food ingestion as described by Camp (1937b). The structures figured by Rhea (1966) are somewhat different from the pinocytotic structures figured by Guttes and Guttes, since Rhea describes them as small, straight canals (0.1–0.4 micron in diameter) open at the surface and extending 25–50 microns or more into the cytoplasm and expanding into vesicles 0.3–2.2 microns in diameter every 5–10 microns. In view of this description, it seems doubtful that these structures are pinocytotic.

Groundplasm

The term groundplasm is usually employed to designate protoplasm other than morphologically distinguishable inclusions or organelles. It is obvious that in an active plasmodium containing dividing nuclei, contractile vacuoles, food particles in the process of being ingested or egested, pinocytotic structures, and so on, it would be impossible to state that a certain proportion of a plasmodium always consists of a certain percentage of groundplasm. Andresen and Pollock (1952) estimated that about 30 per cent of the protoplasm of *P. polycephalum* consists of inclusions; therefore, in the particular samples with which they worked it can be assumed that about two-thirds consisted of groundplasm. In spite of the tremendous increase in our knowledge of the fine structure of plasmodia which has occurred during the last several years, our knowledge of groundplasm is still very meager, and too-positive accounts of its amount as well as its differentiation capabilities must at this time be accepted cautiously. For example, Wohlfarth-Bottermann (1964, p. 108) has stated that the whole mass of groundplasm must be considered as potential fibril-forming material—a very attractive hypothesis but one that must have considerably more substantiation.

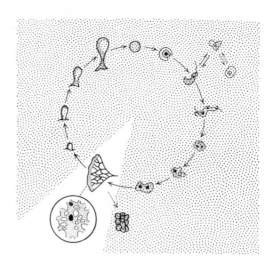

7

Plasmodial Locomotion and Protoplasmic Streaming

Since Corti (Seifriz, 1943) first observed streaming of protoplasm almost 200 years ago, biologists have been fascinated by this striking phenomenon and have studied it intensively. The mode of streaming varies from one type of organism to another, and at least seven different types of streaming have been described. Because the direction of flow in a myxomycete plasmodium typically alternates in a rhythmic pattern, it is often termed shuttle streaming, a term introduced by Seifriz (1943). This type of streaming is the most conspicuous among the streamings of protoplasm because the rate of flow as well as the volume of protoplasm transported is very great compared with those of other cells. Thus, Vouk (1913b) measured the rate of flow in the plasmodium of *Didymium nigripes* as 1250 microns/sec, and Kamiya (1950b) reported a rate of 1350 microns/sec for *Physarum polycephalum*. By comparison, the highest rate reported for any other type of fungus material was the 250 microns/sec reported for hyphae of the ascomycete *Humaria leucoloma* by Jahn (1934). Leaves of *Elodea* spp. are commonly used to demonstrate streaming in plant cells, but compared to the shuttle streaming of plasmodia, the rate is exceptionally slow, since Zurzycki (1951) reported a rate of only 6 microns/sec in *Elodea densa*.

In view of the comparatively spectacular nature of streaming in plasmodia it is not surprising that such material has been used extensively to study protoplasmic streaming *per se*. Much credit must be given to

Seifriz (1943, 1953) for repeatedly calling attention to the extreme suitability of the plasmodia of *Physarum polycephalum* for the study of protoplasmic streaming, and to Kamiya (1940, 1942, 1943) who developed more sophisticated techniques for the study of streaming in plasmodia. Although Pfeffer (1906) suggested that streaming in protoplasts with cell walls is basically different from that in material such as plasmodia, Seifriz (1943) was of the opinion that "there is one basic mechanism of protoplasmic flow and not an entirely different principle for each type of cell." It seems most likely that Seifriz' view is the correct one, and, hence, if the mechanism of protoplasmic streaming can be determined for plasmodia, it is probable that the problem of protoplasmic streaming for most organisms will have been solved. Unfortunately it must be stated that although our knowledge of protoplasmic streaming has increased almost by several orders of magnitude during the past three decades there are many perplexing questions yet to be answered.

LOCOMOTION

Although a plasmodium may show active protoplasmic streaming without locomotion being evident, it is obvious that movement is dependent upon streaming. Seifriz and Urbach (1944) have pointed out that there are four categories of motion to be observed in the plasmodium: (1) protoplasmic streaming, (2) spreading of plasmodium, which does not involve change in volume, (3) growth, which involves change in mass, and (4) locomotion, which involves change in form or position, but not necessarily an increase in area or volume. For the sake of completeness, two other categories of motion should be added to Seifriz' four categories: Brownian movement and independent movement of particles in the protoplasm. There is no evidence that these two additional categories of movement are related to protoplasmic streaming; however, spreading, growth, and locomotion are dependent upon streaming and so an understanding of this phenomenon will probably answer the major questions relative to motion in plasmodia.

Factors Affecting Migration of Plasmodia

Since protoplasmic streaming is basic to the major types of motion in plasmodia, a great amount of research effort has been directed toward explaining this phenomenon. However, some work has been conducted primarily for the purpose of studying locomotion and spreading. Stahl (1884) reported that KNO_3, NaCl, and glycerine would prevent spreading of plasmodia, and Smith and Grenan (1949) found that by increasing sugar concentration in the agar substrate, spreading of *P. polycephalum* plasmodia was progressively reduced. Cohen (1939), working with two-membered cultures, found that advancing plasmodial strands follow streaks of yeast cells. Apparently, as they crawl about over their substrates, plasmodia may excrete materials which they later avoid, since Seifriz (1944) reported that plasmodia would not recross their paths, and he attributed this to excretion of exotoxins. However, our own observations indicate that, whereas it is true that a plasmodium migrating over the agar surface in a Petri dish will usually move over new territory, when the entire surface has been gone over once, a plasmodium that, for one reason or another, has failed to fruit usually continues to migrate over the same territory it has covered before. Whether in nature plasmodia ever recross their paths is not known.

Watanabe, et al. (1938) found that the migration of plasmodia of *P. polycephalum* can be oriented by a weak electric current, and Anderson (1951) reported that the effect of the current was that of inhibition of migration toward the anode rather than stimulation of migration toward the cathode. Anderson (1962, 1964) later found that while differences in potassium content between anterior and posterior regions of non-electrically oriented plasmodia were less than 5 per cent, the posterior reticulated portions of oriented plasmodia contain 30 per cent less potassium than the anterior non-reticulated region. In contrast to potassium, sodium is generally less concentrated in the anterior than in the posterior region, but Anderson pointed out that sodium concentrations are extremely variable. He found that there was no significant difference in protein concentration between oriented and non-oriented plasmodia. Oriented plasmodia lose about ten times as much potassium to the substrate as non-oriented plasmodia, and Anderson considers that potassium has an essential function in migration and postulates that loss of potassium to the substrate may be a primary aspect of the orientation effects of direct current.

PROTOPLASMIC STREAMING

Progressive and Regressive Streaming

Most observations on and experimentation with slime mold plasmodia have been conducted with the phaneroplasmodium type, primarily because of the ease with which the phaneroplasmodium of *Physarum polycephalum* and a few other species can be obtained. Therefore, the present discussion will be confined largely to streaming in this plasmodial type. When a single strand of such a plasmodium is examined under the microscope, a unidirectional flow of protoplasm is first observed; the flow will be seen to gather momentum until it is occurring at a very rapid rate. Flow will then slow down and finally come to a complete halt. After a short period of quiescence, the plasmodium will slowly start flowing in the opposite direction, gradually gain momentum, slow down and stop, and then start flowing in the reverse direction. Occasionally it may be observed that after streaming comes to a halt, when it is resumed flow will occur in the same direction as before, but ordinarily the direction of flow will reverse after a period of quiescence.

It is soon obvious, especially if the advancing front and the retracting ends of a plasmodium are observed, that the other major motions of the plasmodium are due to the basic motion—protoplasmic streaming. More often than not, when durations of flow in each direction are timed, it is observed that the flow in one direction is of longer duration than in the reverse direction. For this reason it has been a temptation to observers to suggest that the slow locomotion of a plasmodium is in the direction of longest duration of protoplasmic flow, and the terms "progressive" and "regressive" streaming have been employed to designate streaming in and away from the direction of plasmodial movement. Vouk (1910) observed the reversal of streaming in plasmodia and referred to one progressive streaming and the immediately following regressive streaming as one rhythm and claimed that rhythm duration is approximately constant. Vouk also stated that streaming in the direction of plasmodial movement (progressive) is always of longer duration than the opposite reverse streaming (regressive) of the rhythm.

Since it is evident that a plasmodium moves in the direction toward which the greater amount of protoplasm is moved, to accept the view of Vouk is to assume that a greater volume of protoplasm is always transported during progressive streaming than during regressive streaming. However, Kamiya (1950a) adequately demonstrated that duration of flow does not necessarily correlate directly with volume of protoplasm transported. This worker devised a simple but very sensitive double-chamber volumeter (Fig. 36) with which he could simultaneously measure the duration of and the volume of protoplasm moved in a single streaming. Kamiya found that progressive flow is not always of longer duration than regressive flow: of 229 rhythms taken at random, there were 135 in which progressive flow had a longer duration than regressive flow, while in the remaining 94 rhythms, regressive flow had a longer duration than progressive flow. Since Kamiya's measurements showed that more than 4 mm^3 of protoplasm are sometimes shifted in a direction in one streaming duration, it is not surprising that plasmodia sometimes appear to move rather rapidly over their substrates.

McManus (1966) has described a unique situation in the minute plasmodium of *Cribraria violacea*. The plasmodium of this species, barely visible to the naked eye as a black speck, was observed during migration

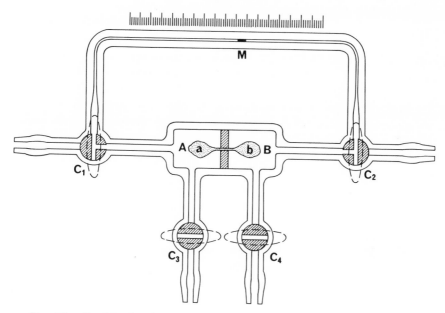

Fig. 36. Double-chamber volumeter. A, B = compartments containing small masses of plasmodium (a, b) connected by single strand. M = index drop. C_1-C_4 = stopcocks. (Redrawn from Kamiya, 1950.)

and seen to flow in one direction only. McManus observed plasmodia continuously for two 40-minute periods and saw no reversal of flow. She described the smaller plasmodia as looking and behaving like large black amoebae, often with a contractile vacuole at the posterior end. This type of plasmodium deserves more intensive study, since it appears to be intermediate between amoebae and typical phaneroplasmodia and could conceivably be used to determine whether protoplasmic flow in amoebae and plasmodia is basically different or whether there is "unity among diversity" as Engelhardt (1957) has stated. Stewart and Stewart (1959) have noted that in plasmodia of *P. polycephalum* flow in one direction can occur for as long as 30 minutes; however, they stated that usually reversal of flow occurs in the range of 0.5 to 10 minutes. Kamiya (1950a) presented data on twenty rhythm durations (progressive plus regressive flow), and all were in the range of 71.6 to 85.0 seconds.

Hypotheses Concerning the Mechanism of Protoplasmic Streaming

Seifriz (1943) listed eleven different hypotheses that had been advanced up to that time in attempts to explain the mechanism of protoplasmic streaming. Thus, streaming has been variously interpreted in terms of: (1) surface tension, (2) hydration, (3) osmosis, (4) sol-gel reversibility, (5) myelin processes, (6) coacervates, (7) autonomous propulsion of particles, (8) kinetic energy, (9) magnetism, (10) electrical forces, and (11) contractility. In all probability some or perhaps all of the above may affect protoplasmic streaming, but to discuss all of these hypotheses in detail is well beyond the scope of the present work. For the student who wishes to examine the details of the various hypotheses the extensive reviews of Seifriz (1943) and Kamiya (1959), with 225 and 428 literature references respectively, are recommended. Seifriz definitely gave preference to an interpretation of streaming based upon rhythmic contraction and relaxation of protoplasm, and Kamiya gave preference to a hypothesis that explains streaming on the basis of a contractile protein system similar to that found in muscle.

Two additional hypotheses should now be added to Seifriz' list of eleven: (12) the diffusion drag force hypothesis and (13) the contraction-hydraulic hypothesis. The principal advocates of the diffusion drag force hypothesis are Stewart and Stewart (1959); this hypothesis will be discussed in some detail in a separate section. Since Andresen and Pollock (1952) and Jahn, et al. (1964) have demonstrated the existence of hydraulic pressure in plasmodial strands, Jahn (1964) refers to a "contraction-hydraulic" system as a possible means of explaining protoplasmic streaming. Jahn's scheme as well as another scheme involving contractile fibrils as the motive force in protoplasmic streaming may in a very broad sense embody both Seifriz' contractility-of-protoplasm hypothesis and the older explanation of streaming on the basis of sol-gel reversibility.

Immediate Source of Energy for Streaming

In view of the great number of investigators who have found Myxomycetes to be excellent experimental organisms, and in view of the spectacular shuttle streaming exhibited by these organisms, it is not surprising that a relatively large number of investigators have concerned themselves with various aspects of streaming. Although there are many facets of streaming, the principal problems involve identification of the energy source for the process, how the energy is released, and the mechanism by which chemical energy is transformed into mechanical work. With respect to the source of energy there is now little doubt that ATP is the immediate source of energy from which the motive force of protoplasmic flow is produced; however, there has been some difference of opinion as to whether the ATP used as the energy source is generated aerobically or anaerobically.

Clark (1888), and later Kitching and Pirenne (1940), reported that the complete removal of oxygen causes cessation of flow in plasmodia of several Myxomycetes, but that renewal of the O_2 supply would restore flow, and the amounts of O_2 necessary to maintain or restore flow were very low (partial pressures of O_2 equivalent to 1–3 mm mercury). Moore (1935) reported that plasmodia of *P. polycephalum* will not survive long periods of anaerobiosis and concluded that the energy for protoplasmic flow is derived through aerobic respiration, but that the respiratory requirements for the maintenance of flow are small. On the other hand, Seifriz and Urbach (1944) reported that streaming in *P. polycephalum* plasmodia continues in atmospheres containing as low as 0.3 per cent O_2 and concluded that respiration is anaerobic or nearly so. Allen and Price (1950) reported that normal streaming occurs until O_2 pressure reaches 2.4 per cent of the atmospheric pressure, the rate of flow decreases slightly under conditions of 1 per cent O_2, and in atmospheres of 0.3 per cent O_2 streaming still continues but growth cannot occur. Loewy (1950) found that in pure nitrogen the plasmodium of *P. polycephalum* disintegrates in 20–80 minutes but the addition of 5 per cent CO_2 removes the toxic effect, and that streaming continues for more than 24 hours in spite of the complete lack of oxygen. Loewy concluded that it was the lack of CO_2 and not the absence of O_2 that was responsible for the cessation of flow. Ohta (1952b), using a device (Fig. 37) similar to that

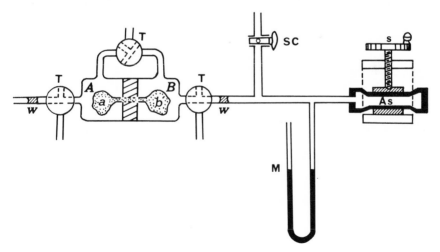

Fig. 37. Diagram of equipment used for measuring the motive force of protoplasmic streaming in a myxomycete plasmodium. The equipment consists of a double chamber (A, B) in which the plasmodium (a, b) is placed. Volume of rubber bulb (As) is controlled by screw S. Pressure exerted on the plasmodium by means of the rubber bulb is measured with manometer M. Sc, stopcock; W, water drop; T, three-way stopcock. (Redrawn from Ohta, 1952.)

employed by Kamiya (a double-chamber volumeter equipped with a means of setting up a hydrostatic counterpressure just sufficient to stop the flow), studied the effects of the removal of O_2 on streaming and reported that it had no effect on motive force generation. He also found that when the plasmodium was placed in fresh air, the motive force was slightly depressed for a while prior to its recovery, and that pure O_2 administered to both compartments of the double-chamber volumeter inhibits generation of the motive force to a certain extent. Citing his own work and that of his associates, Kamiya (1959) states that without exception the conditions that suppress respiration (O_2 uptake) increase the motive force back of streaming. However, he notes that conditions that block the glycolytic process always diminish the motive force when respiration is not affected, and hence he states that this indicates that the energy for streaming is supplied by glycolysis. Thus, the increase in motive force in the anaerobic state or under the influence of KCN or CO can be interpreted as an increase in glycolysis due to the Pasteur effect which has been observed in *P. polycephalum* by Ohta (1954). This latter investigator also reported that he had demonstrated the presence of such enzymes as succinic dehydrogenase, malic dehydrogenase, pyruvic oxidase, and lactic dehydrogenase in homogenates of plasmodium, so it seems probable that the tricarboxylic acid cycle also exists in plasmodium. Since Ohta also reported the production of lactic acid under anaerobic conditions and confirmed the presence of cytochromes *a, b,* and *c* spectroscopically, he inferred that the main path of metabolism is the decomposition of glycogen to pyruvic acid through the action of a series of glycolytic enzymes. Under anaerobic conditions, the pyruvic acid is reduced to lactic acid by lactic dehydrogenase, but in the presence of oxygen, pyruvic acid enters the tricarboxylic acid cycle and is oxidatively decomposed to CO_2, with the cytochrome system as the terminal oxidase. Younggren (1958) analyzed extracts of *P. polycephalum* spectrophotometrically and found no evidence for the presence of cytochromes, but Ward (1956) demonstrated the presence of cytochrome oxidase in this species. Since Ohta and Ward have both demonstrated the presence of a cytochrome system, and since Allen and Price (1950) obtained evidence indicative of the participation of cytochrome oxidase in the normal respiration of plasmodia, it can probably be assumed that a cytochrome system is present.

Prior to Ohta's demonstration of the presence of succinic dehydrogenase, Holter and Pollock (1952) had compared the dipeptidase and succinic dehydrogenase activities of intact plasmodia, plasmodia stratified by centrifugation, and plasmodial homogenates. They suggested that succinic dehydrogenase was localized in the mitochrondria, but that dipeptidase was diffusely distributed in the cytoplasm. Johnson and

Moos (1956) found that homogenates of *P. polycephalum* plasmodia show strong succinoxidase activity, and when homogenate fractions were separated in a refrigerated centrifuge succinoxidase activity was concentrated in the mitochondrial fraction.

Although it has not been proved beyond question, the great weight of evidence at this time is that the ATP which is the immediate source of the energy for protoplasmic streaming is generated anaerobically through glycolysis. Chemically there is no difference between ATP generated through aerobic respiration and ATP generated through glycolysis; however, the matter of location in the protoplasm and hence of availability may be of considerable importance. Since the site of aerobic respiration seems to be the mitochondria where most of the important respiratory enzymes are, and since glycolysis takes place in the groundplasm where the motive force seems to be generated, it is logical to assume that the ATP generated through glycolysis in the groundplasm usually provides the immediate source of energy for streaming, unless it can be demonstrated that ATP diffuses readily from mitochondria into the groundplasm.

Since the energy required for most physiological processes is supplied by the energy-rich phosphate bond of adenosine triphosphate, it was quite natural that attempts to relate this material to protoplasmic streaming were made. Allen and Price (1950) assumed that the source of energy for streaming is the energy-rich phosphate bond, and Kamiya, *et al.* (1957) pointed to the possibility of ATP formed during fermentation being the source of energy, but it was Hatano and Takeuchi (1960) who demonstrated the actual presence of ATP in plasmodia (Fig. 38). These last workers extracted phosphate compounds from the plasmodium of *P. polycephalum* and found that there were about 2.5 micromoles of inorganic phosphorus, 0.2 micromole of ADP, and 0.4 micromole of ATP per gram wet weight on the average. They also found that under conditions of low oxygen tension (0.2 per cent O_2 in cylinder N_2), ATP content did not change significantly. In view of Ohta's (1954) finding that *P. polycephalum* forms a considerable amount of acid under anaerobic conditions and only an insignificant amount under aerobic conditions, Hatano and Takeuchi also suggested that the process of fermentation in plasmodia is glycolysis.

Effects of ATP on Streaming

Other investigators have determined the effects of adding ATP either externally to the plasmodium or internally by microinjection. Thus, Kamiya, *et al.* (1957) treated one-half of a plasmodium in the double-chamber volumeter with 2×10^{-3} M ATP and observed a decided in-

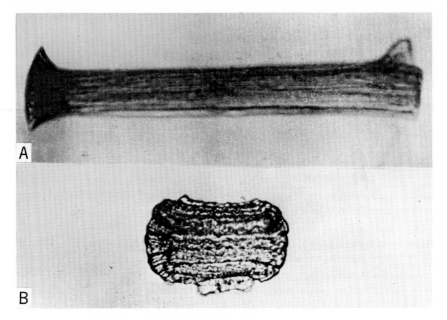

Fig. 38. Contraction of glycerinated rabbit psoas muscle by addition of small portions of barium-insoluble fraction of plasmodium of *P. polycephalum*. A. Muscle before addition. B. A few minutes after addition. (Hatano and Takeuchi, 1960.)

crease in motive force in about six to seven minutes after ATP was administered. No immediate change in viscosity was noted, but accompanying the increase in motive force an increase in viscosity was observed. Adenylic acid (AMP) from muscle and yeast did not produce increases in motive force comparable to those caused by ATP nor were there discernible changes in viscosity. Ts'o, *et al.* (1956a) introduced ATP in low concentration inside plasmodia by microinjection and observed partial liquefaction of the plasmagel and an increased rate of streaming. From such observations as the above it is obvious that the motive force of streaming can be quickly augmented by the addition of ATP, and since this compound also has been demonstrated in plasmodia, there now seems little question that it is the immediate source of energy for streaming.

There is some evidence that the ratio of amount of endoplasm to amount of ectoplasm in a particular region of the plasmodium may affect the generation of motive force. Kamiya and Yoneda (1967) used a triple-chamber system which allowed them to make one region of a plasmodium endoplasm-rich and one endoplasm-poor, and leave one with a normal endoplasm–ectoplasm ratio. Such treatment of plasmodia was accompanied by observable differences (dynamic polarity) in motive forces between regions. Such differences gradually diminished even when the displaced endoplasm was not allowed to flow back into the endoplasm-poor region. Kamiya and Takata (1967) then employed a quadruple-chamber system and found that the patterns of motive force generation in regions with excessive amounts of endoplasm and those with deficient amounts tend to approach each other in time and eventually become indistinguishable. This was interpreted as evidence of a regulatory mechanism which brings an abnormal endoplasm–ectoplasm ratio back to normal. It seems possible that the capacity of a plasmodium to control the state of fibrillar differentiation (Takata, Nagai, and Kamiya, 1967) may be closely related to this regulatory mechanism.

Possible Mechanism of Protoplasmic Streaming

In his 1943 review article, Seifriz gave preference to the hypothesis that protoplasmic streaming is due to the rhythmic contraction and expansion of protoplasm, but in his review Kamiya (1959) gave preference to an hypothesis based upon a contractile protein system known to be present in plasmodia. In a sense, both reviewers were talking about the same general type of system; however, in his later review, Kamiya had the advantage of being able to utilize the findings of a number of investigators obtained over an additional sixteen-year period. Assuming that the immediate source of energy for streaming is ATP, there still remains unanswered the question of how living matter is able to transform chemical energy into mechanical work; however, the work of Loewy and others has pointed in a direction such that hopefully it may soon be possible to describe with reasonable certainty how this may be accomplished.

Since active local contractions of the peripheral plasmagel are known to occur spontaneously in plasmodia and can be induced experimentally by the addition of ATP (Fig. 39), hydraulic pressures may be built up locally in plasmodia. For this reason Jahn et al. (1964) have combined the theory of a spongy structural network in both plasmagel and plasmasol with the contraction-hydraulic theory to explain protoplasmic streaming.

The isolation from muscle of two proteins (actin and myosin) which seem to retain some of the properties of the muscle cell must be considered one of the great achievements of muscle chemistry. These proteins form a complex (actomyosin), and the addition of ATP will not only lower the viscosity of this complex but will cause it to contract when precipitated. Loewy (1950) first reported the isolation of a system similar to actomyosin from the plasmodium of *P. polycephalum*. Addi-

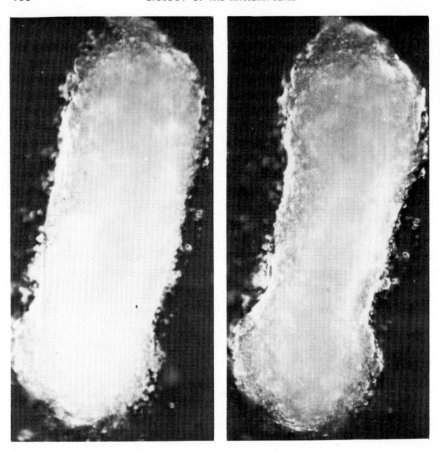

Fig. 39. Strand of plasmodium of *Physarum polycephalum* before (*left*) and after (*right*) application of ATP. Note contraction at central region of strand caused by application of ATP. (Jahn, *et al.*, 1964.)

tion of ATP to a final concentration of 4×10^{-4} resulted in a rapid viscosity decrease of this system, followed by a slower rise to a viscosity greater than initial. Viscosity of the system rose with muscle adenylic acid, but yeast adenylic acid was without effect. Loewy interpreted the slow rise in viscosity that followed decrease in viscosity caused by the addition of ATP as being due to the formation of muscle adenylic acid by the dephosphorylation of ATP. Ts'o, *et al.* (1956a, b, c; 1957a, b) isolated the system first described by Loewy and named it myxomyosin, and this group of investigators, as well as Nakajima (1956, 1957), studied its properties in greater detail. Ts'o, *et al.* (1957a) studied the characteristics of this protein complex by viscosity, sedimentation, birefringence, and electron microscope measurements, and they concluded that the myxomyosin molecule is a long, rigid rod with average length of 4000–5000 Å and a diameter of about 70 Å. On the basis of sedimentation and viscosity data the molecular weight was calculated to be 6,000,000. Since Ts'o, *et al.* (1957b) found that the ATP effect was greater at 0.1° C than at room temperature (24.5° C), they inferred that the reaction is not enzymic but rather a physical-chemical reaction, possibly the binding of ATP to myxomyosin. This latter inference does not agree with the interpretation of Loewy, who believed that the slow rise in viscosity which followed decrease in viscosity caused by the addition of ATP was due to the dephosphorylation of ATP.

More recently, Hatano and Oosawa (1962, 1963, 1964) attempted to isolate an actin-like protein and a myosin-like protein from a plasmodium of *P. polycephalum* and were successful in isolating an actin-like protein (Fig. 40) which would form a complex with muscle myosin. The complex behaved similarly to the actomyosin complex in muscle (Fig. 41). The molecular weight of the actin-like protein was estimated to be about 57,000 which is equal to that of G-actin from muscle. When muscle G-actin was added to a solution of plasmodial actin, addition of 0.1 M

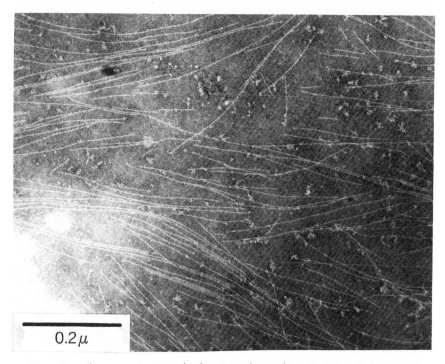

0.2 μ

Fig. 40. Electron micrograph showing plasmodium F-actin. Polymerization induced on addition of 0.1 M KCl. × 135,000. (Photograph, courtesy of S. Hatano.)

Fig. 41. Superprecipitation of actomyosin complex synthesized from actin-like protein from plasmodium and myosin A from rabbit striated muscle. *Left:* Control (no ATP). *Right:* Superprecipitation on addition of 1.5 mM ATP. (Courtesy of S. Hatano.)

KCl or 2 mM MgCl$_2$ caused a copolymerization of these two. In a later communication (Hatano, *et al.*, 1965), the Japanese investigators also reported the isolation of a contractile myosin-like protein, one of the components of which they named myosin A. As noted above, Hatano and his associates reported the cross-complexing of plasmodial actin with muscle myosin, and in a later report Oosawa, *et al.* (1966) reported the successful reciprocal cross-complexing, i.e., plasmodial myosin with muscle actin.

Plasmodial Fibrils

Whether or not contractile protein molecules can be proved to provide the mechanism for the conversion of the chemical energy of ATP to the mechanical work of streaming may depend in part upon the incontrovertible establishment of the presence of fibrils in living plasmodia. Sponsler and Bath (1953) obtained fibers of various sizes in electron micrographs of material obtained by macerating P. polycephalum plasmodia and drying the resultant suspension on electron microscope grids. Kishimoto (1958) reported the existence of network-like structures as a result of his electron microscope studies. Stewart and Stewart (1960a) objected to the use of such crudely prepared materials as those used by Sponsler and Bath for the demonstration of fibrils, and they fixed plasmodia of P. polycephalum in cold 1 per cent osmic acid in veronal-acetate buffer at pH 7.0. The fixed plasmodia were then embedded in methacrylate, sectioned, and examined with the electron microscope. They were unable to observe any fibrous structure regardless of section orientation with respect to axis of streaming, and hence they stated that the type of structure they observed seemed more consistent with the requirements of Rashevsky's (1948) diffusion drag-force hypothesis than with the requirements of a contractile network analogous with muscle.

Wohlfarth-Bottermann (1962, 1964) demonstrated a fibrillar network in plasmodia of P. polycephalum. This network was composed of filaments 70 Å in diameter—the same size as that reported by Ts'o, et al. (1957a) for myxomyosin filaments. The fibrils were birefringent and displayed ATPase activity, and Wohlfarth-Bottermann concluded that the fibrillar network functions in streaming and locomotion. Birefringent fibrils have also been reported in plasmodia by Nakajima (1964) and Nakajima and Allen (1965). However, Terada (1962) made a specific search for fibrils and could not find them.

McManus (1965), using fixation techniques similar to those of Stewart and Stewart (1960b), found three distinct types of fibrils (granular, tubular, and ones resembling the mitotic filaments, such as in Pelomyxa carolinensis) in plasmodia of Didymium clavus, Clastoderma debaryanum, and Metatrichia vesparium and also in an unidentified yellow plasmodium. She failed to find fibrils in the aphanoplasmodium of Stemonitis fusca and noted that fibrils were most frequent and most clearly differentiated in the protoplasmodium of C. debaryanum (Fig. 42), in which streaming was sluggish and intermittent.

More recently, Rhea (1966) has conducted extensive electron microscopic studies on motile plasmodia, microplasmodia (Daniel and Rusch, 1961), and spherules of P. polycephalum. He failed to find the tubular type of fibril which was one of the types described by McManus, but he did find internal fibrils in motile plasmodia and in microplasmodia; the existence of internal fibrils in spherules was not definitely established. Internal fibrils consisted of filaments about 55 Å in diameter and were found in or subjacent to the hyaline cortical cytoplasm. The fibrils were

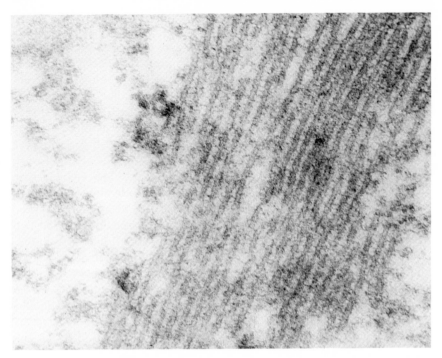

Fig. 42.   Plasmodium of *Clastoderma debaryanum* showing fibrils.   ✕ 105,-000.   (McManus, 1965.)

occasionally in contact with the plasma membrane of free surfaces, but usually were more closely associated with the plasma membranes of invaginations. Rhea stated that if they are contractile, "the fibers are so positioned in circular and longitudinal arrays as to bring about changes in diameter and length associated with cytoplasmic streaming and motility." External filaments similar to those that had been observed by McManus (1965) were also observed by Rhea, who noted that all plasmodia were encapsulated in a fibrillar network composed of branched and curved filaments 30–75 Å in diameter and of indefinite length. Because of their morphological similarity to internal fibrils, Rhea suggested that external fibrils might have a role in providing restoring forces during streaming and motility.

Nakajima and Allen (1965) found birefringent fibrils throughout the ectoplasmic region of plasmodia of *P. polycephalum* and stated that some fibrils exist for only a few minutes, but that others exist for a longer period of time. In the larger plasmodial strands, the fibrils were oriented parallel to the strand or were arranged in a circular or spiral manner along the periphery of endoplasmic channels. It is interesting to note that Rhea as well as Nakajima and Allen reported a peripheral position of fibrils, and that the latter workers expressed the opinion that streaming may be explained in terms of coordinated contractions taking place in the fibrils. The fact that some fibrils had an existence of short duration might possibly explain why several investigators failed to find such structures.

In 1965, Kamiya and Kuroda prepared glycerinated plasmodia by a method comparable to that used by Szent-Györgyi (1951) for muscle fibers, and studied contraction induced by application of ATP. They found that contraction in the fan-shaped anterior portion is in a radial direction (perpendicular to the advancing front), but that in a plasmodial strand contraction occurs perpendicularly and not longitudinally to the axis. Nagai and Kamiya (1966) then found in their electron microscope studies that fibrils are localized in regions where contraction takes place in glycerinated models. They reported that at the advancing front of the plasmodium filament bundles tend to be oriented radially, whereas in the walls of a plasmodial strand they run mainly circularly in the plane perpendicular to its axis. Such observations support the view that fibrillar structures may be causally responsible for local contraction. By applying external pressure to a portion of a plasmodium, Takata, Nagai, and Kamiya (1967) produced endoplasm-rich and endoplasm-poor regions in the same plasmodium and compared their fine structures. There were well-developed fibrillar bundles in the groundplasm of the ectoplasmic layer of the endoplasm-rich region but scarcely any fibrillar differentiation in the groundplasm of the endoplasm-poor region, and these investigators suggested that fibrillar bundles might be converted to another form when the normal endoplasm–ectoplasm ratio is disturbed by the squeezing out of endoplasm.

Thus, more and more evidence is accumulating to support the view that fibrils are present in plasmodia since they have been encountered in at least nine different investigations. Whether or not these fibrils are actually composed of an ATP-sensitive protein complex remains to be proved. On the other hand, it does not seem that visible fibrils need necessarily be present to explain protoplasmic streaming on a contractility basis. Bishop (1964) has objected to what he terms an unnecessary search for fibrillar systems in amoeboid cells, since he believes that motility could be accounted for on a molecular basis rather than demanding a visible fibrillar organization as the only suitable explanation. Park and Robinson (1967) have proposed that the formation of vacuoles in the plasmodium is related to protoplasmic streaming, since their formation attracts water from the groundplasm and hence increases the viscosity of the cytoplasm. Increased viscosity would create a tension in fibrils which appear to be responsible for protoplasmic streaming.

Diffusion Drag-Force Hypothesis

Stewart and Stewart (1959) made cinephotomicrographic analyses of protoplasmic movements of plasmodia of *P. polycephalum* and six unidentified plasmodia. From their studies, they suggested that an explanation of streaming based upon Rashevsky's (1948) diffusion drag-force hypothesis was more compatible with their observations. These investigators were able to distinguish three reversible states of protoplasm in viable plasmodium:

> *State I*—flowing protoplasm.
>
> *State II*—protoplasm that coexists with State I but does not flow. It is rigid enough to confine and direct the flow of State I in channels and exhibits Brownian movement indistinguishable from that of State I.
>
> *State III*—protoplasm that has set to a relatively rigid gel. Its formation may be induced by a variety of mildly noxious agents or by excessive mechanical manipulation. There is no Brownian movement except in the vacuoles.

These investigators stated that since three different gel-like states exist in addition to the liquid state in plasmodia, "classical sol-gel terminology is an oversimplification and may be misleading in considering mechanisms for protoplasmic flow." Their principal objection to an interpretation of protoplasmic streaming based on the generation of the motive force by myxomyosin plus ATP appears to be based on the fact that no detailed mechanism has been described. They do suggest, however, that since the configuration of myxomyosin can be affected by ATP, it may function as a labile structural protein which, by controlling the relation between States I and II, could control flow pattern but not be the direct source of motive power.

Since the flow of mass that occurs when a solute diffuses down a concentration gradient has a flow of momentum associated with it, there is a continuous transfer of some of this momentum to other types of molecules, and thus a force is exerted on adjoining molecules by diffusing molecules and they are dragged along with them. The Stewarts prefer to explain motive-force generation in plasmodia by postulating the establishment of concentration gradients of "some particular compound(s) with appropriate magnitude, direction and distributions" through metabolic processes in the protoplasm. The diffusion drag-force hypothesis is an attractive one, but it seems to have few supporters. It would, of course, be virtually impossible to substantiate it in plasmodia with present techniques. It is generally agreed that motive force is generated throughout the protoplasm, and therefore identification of the metabolic compounds postulated by Stewart and Stewart, establishment of the fact that they formed concentration gradients, and above all an explanation of why these gradients are reversed periodically would present rather formidable tasks.

Stewart and Stewart also claim that a caterpillar-like action of long contractile molecules (ATP-sensitive myxomyosin) at the edges of channels of protoplasmic flow, as a mechanism for generating motive force, is not compatible with the truncated parabolic velocity profile (Fig. 43)

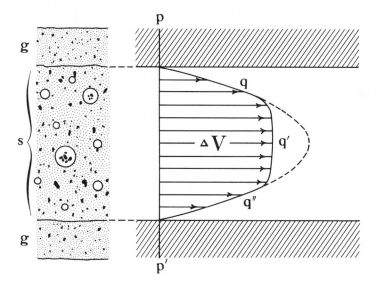

Fig. 43. Distribution of streaming velocity in a strand of plasmodium. *Left:* Diagram of microscopic view of strand; g = plasmagel (ectoplasm), s = flowing plasmasol (endoplasm). *Right:* Diagrammatic representation of velocity distribution; dotted line indicates parabola extrapolated from peripheral lines. (Redrawn from Kamiya, 1950.)

that Kamiya (1950a) has established for flow in *P. polycephalum*. On the contrary, Jahn, *et al.* (1964) state that the velocity profile is exactly the type that would be expected from pressure flow.

Jahn (1964) has objected to the diffusion drag-force hypothesis as a means of explaining protoplasmic streaming for a variety of reasons, the principal one being that it is not supported by published experimental evidence in any other material. For a more detailed criticism of this hypothesis the work of Jahn should be consulted.

INDEPENDENT MOVEMENT OF PARTICLES

Unexplained by any general theory of protoplasmic flow is the apparently independent movement of various types of individual particles in the protoplasm. Stewart and Stewart (1959) observed such movement in plasmodia and stated that it can be in any direction with respect to flow—even against it. Speed of movement of a particle was relatively constant, and paths were long compared with those in Brownian movement. They noted that direction of movement could change abruptly and stated that movements were not simple recoils from single impulsive forces. They calculated the work performed in the movement of a single 2-micron particle over a distance of 7 microns as about 10^{-11} ergs, which is equivalent to the hydrolysis of about 20 ATP molecules.

While Stewart and Stewart imply that diffusion drag forces can explain independent movement of particles, Jahn (1964) claims that such movement can be caused by contraction of either protein molecules or fibers in the plasmasol, and that such contraction could be an active contraction caused by ATP or a passive contraction due to kinetic forces. Obviously at this time the issue is not settled, but it seems probable that once the mechanism of protoplasmic streaming is elucidated to the satisfaction of all, the problem of independent movement of particles can then be better explained.

SUMMATION

While the problem of the mechanism of protoplasmic streaming in plasmodia has not been solved yet, at our present stage of knowledge a very reasonable working hypothesis is that it involves a system similar in many respects to the actomyosin complex from muscle. The presence of an ATP-sensitive contractile protein complex in plasmodia has been well established, and more and more evidence is accumulating to substantiate the view that fibrils are present in plasmodia. Evidence in support of the hypothesis will be much stronger if it can be demonstrated that the fibrils observed by the several investigators are in fact composed of the ATP-sensitive protein complex. If this is accomplished, the next step must be to conduct a much more thorough study of the ultrastructure of plasmodia in order to obtain a more complete understanding of fibril orientation and positioning in the plasmodium, since a correct interpretation of how their mechano-chemical properties are able to induce shuttle streaming may depend upon this point. If a wave of contraction could be demonstrated to be present and if it could be shown to be due to contraction and relaxation of peripherally placed fibrils in a strand of plasmodium, it would be easy to understand how pressures could be built up in the channel that would result in the flow of protoplasm. Seifriz (1937) noted that peristaltic-like waves of local contraction of channel walls could provide a mechanism to explain streaming, but Kamiya (1950c) could detect no such waves. Stewart and Stewart (1959) noted that changes in channel diameter do occur but that such changes are not in the form of peristaltic waves. However, the question of peristalsis or no peristalsis is still not answered, since Rhea (1966b), using evidence from time-lapse microcinematography, electron microscopy and electrophysiology to support the pressure-flow or contraction-hydraulic explanation of streaming, reported that flow of protoplasm results from a contractile wall mechanism that moves in a peristaltic-like fashion along plasmodial strands. Even if it ultimately proved that no peristalsis occurs, and even if the fibrils observed by so many different investigators should be proved to play no direct role in providing the mechanism for transforming chemical energy into mechanical work, it is still possible that a protein contraction-expansion system could explain the mechanism of streaming on a molecular rather than on a visible contractile-fibril basis.

Even if the above hypothesis can be proved beyond all doubt, the major problem remains to be solved. Much of the experimentation that has been conducted on protoplasmic streaming has been done with isolated bits of plasmodium, and the fact that a plasmodium represents a very complex organism although it may appear to be only a naked fan-shaped mass of protoplasm has been ignored. Over three decades ago Moore (1933, 1934, 1935) presented evidence that suggested submicroscopic structure in plasmodia, and Winer and Moore (1941) showed that the potential for streaming resided in relatively small bits of protoplasm. Ohta (1952a) was able to measure motive force in a plasmodium with a total weight of 1.5 mg and found that the magnitude of the force was slightly greater than that of a plasmodium weighing 100.2 mg. Stewart and Stewart (1961a) found unidirectional circular streaming patterns in plasmodia of *P. polycephalum* (Fig. 44), and because of the absence of any value or ratchet-like mechanism suggested that whatever generates motive force must be distributed throughout the system.

If the ATP which seems to be the immediate source of energy for streaming is produced throughout the groundplasm of a plasmodium by glycolysis, as the evidence to date strongly suggests, and if a contractile protein complex also exists throughout the groundplasm, a mechanochemical system exists in all localities in the organism. Therefore, as one examines a plasmodium spread over a moist surface such as agar it is not surprising that in one strand of the plasmodial network streaming occurs in one direction, and that in a nearby strand flow is in the opposite direc-

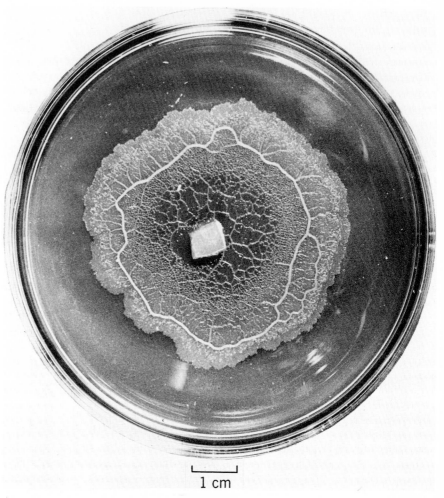

Fig. 44.   Plasmodium of *P. polycephalum* showing continuous large circular vein.   (Stewart and Stewart, 1961.)

tion. In fact, a rapid examination of an active plasmodium will reveal a great many different directions of flow, and it seems rather remarkable that the plasmodium does not either form a very non-fan-like heap of protoplasm or tear itself apart into a great number of small bits. Both of these events occur occasionally, but ordinarily the plasmodium maintains its network-like form and performs as a unit, which is evidence that some type of overall coordinating mechanism is functioning. The major problem, then, is that of determining the nature of the coordinating mechanism, regardless of the method whereby chemical energy is transformed into mechanical work.

Knowledge of the coordinating mechanism will have ramifications far beyond a mere understanding of the mechanism of streaming and may well serve to provide us with a better understanding of certain species differences that have long been observed but whose underlying mechanism appears not to have been questioned. By way of exemplifying this point one need only look at two closely related species such as *Arcyria nutans* and *Arcyria cinerea*. Both are members of the same genus and have many common morphological features, but the former develops closely packed sporangia and the latter usually forms scattered sporangia. At sporulation time, the plasmodium of *A. nutans* flows into a large heap from which discrete but closely placed sporangia are delimited, while the plasmodium of *A. cinerea* flows into a number of separate small masses, each of which becomes a sporangium. The formation of plasmodiocarps and aethalia instead of separate sporangia probably represents another facet of this same situation. It seems obvious that the coordinating mechanisms of *A. nutans* and *A. cinerea* cease functioning at different points in their cycle just prior to sporulation, or perhaps the mechanisms actually change but in different ways. To investigate and elucidate such problems will not be easy and like the investigation of many of the other subtle biochemical mechanisms of these organisms, will depend upon the development of pure culture methods in which the organisms can complete all phases of their life cycles under conditions similar in as many respects as possible to their normal habitats, with the exception that a biological environment has been eliminated.

Hatano and Nakajima (1961) and Nakajima and Hatano (1962) have reported the presence of acetylcholinesterase in the plasmodium of *Physarum polycephalum*. This enzyme, which catalyzes the breakdown of acetylcholine into choline and acetic acid is known to play an important role in nerve impulse transmission. The Japanese investigators reported the presence of both a specific acetylcholine hydrolyzing enzyme (AChE) and a non-specific choline esterase (ChE) in plasmodium. On the basis of results obtained in studies of the effects of 10^{-2} M caffeine on oxygen uptake and protoplasmic streaming, it was concluded that the specific AChE may play a role in protoplasmic streaming. Hoitink and Van Dijk (1967) have also reported the presence of acetylcholinesterase and acetylcholine in the plasmodium of *Physarella oblonga* and found that adrenaline and noradrenaline effected a shortening while acetylcholine effected a lengthening in the duration of protoplasmic streaming. It is tempting to suggest, as have Nakajima and Hatano, that perhaps a plasmodium may have a functional "neuromotor system," but evidence at this time is insufficient to warrant such a conclusion.

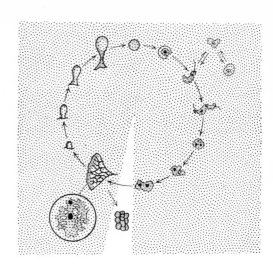

8

The Sclerotium

Spores, swarm cells, zygote, plasmodium, and fructification obviously are all necessary for the completion of the myxomycete life cycle; however, there is another structure that may play an important role in the survival of a myxomycete even though its formation is not necessary for successful life-cycle completion. This is a resistant structure which may be formed directly from the plasmodium when it is subjected to adverse environmental conditions; it represents a resting or dormant state of the plasmodium and is usually referred to as the sclerotium. DeBary (1866) first applied the name sclerotium to such structures, although they had undoubtedly been seen earlier by others, since deBary (1887) expressed the opinion that they had probably been seen by Corda in *Stemonitis* and also that sclerotia were some of the forms on which Persoon based his fungus genus *Phlebomorpha*.

Since the assimilative phase of a myxomycete consists of unprotected protoplasm, it would be surprising to find that it could withstand extremes of various environmental factors, and hence it is a very vulnerable structure. On the other hand, the sclerotium consists of dryer protoplasm and may enable the plasmodium to survive during a period of unfavorable environmental conditions. The sudden appearance of an active plasmodium on decaying wood after a day or two of mild weather in winter may well be due to the fact that the plasmodium had its origin in a sclerotium, since there is little evidence that an extensive plasmodium could have been formed so quickly if it had originated in the usual manner as a zygote. DeBary (1887) states that *Fuligo* and *Didymium serpula* are known by direct observations to persist as sclerotia during the cold, dry season and then pass into the active plasmodial state with the advent of damper and warmer weather.

Jump (1954) has correctly pointed out that relatively little attention was given to the sclerotium by earlier workers—presumably because of the unessential position it occupies in the life cycle. In general, the sclerotium has had its principal value to the myxomycete investigator as a structure from which an active plasmodial culture can be obtained quickly and easily.

Earlier workers attributed sclerotium formation to shifting of environmental conditions, and thus variation of temperature, moisture, nutrient conditions, or a combination of these and possibly other unknown factors were considered by deBary (1887), Lister (1888), Miller (1898), Constantineanu (1907), and others to be responsible for induction of the formation of a dormant sclerotium. Both moisture and temperature often appear to have been considered as major factors in the sclerotization process. For example, deBary (1887) considered cooling below a certain minimum to be among the factors concerned, and Macbride (1922) stated that lack of moisture and low temperature induce plasmodia to enter the "resting stage."

LONGEVITY OF SCLEROTIA

There is no close agreement among the various investigators concerning how long the dormant protoplasm of a sclerotium may remain alive and capable of giving rise to an active plasmodium when placed under suitable conditions of moisture and temperature, but it is quite evident that sclerotia do not have longevities that even approach those of myxomycete spores. DeBary (1866, 1887) stated that, in general, sclerotia do not retain their viability for more than seven or eight months, although some sclerotia of *Didymium serpula* remained viable for more than a year. Lister (1888) reported that five-month-old sclerotia of *Badhamia utricularis* revive within three or four hours after being moistened, and later (1894) he stated that sclerotia of this species can be revived after three years. Jahn (1919) also studied the longevity of *B. utricularis* and found the maximum to be 40 months. Jahn suggested that variations in longevity might be due to differences in external conditions during drying. Schinz (1920) claimed a much greater longevity for *B. utricularis*, since he reported that he could "with greatest ease" revive sclerotia of this species that had been in the dry state for seven years. Howard (1931a) did not attempt to determine maximum longevity of sclerotia of *Physarum polycephalum* but did state that sclerotia could be reactivated after eight months in the laboratory. Gehenio (1944) studied the longevity of over 100 sclerotia of *P. polycephalum* and found a rapid loss of vitality in all cases: only 70 per cent of initially viable sclerotia "germinated" after one year; about 10 per cent after two years; none after three years. While Hodapp (1942) was primarily interested in determining what factors influence sclerotization in *P. polycephalum*, he did note that viability was considerably reduced after 8–13 months. In 1843, Léville (cf. deBary, 1887; Gehenio, 1944; Jump, 1954) reported that the sclerotium of an unknown species was viable after 20 years. Gehenio believes that a myxomycete sclerotium may have been involved, but Jump considers Léville's account to be somewhat dubious. In spite of Léville's account and the seven-year longevity that Schinz reported for sclerotia of *B. utricularis*, the reports of other investigators seem to indicate that in general the longevity of sclerotia is about three years or less. However, since studies have been made on a relatively small number of myxomycete species, the above estimate must be considered tentative and hence may have to be revised as additional information is obtained.

Lonert (1965), working at the Turtox Laboratories, has reported the development of a practical method for preparing sclerotia of *P. polycephalum*. Basically the method involves overfeeding with rolled oats and drying at temperatures ranging from 65° to 90° F. Storage under refrigeration produced no change in vitality of sclerotia, but storage at room temperature or prolonged desiccation increased the length of time required for transformation of sclerotia to plasmodia from an original 2.5 hours (immediately after formation) to 7 and 17 hours, respectively. Sclerotia so prepared were viable after 12–16 months, and Lonert has stated that "circumstances permitting" a report on the viability of these sclerotia will be given at 5-year intervals. Since this represents an attempt to determine longevity of sclerotia prepared and stored under a standard set of conditions, subsequent reports will be awaited with interest.

STRUCTURE AND FORMATION OF SCLEROTIA

In external appearance, sclerotia often appear to have a dry and horny consistency, and sclerotia of the same species may show considerable variation. Thus, the sclerotia of *P. polycephalum* may be reticulate resembling an active plasmodium, a thick irregular mass, or a structure intermediate between the two. Nauss (1943) described the sclerotium of *Metatrichia vesparium* as consisting of many isolated globules of resting protoplasm, and her photograph shows the globules appearing as randomly scattered, short strings of loosely strung black beads. However, Wollman (1966) illustrates the sclerotium of this species (Fig. 45) as a closely packed sheet of nearly isodiametric spherules, in general similar to the sclerotium figured by Jump (1954) for *P. polycephalum* (Fig. 46). Variations in color may also occur in sclerotia of the same species; for example, sclerotia of *P. polycephalum* may vary from pale yellow to orange-brown.

In sclerotia of *Stemonitis fusca* and *Arcyria cinerea* Alexopoulos (1963) has observed structures similar to the isolated globules described by Nauss for *M. vesparium,* and Wollman (1966) has shown that sclerotia of *Comatricha nodulifera* consist of isolated globules. Alexopoulos (1964a) has noted that aphanoplasmodia do not form on agar unless the surface is covered with at least a thin film of water. Even after plasmodia are formed they fragment into small globules which proceed to encyst if permitted to dry. When rehydrated the cysts coalesce, and plasmodia are reconstituted in a few minutes. In a later paper (1966), he suggests that the process of sclerotization in aphanoplasmodia is different from that in phaneroplasmodia, since instead of aggregating the strands segment, and the plasmodium forms a large number of macrocysts distributed in the same position as the plasmodial

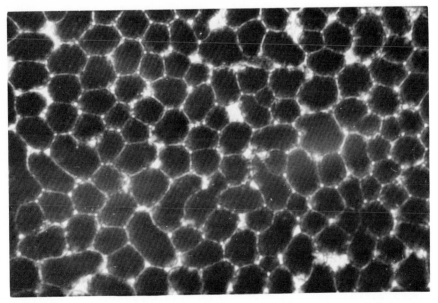

Fig. 45.   Sclerotium of *M. vesparium* showing closely packed dark spherules. × 180. (Wollman, 1966. Courtesy Constance Wollman.)

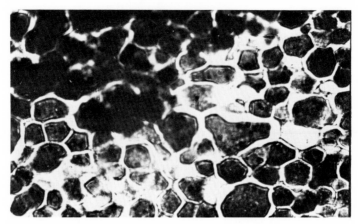

Fig. 46.   Sclerotium of *P. polycephalum* showing spherules.   × 430.   (Jump, 1954.)

network at the time of sclerotization. Wollman (1966) has figured the same general type of sclerotium (Fig. 47) for *Calomyxa metallica*.

According to Jump (1954) sclerotia of *P. polycephalum* are very constant in their internal structure, being made up of small cells. DeBary (1887) had observed these cells, which Jorgensen (1925) called sclerotiospores and Brandza (1928) later termed spherules (Fig. 46). Jump reported that the spherules of *P. polycephalum* sclerotia vary with respect to size and number of nuclei. He examined 100 such cells which were spherical to ovoid in shape and varied in length from 10 to 25 microns. The number of nuclei varied from 0 to 14 with a mean of 4.2 per cell. DeBary (1887) did not see nuclei but assumed that they were present and reported a size range of 25–40 microns for spherules. This latter worker apparently did not study *P. polycephalum,* so the discrepancies between Jump's and deBary's reported sizes may be a reflection of species differences. Although there is little evidence that characteristic differences occur between sclerotia of different species, this lack of evidence is due primarily to the fact that the sclerotia of only a few species have been studied; however, such differences might reasonably be expected to occur.

Jump's studies, which represent the most thorough investigation of sclerotia yet performed, were concerned not only with the sclerotization process (which he terms encystment) but also with the process of plasmodial reconstitution which he terms excystment. This investigator found that sclerotia may form as a result of desiccation, constant temperature of 5° C, 0.5 M sucrose, certain heavy metals (Fe, Cu, Zn), starvation, certain contaminating fungi, or low pH. Since Jump found

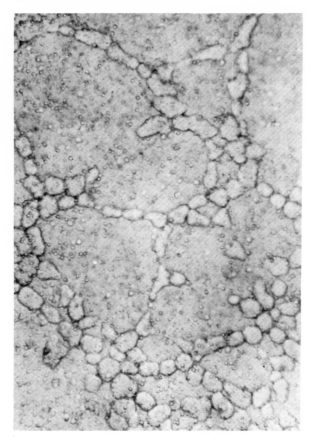

Fig. 47. Sclerotium of *Calomyxa metallica* showing spherules distributed in the same position as the plasmodial networks at the time of sclerotization. × 180. (Wollman, 1966. Courtesy Constance Wollman.)

that all of these agents except desiccation resulted in the formation of sclerotia that were plastic and moist rather than hard and dry, he suggested that the term cystosorus would be a more appropriate term than sclerotium for this dormant structure. He further suggested that the term macrocyst be substituted for spherule. Each spherule is surrounded by a membrane, and when plasmodia are dried rapidly there are formed pseudoplasmodia in which the macrocysts have incomplete membranes or none at all, and the nuclei are distorted. Jump described sclerotization as an orderly process in which the following sequence of events occurs: (1) cessation of streaming, (2) gelation of the whole structure, (3) distribution of nuclei, (4) depositing of wall, (5) completion of macrocyst formation, (6) hardening of the sclerotium, and (7) shrinkage of nuclei to about one-half diameter. In excystment (plasmodial reconstitution), the above processes are reversed.

FACTORS INFLUENCING THE FORMATION AND VIABILITY
OF SCLEROTIA

Hodapp (1942) considered only the factors of temperature and moisture in his studies of the sclerotization process in *P. polycephalum*. He induced desiccation of plasmodia in sealed chambers over solutions of H_2SO_4 of various concentrations and found that at 25° C all sclerotia formed in desiccation periods of 25–70 hours were viable. In contrast to Jump's findings, Hodapp reported that at 5°–6° C gradual death rather than sclerotization of plasmodia occurred. At sclerotization temperatures of 7°–10°, 15°, 25°, and 35° C, no viable sclerotia could be produced in desiccation periods of less than 18, 12, 4, and 3.5 hours, respectively. The water content of viable sclerotia was higher than that of non-viable sclerotia which had been treated in the same manner (12.3 per cent by weight as compared with 7.1 per cent). Hodapp's findings with respect to the effect of too-rapid desiccation are in keeping with the earlier findings of Brandza (1928) who sclerotized young plasmodia of *Didymium serpula, Craterium minutum,* and *Physarum contextum* under conditions of rapid and slow desiccation and found that rapidly formed (2 hours) sclerotia were not viable while slowly formed sclerotia were. Camp (1936) reported that viable sclerotia of *P. polycephalum* could be produced by allowing plasmodia to dry slowly on moist filter paper under a bell jar at room temperature, and recommended a drying period of about 24 hours. That plasmodia will form sclerotia if properly desiccated has been shown by many different investigators; however, the results obtained by Jump reveal that desiccation need not necessarily occur during sclerotization.

From the above accounts it is apparent that the process of sclerotization is not merely a simple drying up of the plasmodium but involves physiological changes (some of which result in obvious morphological changes) that require a certain minimum amount of time for their completion. Not only does too-rapid desiccation prevent the formation of viable sclerotia, but Luyet and Gehenio (1944) have shown that desiccation may have a lethal action on sclerotia. These investigators found that sclerotia of *P. polycephalum* suffer either a decrease in or a complete loss of viability when dehydrated by an exposure of several days over such desiccants as calcium chloride, silica, or phosphorus pentoxide, and that desiccation in a vacuum produces the same lethal results. They found that loss of viability does not parallel decrease in water content but occurs after no further dehydration occurs. Hence they point out that the immediate effect of water removal from the sclerotium seems to be to render the dormant protoplasm vulnerable rather than to kill it. In a later paper Luyet and Gehenio (1945) investigated the relation of temperature to killing time for sclerotia of *P. polycephalum* and found that 50 per cent killing time varies from 20 minutes at 90° C to about 28 hours at 50° C; they also reported that in a vacuum or over a desiccant the lethal action of heat is more pronounced than in air. In view of their results, sclerotia do not appear to be able to withstand as high temperatures as may have been supposed. Moist heat appeared to be even more lethal, since at 70° C sclerotia were killed in water vapor in five minutes, whereas in liquid water at the same temperature death occurred in ten seconds; thus, resistance of sclerotia to heat is less than resistance of most dormant protoplasms. The results of Luyet and Gehenio suggest that, while the sclerotium is a dormant structure which might well enable the plasmodium to survive certain adverse environmental conditions, it would not be effective long against extremes of temperature or dryness.

That desiccation is not a requisite for the morphological changes that occur in sclerotium formation is evidenced by the fact that Stewart and Stewart (1961b) found that shake cultures of *P. polycephalum* grown in the dark in liquid medium formed sclerotia in 5–7 days at 22° C. Hemphill (1962) described the technique for obtaining sclerotia in shake culture, and Rusch (1968) states that sclerotia are routinely prepared in the laboratory in shaken flasks. Guttes and Guttes (1963) reported that when microplasmodia were transferred to non-nutrient medium, which was the nutrient medium of Daniel and Rusch (1961) without an energy source, after 12 hours the fragments of microplasmodia began to assume globular shapes and within the next few hours started to form spherules. Microplasmodia placed in nutrient medium did not begin to form spherules until more than 120 hours after transfer. Alexopoulos (1966) has reported that aphanoplasmodia were also observed to sclerotize in culture under water. From the findings of Guttes and Guttes, it would appear that depletion of nutrients and possibly aging of the plasmodium both may contribute to the initiation of sclerotization.

BIOCHEMISTRY OF SCLEROTIUM DORMANCY

Sullivan (1953) attempted to investigate the biochemistry of dormancy in *P. polycephalum* and compared his analyses of sclerotia with those of active plasmodia. He found that the percentage of bound water of sclerotia (0.67 per cent) was about one-half that of active plasmodia (1.26 per cent), but he regarded this decrease in bound water content as simply a reflection of major changes in carbohydrate metabolism since water-insoluble, long-chain polysaccharides, glycogen, and reducing sugar were present in decreased amounts in sclerotia. Sullivan's analyses revealed that sclerotia contained much reduced amounts of mucoproteins but that their lipid content was nearly twice that of active plasmodia. He suggested that lipid increase is directly correlated with carbohydrate decrease.

ORIGIN OF SPHERULE MEMBRANES

In an attempt to determine the possible origin of the membranes surrounding the individual spherules, Stewart and Stewart (1961b) fixed sclerotizing plasmodia at intervals, sectioned them, and made electron microscope observations. During the process of sclerotization, vesicles appeared to line up and fuse, contributing their membranes to the surfaces of the spherules being formed. Since a tremendous increase in surface membranes occurs during spherule formation, it seems quite probable that these membranes are formed from previously existing membranes or structures that have the potential for becoming membranes quite rapidly. Stewart and Stewart also made the interesting observation that while plasmodial mitochondria were pleomorphic, spherule mitochondria were smooth and oval and contained many dense particles.

SIGNIFICANCE OF SCLEROTIA AND GENERAL CONCLUSIONS

From the above brief account it is apparent that (1) the sclerotization process can be induced by several means of which desiccation is only one, (2) we have fairly complete information concerning the morphology of mature sclerotia of several species, (3) major changes in metabolism occur during the change from active plasmodium to dormant sclerotium, and (4) much work yet remains to be done especially with respect to sclerotization of protoplasmodia and aphanoplasmodia and the biochemical changes that occur during sclerotization. With reference to the last point mentioned, it might be most fruitful to apply and extend the methods of Sullivan to plasmodia in various stages of the sclerotization process to determine whether biochemical changes correlate in any way with the sequence of events observed by Jump during the sclerotization of *P. polycephalum*. Such work might well also be supplemented with careful cytochemical investigations.

Although the sclerotium does not constitute a stage necessary for lifecycle completion of a myxomycete, many investigators who have cultured *P. polycephalum* have probably observed a curious and marked increase in vitality of plasmodia when they are sclerotized and then reactivated. How the process of sclerotization contributes to this increase in vitality is still unexplained, but that it does occur indicates that events far more complex than simple desiccation of protoplasm and formation of spherules occur during sclerotium formation.

Alexopoulos (1964a) has suggested that under conditions where aphanoplasmodia (and possibly protoplasmodia) are about to enter the sporulation stage and the substrate (such as tree bark) dries before sporulation takes place, the plasmodia sclerotize. Then, when the substrate again becomes wet, plasmodia are quickly reconstituted and sporulation soon occurs. Such a sequence of events could explain the rapid development of sporophores on bark in moist chambers, but as yet this suggestion has not been verified experimentally.

Although the fungal affinities of the Myxomycetes have not been established beyond question, the fact remains that they possess sufficient characteristics in common with fungi to have been grouped with such organisms for many years. A morphological similarity to certain structures in some of the Eumycotina is exhibited by various sclerotia. The rounding up of cells of hyphae in some Eumycotina with the subsequent formation of chains of oidia (thin-walled) or chlamydospores (thick-walled) is by no means an uncommon event. In many respects, the formation of chains of globules during sclerotium formation of *M. vesparium* as described by Nauss (1943) is reminiscent of chlamydospore formation in the Eumycotina, and Wollman's (1966) illustration (Fig. 47, page 155) of the sclerotium of *Calomyxa metallica* as well as Alexopoulos' (1966) illustration of a sclerotizing plasmodium of *Arcyria cinerea* are highly suggestive of oidial formation in anastomosing hyphae. Thus, the sclerotization of a myxomycete plasmodium may be considered analogous to the formation of intercalary asexual spores in the Eumycotina. Furthermore, like oidia and true chlamydospores, when sclerotia "germinate" they produce assimilative structures identical to those from which they were formed.

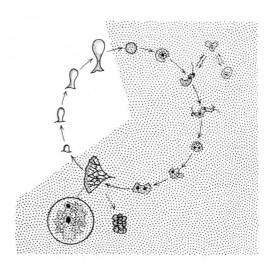

9

Sporulation

When once the relation between the viscous, protoplasmic assimilative plasmodium stage and the matured fruiting structures had been established, the fascinating transitional stages of a large number of species were in all probability observed by quite a few investigators. This transition from a moist, net-like, viscous protoplasmic body with its concomitant series of color and structural changes into a single mature fruiting body or group of fruiting bodies is one of the most spectacular phenomena in biology. One such developmental series is illustrated in Fig. 48, and for the student especially interested in this phase of myxomycete study the papers of Jahn (1931), Emoto (1933b, 1934a, 1934b), and Gray (1937, 1938, 1949) are recommended.

One of the more striking features of reproduction in a myxomycete, as compared with this process in the Eumycotina, is that typically the entire assimilative structure is converted into one or more fruiting bodies, and hence only rarely do the somatic and reproductive phases exist simultaneously in the same individual. This process of sporulation is an inexorable one, and once a plasmodium starts to enter the reproductive stage a critical point is reached at which it is impossible to reverse the change. At the present time, there is no known way of predictably maintaining the plasmodium as an active assimilative body after it is committed to sporulation.

The factors responsible for the sudden cessation of assimilation in the myxomycete plasmodium and the subsequent initiation of the reproduc-

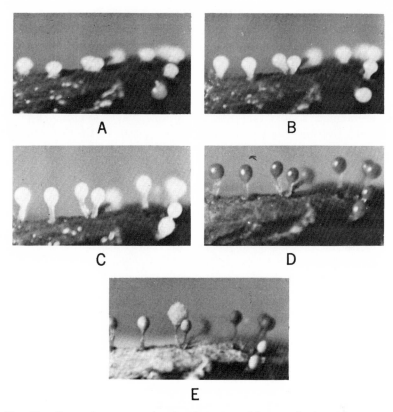

Fig. 48. Several stages in the development of fruiting bodies of *Hemitrichia stipitata*. × 4. (Alexopoulos, 1962. Reproduced by permission of John Wiley & Sons, Inc. Courtesy J. L. Koevenig.)

tive phase are still not clearly understood, although a variety of environmental factors have been linked definitely to the fruiting process by various investigators. DeBary (1864) studied sporangium formation in *Physarum sulphureum, Didymium serpula, Fuligo septica,* and *Stemonitis axifera* and noticed that sporangia usually began to form in the afternoon or late evening and that development was completed by the middle of the next day. Miller (1898) observed that for the most part sporangia of *Physarum cinereum, Didymium difforme, D. nigripes,* and *D. melanospermum* developed at night. Apparently the nocturnal formation of myxomycete sporangia is quite common since it has also been described by Jahn (1899, 1901), Lister (1888), and Howard (1931a), and it has been a common experience to many who have attempted to observe the sequence of morphological changes during sporangium development that such observations usually must be made at night. Goodwin (1961), in her studies of morphogenesis in *Comatricha,* observed that fruiting bodies usually developed during the pre-dawn hours, but found that if she placed cultures at 15° C overnight, the fruiting process was slowed down, and that sporangia in all stages of development were available between 7:30 and 9:00 A.M.

In the course of her studies on several species of *Didymium,* Cayley (1929) obtained results that led her to the suggestion that a definite rhythmical fruiting (varying with species) exists in the Myxomycetes. Thus, she found that *D. difforme* possesses a much shorter assimilative phase than either *D. nigripes* or *D. squamulosum* but concluded that the factors causing plasmodia to form fruiting bodies are "still a complete mystery" (p. 234). Seifriz and Russell (1936), from their observations of fruiting of *Physarum polycephalum,* also concluded that rhythmical fruiting was an innate characteristic of Myxomycetes.

The fruiting process of *P. polycephalum* was also studied by Camp (1937a), who found that the length of the vegetative phase was very much shortened by withholding of nutrient materials. On the basis of his results, Camp concluded that the primary factor responsible for the induction of the reproductive phase was exhaustion of the nutrient supply.

LIGHT AND SPORULATION

Gray (1938) conceded that fruiting rhythms might well exist in Myxomycetes but expressed the opinion that unless such rhythms were so innate as to be inalterable, it should be possible by proper manipulation of environmental factors to lengthen or shorten the assimilative phase. Using yellow-pigmented plasmodial types: *Physarum polycephalum, P. tenerum, Fuligo septica,* and *Leocarpus fragilis;* non-pigmented plasmodial types: *P. compressum, P. nutans, Stemonitis axifera, S. fusca, Comatricha typhoides, Hemitrichia clavata, H. stipitata, Lamproderma arcyrionema,* and *Trichia persimilis;* and one "variable" plasmodial type, *Didymium iridis,* Gray concluded that light is required to initiate reproduction in yellow-pigmented forms (Fig. 49), but that non-pigmented forms sporulate equally well in light or in darkness. This latter finding is in keeping with the observations of Vouk (1910), who noted that non-pigmented plasmodia would fruit in either light or darkness. Under conditions of continuous illumination the time required for fruiting of *P. polycephalum* varied inversely with light intensity. When starved cultures of the same species were exposed to continuous illumination, the same relationship between intensity and time required for fruiting existed but the time was markedly shortened. The relation of light intensity to time required for fruiting in fed and starved cultures of *P. polycephalum* is shown in Table 14.

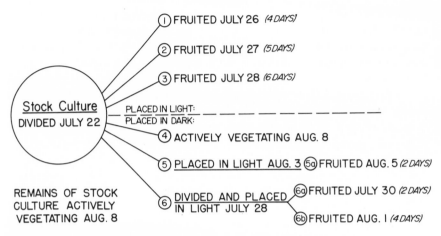

PHYSARUM TENERUM REX

Fig. 49. History of a single plasmodium (and its subcultures) of *Physarum tenerum* Rex showing the relationship of light to sporulation. (Redrawn from Gray, 1938.)

Table 14. The relation of light intensity (under conditions of continuous illumination) to fruiting in *Physarum polycephalum*. (Gray, 1938.)

Lamp Size (watts)	Hours Required for Fruiting	
	Fed Cultures	Starved Cultures
60	288	87
100	264	81
150	240	78
200	216	—
400	144–216	68

Continuous versus Intermittent Illumination

Since data presented in Table 14 were obtained from studies conducted with continuously illuminated cultures, the inference might be drawn that the rapidity with which the onset of the reproductive stage occurs depends wholly upon the total amount of illumination to which the plasmodium is exposed, although the relationship is not necessarily a straight-line one. However, Gray also used alternating light and dark periods (8 hours light, 16 hours dark) and obtained fruiting in cultures so treated with 33 per cent of the total illumination to which continuously illuminated cultures were exposed. Although the intermittently illuminated cultures required a longer period of time for sporulation, the additional time amounted to only about 14 per cent of the time for fruiting of continuously exposed cultures. These findings are in keeping with the earlier findings of Skupienski (1928), who, in his discussion of the plasmodial behavior of *Didymium difforme,* stated, ". . . if one submits a well-expanded plasmodium to the action of light rays, coming from a well-defined source, for two minutes only, and if one repeats this short illumination every two hours, the fruiting of the plasmodium in question is surely accelerated."

Light Intensity

Reinhard (1952; cf. Stosch, 1965) studied the relation of light intensity to fruiting of *Didymium nigripes* but used a wider range of intensities than had Gray and found that after a certain optimum intensity was reached, further increases led to decreased percentages of fruiting. Thus, at 40 Lux no cultures sporulated; at 100 Lux, 21.1 ± 1.9 per cent; at 600 Lux, 100 per cent; while in the range of 1100 to 3000 Lux, fruiting decreased from 83.8 ± 10.9 per cent to 24.0 ± 5.1 per cent.

In a later paper Gray (1949) reported on the relation of light to fruiting of *Physarella oblonga* and *Physarum didermoides.* The non-pigmented species fruited equally well in light or dark, but *P. oblonga,* the yellow-pigmented species, appeared to require light for fruiting. Thus, only 2 cultures of 50 of this latter species fruited in darkness, whereas 40 of 60 cultures fruited when illuminated. In a later, more extensive investigation of *P. oblonga,* Gehenio and Luyet (1951) verified the general premise that light is required for fruiting of this species. All of their cultures that were exposed to continuous illumination from a 100-watt lamp or intermittently to diffuse daylight formed sporangia, while none of the cultures maintained in the dark (48 experiments) ever sporulated. Gehenio and Luyet also found that intermittent daylight induced sporulation more quickly than continuous artificial light, but since no light-intensity data were reported it is impossible to draw any inferences concerning the relative effectiveness of continuous versus intermittent illumination from their data. These workers noted that starved cultures sporulated more rapidly than fed cultures, but starvation alone will not induce sporulation; i.e., it cannot replace light.

Sobels and van der Brugge (1950) investigated the effect of light upon sporulation and also found that light is necessary for the fruiting of *P. polycephalum* as well as *Badhamia utricularis,* another yellow-pigmented species. Working with both pure and two-membered cultures which were exposed to natural light, these investigators reported that both species required a much longer time for sporulation during the winter months than during the summer months and attributed this difference to differences in light intensity at different seasons. Since no data on either temperature or light intensity were presented, it is impossible to determine which factor (temperature or light) was primarily responsible for the observed differences in time required for fruiting.

Wavelength

In his 1938 studies Gray, using a tungsten lamp as the light source with variously colored glass filters, found that the shorter wavelengths of visible light appeared to be most effective in the initiation of sporulation. Later, Gray (1953) verified this through the use of more refined techniques. Starved cultures of *P. polycephalum* were used, and all experiments were conducted at 25° C with the initial pH of the liquid in the culture chambers being adjusted to 3.0. A large mercury vapor lamp was used as a light source, and the radiations of various wavelengths of the resultant discontinuous spectrum were isolated by the insertion of a series of liquid filters between the lamp and a black paper-lined chamber in which cultures were irradiated continuously. Data obtained from these studies are presented in Table 15.

Table 15.   The relation of wavelength of light to fruiting of *Physarum polycephalum*. (Gray, 1953.)

Wave-length (Å)	Intensity erg/cm^2/sec	No. of Cultures	No. that Fruited	Percentage Fruiting	Average No. of Hours Necessary for Fruiting
4360	288	61	55	90.1	51.4
5460	224	17	14	62.3	76.0
5770–5790	392	38	9	23.7	120.0

In his work with *Didymium nigripes*, Straub (1954) found that this species would not sporulate in the dark or in green light but would sporulate in white, blue, or red light or with ultraviolet (350–390 mμ) illumination. Within certain limits, the length of the illumination period required varied inversely with light intensity, thus providing a confirmation of Gray's 1938 findings with respect to light intensity. Straub also found that the length of the period of illumination required for sporulation could be shortened by feeding plasmodia on previously illuminated plasmodia. This latter finding suggests the existence of a substance or substances synthesized photochemically that initiate the onset of the reproductive phase. Lieth (1954) separated four pigments electrophoretically from the reddish-brown plasmodia of *D. nigripes*, but a study of their absorption spectra led him to the conclusion that none of these pigments was directly responsible for the absorption of the energy necessary for sporangium formation. In a later paper Lieth (1956) verified Straub's report that *D. nigripes* sporulated under violet, blue, and red light but not under green or infrared. This investigator also reported that green light actually inhibits fruiting because when red light sufficient to initiate sporulation was supplemented with increasing amounts of green light the percentage of plasmodia that sporulated was greatly decreased. In a more recent paper Rakoczy (1967) confirmed the finding that lights of different wavelengths may be antagonistic in their action. She irradiated plasmodia of *Physarum nudum* simultaneously with blue light of sufficient intensity to induce 50 per cent sporulation and lights of wavelengths ranging from 504 to 669 mμ. Wavelengths up to and including 520 mμ acted synergistically. When accessory light of 541 mμ was used, the percentage of sporulating plasmodia increased with increase in intensity, but after a certain point the percentage decreased from 50 to a lesser rate. Wavelengths of 557, 581, and 602 mμ were inhibitory, but those of 612 and 622 mμ showed no activity. Light of 557 mμ wavelength had the highest inhibitory activity.

In 1961, Gray reported the successful laboratory cultivation of another yellow-pigmented species, *Physarum flavicomum*. Using starved cultures he obtained no sporulation in 50 cultures maintained in darkness, but he did observe sporulation in 46 of 50 cultures that were continuously illuminated by light from large neon lamps. Data obtained from the illuminated cultures are presented in Table 16.

Table 16.   The relation of light to sporangium formation by *Physarum flavicomum*. (Gray, 1961.)

Expt. No.	No. of Cultures	Number Fruiting in:			Total No. of Cultures Fruiting	Percentage Fruiting
		2 Days	3 Days	4 Days		
1	4	0	0	2	2	50%
2	4	0	1	3	4	100%
3	8	0	2	4	6	75%
4	7	0	4	3	7	100%
5	7	4	3	0	7	100%
6	20	14	6	0	20	100%
Totals	50	18	16	12	46	

Age of Illuminated Plasmodia

Rakoczy (1962) reported the results of her studies on the effect of light upon still another yellow-pigmented species, *Physarum nudum,* and noted that light is also necessary for fruiting of this species. If plasmodia were cultured for seven days in the light and then transferred to darkness, none ever formed fruiting bodies and all died in 15–18 days —similar to those maintained continuously in the darkness. When plasmodia were illuminated for 24 hours at the ages of two, four, six, and eight days and then placed in darkness, fruiting was not initiated, but a 24-hour light period applied to ten-day-old cultures resulted in fruiting in about 50 per cent of the cultures. When 12- and 14-day-old cultures were illuminated for 24 hours and then returned to darkness, fruiting occurred in all cultures after they were placed in the dark. On the basis of these results Rakoczy postulated that the initiation of fruiting is dependent upon the presence of a hypothetical "Substance B," which is formed by photochemical reaction from another hypothetical compound, "Substance A," which is formed during vegetative growth in either light or darkness. Thus, the amount of Substance B formed is proportional to the initial concentration of Substance A which presumably varies directly with age. This hypothesis may be used to explain the failure of young (2–8 days old) plasmodia to fruit after a 24-hour illumination period, whereas 10-, 12-, and 14-day-old plasmodia were able to fruit after such a period of illumination. It may also be used to interpret the results obtained by Gray (1938) using interrupted light periods. When plasmodia of *P. polycephalum* were illuminated for only eight hours out of each 24, the time required for fruiting was 13 days—only two days longer than that required by cultures continuously illuminated. Thus, if fruiting time is directly related to total quantity of illumination, the cultures that were intermittently illuminated should have required 33 days for fruiting rather than 13. Apparently total quantity of illumination is related to fruiting only after plasmodia are of sufficient age. Thus, Straub (1954) found that 38.5 per cent of ten-day-old cultures of *Didymium nigripes* that had been cultured in darkness fruited after being illuminated for five hours with light of 1000 Lux intensity, while 100 per cent fruiting was observed in cultures of similar age illuminated for ten hours with light of the same intensity.

Pigmented versus Non-pigmented Plasmodia

In contrast to Gray's (1938, 1953, 1961) conclusion that light is necessary for the initiation of sporulation in yellow-pigmented plasmodia but not for non-pigmented plasmodia, different opinions have been expressed by other investigators. For example, Scholes (1962) reported that light is not necessary for sporulation in *Fuligo septica* and was unable to relate this process with any factor other than age of plasmodium. She found that older cultures (i.e., those from which no subcultures had been made) exhibited a much higher percentage of fruiting than younger cultures.

Koevenig (1963) found that the plasmodium of *Physarum gyrosum* is white if cultured in the dark but will develop a yellow pigment if exposed to light, and that the plasmodium always turns yellow prior to fruiting. He concluded that light and the depletion of nutrients were necessary for sporulation, and he raised interesting questions about whether the plasmodium of this species should be considered pigmented and, if so, is the pigment necessary for sporulation. Fergus and Schein (1963) also studied *P. gyrosum* and reported that no sporangia were ever formed by plasmodia that were kept in the dark. These latter workers also demonstrated with this species that time required for fruiting varied inversely (although the relationship was not a straight-line one) with light intensity—thus verifying Gray's (1938) earlier findings with *P. polycephalum*. The plasmodia of *Physarum nicaraguense* are either white or cream-colored [the variable plasmodial type of Gray (1938)?] and according to Solis (1962) require light for the initiation of sporulation.

It seems possible that there also may be some exceptions to Gray's general conclusion that light is not necessary for initiation of sporulation in non-pigmented plasmodial types. Thus, McManus (1961a) reported that the non-pigmented aphanoplasmodia of *Stemonitis fusca* will not sporulate unless they are exposed to light, and Fergus and Schein (1963) have emphasized Straub's (1954) report that *white* plasmodia of *Didymium nigripes* require light. Unfortunately, the plasmodium of *D. nigripes* can scarcely be considered non-pigmented in view of Lieth's (1954) isolation of four separate pigments from the plasmodium.

While the possibility of exceptional cases being found is most certainly not ruled out, the preponderance of evidence to date indicates that species with yellow-pigmented plasmodia require light for sporulation, but that species with white or colorless plasmodia do not. The report of McManus (1961a) that the non-pigmented plasmodia of *Stemonitis fusca* will not form fruiting bodies unless they are exposed to light should be further checked, since this represents the only report of such plasmodia requiring light for fruiting. It seems possible that certain *seemingly* non-pigmented plasmodia which may require light for sporulation actually contain pigment(s) in minute quantities that are not detectable by the human eye. This possibility is strengthened by Lieth's isolation of several pigments from a plasmodium that Fergus and Schein term white.

ULTRAVIOLET RADIATION AND SPORULATION

In most of his studies Gray (1938, 1939b, 1953, 1961) was concerned with the relation of visible light to the initiation of the fruiting process, but in 1941 he reported results of studies in which the effects of polychromatic ultraviolet radiation on protoplasmic streaming and fruiting in *Physarum polycephalum*, *P. didermoides*, and *Physarella oblonga* were examined. The total intensity of radiations (2200–4000 Å) to which plasmodia were exposed was 4665 ergs/cm²/sec, of which wavelengths between 2850 and 4000 Å supplied 2948 ergs/cm²/sec, and wavelengths between 2200 and 2850 Å supplied 1717 ergs/cm²/sec; there was also some radiation of wavelengths less than 2200 Å. It was found that streaming was still evident in some of the yellow-pigmented plasmodia of *P. oblonga* after a ten-minute irradiation period while in the non-pigmented plasmodia of *P. didermoides* only one culture of four was still streaming after a three-minute irradiation period and none of four was streaming after a five-minute irradiation period. When *P. polycephalum* and *P. didermoides* were irradiated for varying periods of time and then placed under conditions favorable for fruiting, *P. polycephalum* would fruit in visible light after a 1.5-hour period of irradiation with ultraviolet, but not after 2.0 hours of irradiation, while *P. didermoides* (non-pigmented) would fruit in darkness after a 1.0-hour period of irradiation with ultraviolet, but not after a 1.5-hour irradiation period. Thus, the yellow-pigmented *P. polycephalum* appears to be better able to withstand the lethal effects of ultraviolet radiation than does the non-pigmented *P. didermoides*. In general, the longer the irradiation period the longer the time required for sporulation of *P. didermoides* (Table 17); no attempt was made to investigate this particular point for *P. polycephalum*. Gray made no effort to determine whether ultraviolet radiations are effective in the initiation of sporulation in the yellow-pigmented forms (*P. oblonga* and *P. polycephalum*); however, Straub (1954) has reported that long-wave ultraviolet (350–390 mμ) is effective for the induction of sporulation in *D. nigripes*, and Daniel and Rusch (1962a) found that wavelengths between 350 and 500 mμ were effective in inducing sporulation of *P. polycephalum*. With the lethal effects of short-wave ultraviolet so generally recognized, and in view of the greater sensitivity of the non-pigmented *P. didermoides* to ultraviolet, it might well be worthwhile to make large collections of Myxomycetes from natu-

Table 17.   The effect of ultraviolet radiation upon fruiting of *Physarum polycephalum* and *P. didermoides*. (Gray, 1941.)

Length of Radiation Period	Species	Number of Cultures	Number That Fruited	Average Time for Fruiting
1 minute	(*P. polycephalum*	5	5	<48 hours
	(*P. didermoides*	1	1	28.0 days
3 minutes	(*P. polycephalum*	5	5	<48 hours
	(*P. didermoides*	1	1	26.0 days
5 minutes	(*P. polycephalum*	5	5	<48 hours
	(*P. didermoides*	14	12	24.9 days
7 minutes	(*P. polycephalum*	5	5	<48 hours
	(*P. didermoides*	4	2	33.5 days
10 minutes	(*P. polycephalum*	5	5	<48 hours
	(*P. didermoides*	14	12	35.7 days
15 minutes	*P. didermoides*	10	8	40.1 days
30 minutes	*P. didermoides*	18	9	38.8 days
45 minutes	*P. didermoides*	5	4	45.0 days
1 hour	(*P. polycephalum*	5	5	<48 hours
	(*P. didermoides*	13	4	41.2 days
1½ hours	*P. polycephalum*	10	10	<48 hours
2 hours	(*P. polycephalum*	5	0	—
	(*P. didermoides*	11	0	—
3 hours	*P. didermoides*	8	0	—

ral habitats (shaded and unshaded) and note whether or not there is a preponderance of forms with pigmented plasmodia occurring in unshaded habitats where there would be much higher intensities of shortwave ultraviolet; non-pigmented plasmodia might reasonably be expected to be killed after relatively short periods of exposure.

In a more recent investigation Rakoczy (1963) found that ultraviolet radiation of wavelengths 333–400 mμ was effective in initiation of sporulation of *Physarum nudum*. She found that ultraviolet induces sporulation at very low intensities but that generally 100 per cent sporulation was never obtained at any intensity, and that after surpassing a certain limiting value the percentage of plasmodia that formed sporangia quickly fell to 0. The relationship between intensity at various wavelengths and sporulation is shown in Fig. 50.

INFRARED RADIATION AND SPORULATION

Little work seems to have been done on the possible relation of infrared radiation to sporulation. Gray (unpublished research, 1939) found that infrared was not effective in initiating sporulation of *P. polycephalum* or *Physarella oblonga,* and Straub (1954) found that infrared did not

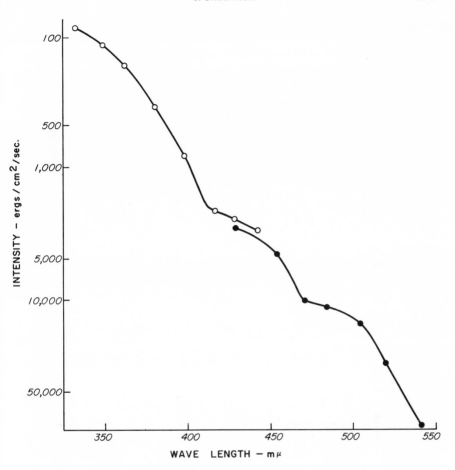

Fig. 50.   Intensity of light of various wavelengths required to obtain 50
per cent fructification in *Physarum nudum*.   (Redrawn from Rakoczy, 1963.)

induce *D. nigripes* to fruit. Straub's report was later verified by Lieth
(1956). Since there are no data that indicate that infrared can initiate
sporulation, it may be assumed at this time that radiation in this part of
the spectrum is ineffective.

NIACIN REQUIREMENTS OF *Physarum polycephalum*

Most of the above observations may be criticized on the grounds that
they were not conducted with axenic cultures, and for that reason the
investigations of Daniel and Rusch (1958, 1962a, 1962b) are of special
significance in the elucidation of the factors responsible for the initiation
of the reproductive process. These workers cultured plasmodia of *P.*

polycephalum in liquid, shake, bacterium-free culture on tryptone-yeast extract-glucose medium for three days after which time the small, discrete plasmodia that had developed were harvested and allowed to fuse into a single plasmodium. This was incubated for four days at 21.5° C in the dark on a CaCO$_3$-buffered salts medium which contained 0.01 per cent niacin and 0.01 per cent niacinamide. After four days' incubation, the cultures were exposed to light for two hours and returned to darkness; sporulation was completed in 12 to 16 hours. According to Daniel and Rusch the obligatory conditions for sporulation of *P. polycephalum* are: (1) an optimal growth age occurring just prior to maximal growth and at a time when medium nutrients are exhausted, (2) four days of incubation on a medium containing only inorganic salts and niacin or tryptophane (both DPN and TPN can also serve as niacin sources), and (3) subsequent illumination with light of wavelengths between 350 and 500 mμ. Since for the development of light sensitivity at least three days of dark incubation with niacin or its precursors is necessary, Daniel and Rusch concluded that either a distal metabolite of niacin is required for sporulation or that niacin induces metabolic changes that bring about light sensitivity. Niacin analogs had an inhibitory effect on sporulation if added at the beginning of dark incubation but did not inhibit if added at the end; thus, niacin *per se* does not seem to be responsible for light sensitivity. The exact action spectrum for sporulation of *P. polycephalum* is as yet not known. Daniel and Rusch found that wavelengths between 350 and 500 mμ were effective, while Gray (1953) obtained fruiting in cultures exposed to light of wavelengths 4360, 5460, and 5770–5790 Å.

While light is unquestionably necessary for the induction of fruiting in all those species with yellow-pigmented plasmodia that have been studied critically, the findings of Daniel and Rusch indicate that nutritional factors are also involved. This is further borne out by the findings of Sobels and van der Brugge (1950) that pure cultures of *Badhamia utricularis* require an abnormally long time for fruiting, an observation similar to that made by Lazo (1961) on *P. polycephalum, P. didermoides,* and *F. septica.*

Since virtually nothing is known regarding the factors responsible for the initiation of sporulation in non-pigmented plasmodia, a very fruitful investigation might well be conducted in the area of nutritional studies on non-pigmented types in pure culture.

PLASMODIAL PHOTORECEPTORS

The relation between pigmentation and a light requirement for sporulation has quite naturally drawn attention to the possibility that plasmodial pigments might be photoreceptors. Thus, Gray (1953) prepared a crude acetone extract of the pigment of *P. polycephalum* and determined its absorption spectrum. Since blue light (4360 Å) was most effective in the induction of fruiting, green light (5460 Å) next most effective, and yellow light (5770–5790 Å) least effective, it is apparent that the action spectrum agrees favorably with the absorption spectrum (Fig. 51). Hence, it seems quite possible that the yellow pigment is the

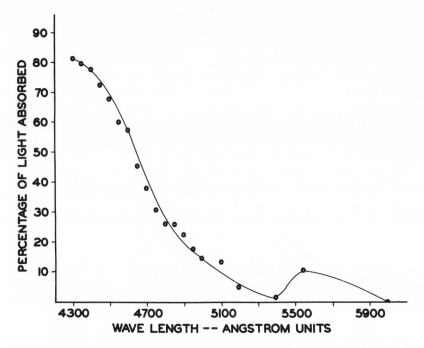

Fig. 51. Absorption spectrum of acetone extract of *Physarum polycephalum* pigment. (Gray, 1953.)

photoreceptor, an hypothesis in which Daniel and Rusch (1961) concur. However, Daniel (1966) has noted recently that the effect of light on respiration modifies this possibility.

Nature of Plasmodial Pigments

Allman (1955) found that the yellow pigment of *P. polycephalum* may be completely extracted in methanol. Wolf (1959) used this extraction procedure and demonstrated both by paper and by column chromatography that the plasmodium contains two yellow pigments, both of which were identified as pteridines. On the basis of spectral properties and shift in light absorption with changes in pH, Wolf concluded that only one pigment (Component 1) has the characteristics of the photoreceptor. There was no indication that the amounts of these pigments were different in light-grown and dark-grown cultures, and hence it appears that it is not Component 1 *per se* that initiates the fruiting process, but that it is triggered by the interaction of this compound with light. Wolf found no traces of yellow pigments in mature sporangia, which indicates that the yellow-pigment characteristic of plasmodia disappears upon fruiting. Component 2, which Wolf does not consider to be the photoreceptor, may have no relationship whatsoever to the fruiting process; however, Wolf suggests that it conceivably might be either a precursor or a degradation product of Component 1. Rakoczy (1963) studied the effect of light on the fruiting of *Physarum nudum* and, on the basis of the action spectrum she obtained, concluded that if the pigments of this species (which have not been studied) are identical with those described by Wolf, it is not Component 1 but Component 2 that is involved in the absorption of radiant energy.

Dresden (1959) is in disagreement with Wolf on the chemical nature of the yellow pigment(s), since he concluded that the yellow color of plasmodia of *P. polycephalum* is due to a peptide-type pigment. Kuraishi, *et al.* (1961), in their report on the mass culture of this species and the purification of its plasmodial pigments, found that three main pigments (A, B, and C) could be extracted in 80 per cent acetone and separated chromatographically. Pigment A could be readily converted into B, and B into C. These workers denied that the pigment was either a pteridine or a peptide, but offered no suggestion as to its chemical nature.

Brewer (1965) obtained three purified pigments extracted from plasmodia of *P. polycephalum* with aqueous acetone and designated them A, B, and C. Pigments A and B were considered naturally occurring plasmodial pigments, but Pigment C was thought to be an isolation artifact of Pigment B. Pigment A is a water-soluble, non-aromatic hydrochloride compound containing a hexaene chromophore. Brewer stated that it probably contains the amide function and one or more strongly basic nitrogen functions. The molecular weight of Pigment A was not determined, but elemental analysis indicated a percentage composition as follows: C, 59.85; H, 7.31; O, 14.67; N, 7.34; Cl, 6.57; and P and ash negligible. On the basis of spectral evidence, Pigment B was considered to be an amphoteric compound containing a polyene chromophore—probably a conjugated heptaene; it contained the carboxyl function, was alkali soluble, and the absorption maximum and extinction were found to be pH dependent. The molecular weight of Pigment B was not determined, but elemental analysis yielded an empirical formula of $C_{61}H_{67}O_{18}N_3$. Pigment C was almost identical to Pigment B in its properties, but ultraviolet absorption occurred at about 25 mμ longer wavelength. Esterification of Pigment C yielded a compound with ultraviolet absorption similar to that of Pigment A. Hydrogenation of Pigment C yielded the only crystalline derivative of *P. polycephalum* pigments so far isolated. Brewer noted that Pigments A and B do not fall into any well-recognized group of naturally occurring polyene compounds. Daniel (1966) states that his observations indicate that a carbonyl group is an essential part of the chromophore of a pigment component of *P. polycephalum*. He found a pigment component that would react with hydroxylamine, 2,4-dinitrophenylhydrazine, and semicarbazide. Since semicarbazide reacts with Schiff bases, Daniel expressed the opinion that the strong basic nitrogen function observed by Brewer could be explained on the basis of a quaternary form of a Schiff base.

Nair and Zabka (1966) recently extracted plasmodial pigments from *Physarella oblonga, Physarum gyrosum, P. polycephalum, Didymium iridis,* and *D. squamulosum* with either boiling methanol or 95 per cent ethanol and attempted to separate the components by paper chromatography. They reported one component for *P. gyrosum,* three for *P. oblonga,* four for *P. polycephalum,* six for *D. iridis,* and none for the white plasmodium of *D. squamulosum.* Absorption spectra were prepared for the various components, and certain chemical tests for flavonoid compounds were performed. A flavone was reported in *P. gyrosum,* and a phenolic compound was reported in *P. polycephalum* and *D. iridis,* but otherwise there was no evidence presented regarding the identity of the many pigments recovered by the methods they employed.

From the above widely divergent accounts, it is evident that the important pigment component, whose role as a photoreceptor in the initiation of morphogenesis is now established almost beyond question, still remains without positive identification. By the very nature of its role, this component can reasonably be assumed to be somewhat labile, and the widely differing accounts concerning number and possible chemical identity of pigment components of the same species may possibly be a reflection of its labile nature. The need for further work of the type performed by Brewer in this area seems quite evident!

Lieth (1954) was able to separate four pigments by electrophoresis from an extract of the red-brown plasmodium of *Didymium nigripes,* but after studying the absorption spectra (Fig. 52) of these pigments he concluded that they cannot be directly responsible for absorbing the necessary energy for sporangium formation. It is interesting to note, however, that Lieth's "Pigment V—" (*a* in Fig. 52) has an absorption

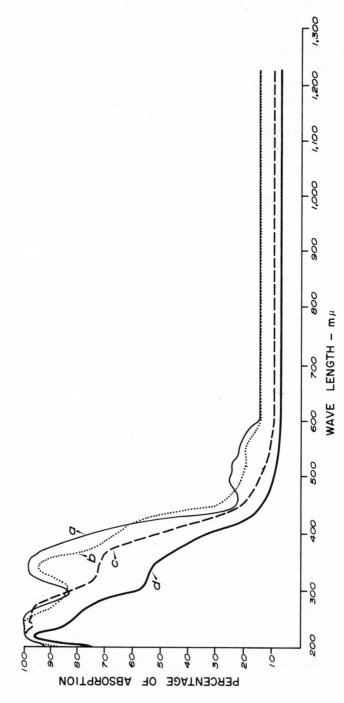

Fig. 52.   Absorption spectra of pigments of *Didymium nigripes*. (Redrawn from Lieth, 1954.)

spectrum in the range of 4000–6000 Å, which is similar to that reported by Gray (see Fig. 51) for *P. polycephalum.*

Gray (1953) found that relatively large quantities of riboflavin are synthesized in cultures of *P. polycephalum* maintained by the moist-chamber method of Camp (1936), and he suggested that part of the yellow coloration of the plasmodium may be due to the presence of this B-vitamin. Data from these analyses are presented in Table 18. It

Table 18. The synthesis of riboflavin in moist chamber cultures of *Physarum polycephalum.* (Gray, 1955.)

Expt. No.	Age of Culture (days)	Rolled Oats Fed (grams)	Riboflavin in Rolled Oats (micrograms)	Total Riboflavin in Culture (micrograms)	Riboflavin Increase (micrograms)	(per cent)
1	4	6.0	46.5	470	423.5	910
2	4	8.6	66.7	264	197.3	296
3	3	4.3	33.3	228	194.7	584

may be seen that there can occur as much as a nine-fold increase in ribo-flavin during a four-day culture period. Since these analyses were not conducted on pure cultures, there is no direct evidence that riboflavin is synthesized by plasmodia nor is there any evidence that riboflavin is involved in initiating the fruiting process. However, in view of the known photolabile nature of riboflavin and also in view of the fact that light is essential for the initiation of sporulation in *P. polycephalum,* the possibility does exist that riboflavin in some way may be involved in the initiation of sporulation.

RELATION OF OTHER FACTORS TO SPORULATION

In addition to light, a variety of other environmental factors have been associated with the fruiting process by various workers. Thus, Hawker (1952) points out that partial desiccation, nature of substrate, acidity of substrate, and injury have been postulated as causing the initiation of sporulation. Unfortunately, many of these postulates are based on more or less casual observations and have not been substantiated by experimentation.

Nutrients and Moisture

Klebs (1900) found that plasmodia of *Didymium difforme* and *D. squamulosum* could be maintained in active condition for an indefinite period by frequent transfer to fresh nutrient material, but sporangia were soon formed if a portion was transferred to a moist, nutrient-free substrate. The implication was that removal of nutrient resulted in the initiation of the reproductive process, an implication that well fits Klebs' postulate which states that the conditions favorable for reproduction are unfavorable for vegetation and vice versa. Camp (1937a) cultured *P. polycephalum* on wet filter paper in a moist chamber using rolled oats as a source of nutrients and reported that, with other conditions being favorable, plasmodia would live and grow as long as food was available; however, if the oats were not replaced, sporulation would occur. The findings of Klebs and of Camp seem to indicate that the exhaustion of nutrients is a primary factor in the initiation of the fruiting process. While it is true that starved cultures of *P. polycephalum* will fruit in a much shorter period of time than fed cultures (see Table 14, page 163), this process is initiated only if the plasmodia are illuminated. There is need for a great amount of investigation of the type conducted by Daniel and Rusch, since these workers have shown that the nature of the nutrients supplied to a plasmodium during the initial growth period in darkness will determine whether fruiting will occur after a suitable period of time in the light.

Schure (1949) has obtained results with *Mucilago crustacea* that indicate that either nutrition or moisture, or a combination of both, are related to sporulation. When spores were germinated in tap water, the young plasmodia that formed were fed on baker's yeast and then transferred to agar in which yeast was incorporated. Plasmodia would never sporulate on the agar medium, but when they were allowed to spread on moist, porous flower pots sporulation was obtained.

Acidity of Substrate

Hydrogen-ion concentration of the substrate undoubtedly influences sporulation, and Emoto (1938) reported that of over a hundred collections (106 species) of fruiting bodies from their natural habitats, nearly all were from substrates of acid reaction. Gray (1939b) found that, in general, high acidity (pH 3.0) was most favorable for fruiting of *P. polycephalum*. However, he found that the factors of pH and temperature were interrelated and that in the temperature range of 21° to 32.5° C, the lower the temperature the wider the pH range over which the organism could sporulate (Fig. 53). In his studies of *Fuligo cinerea,* Collins (1959) also found that both temperature and pH affected fruiting and obtained results in general agreement with those of Gray. At 30° C no fruiting occurred, regardless of the pH of the substrate. Since similar results were obtained by Gray with *P. polycephalum* at 35° C, an

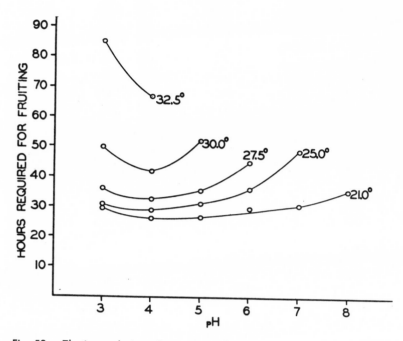

Fig. 53. The interrelation of pH and temperature to sporulation of *Physarum polycephalum*. (Gray, 1939b.)

obvious difference in maximum temperature for sporulation exists between these two species. At 25° C, 75 per cent of the cultures of *F. cinerea* fruited at pH 3.0; 90 per cent at pH 4.0 and 5.0; and diminishing percentages up to pH 8.0. At 20° C, pH has little effect on fruiting—at least 80 per cent of the cultures fruited at all pH values (3.0 to 8.0), and at pH 4.0 and 5.0, 100 per cent of the cultures fruited. These results strengthen the view that at lower temperatures the pH range over which sporulation may occur is wider than at high temperatures.

Internal Acidity

Gray (1953) has presented evidence indicating that for *P. polycephalum* the effect of H-ion concentration may well be an indirect one, and that its primary effect is on the light-absorbing capacities of the photoreceptor pigment. Absolute methyl alcohol extracts of the plasmodial pigment were prepared, portions were added to equal volumes of thallate buffer at various pH values, and the pH values of the resultant solutions were measured. The light absorption spectra that were obtained with four of these solutions (pH 2.9, 4.2, 6.4, and 8.4) are presented in Fig. 54. From this figure, it is evident that the more acid

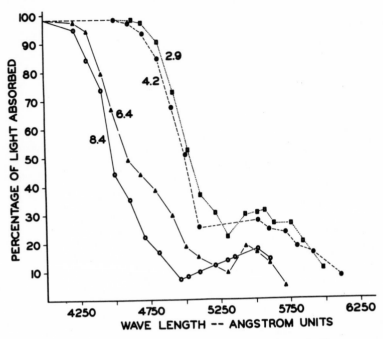

Fig. 54. Absorption spectra of plasmodial pigment of *Physarum poly-cephalum* under varying conditions of pH. (Gray, 1953.)

the solution in which the pigment is dissolved, the greater the amount of light (4000–6000 Å) absorbed. Thus, it is probable that the more rapid onset of sporulation that occurs under conditions of relatively high acidity is simply due to the fact that greater amounts of light in the effective range are absorbed.

The observations of Seifriz and Zetzmann (1935) regarding internal conditions of pH and sporulation are most fascinating but cannot be interpreted at this time. These investigators found that *P. polycephalum* contains a pigment that is a natural pH indicator, which at a pH of < 1.0 is deep chrome in color; but as it is placed in successively less acid buffer solutions it changes in color through orange, golden yellow, light yellow, green-yellow, and finally yellow-green at a pH > 8.0. In active three-day-old plasmodia, the color was similar to that of the pigment in buffer at pH 6.2, but if the plasmodium fruits the color is green (ca. pH 7.5). Thus, as the plasmodium enters the reproductive phase, conditions in the plasmodium at the site of the pigment pass from a slightly acid reaction to one that is slightly alkaline. Seifriz and Zetzmann did not determine the absorption spectrum of their pigment, and hence it is not known if they were dealing with the pigment considered to be the photoreceptor by other investigators.

Temperature

The exact temperature limits for sporulation have never been recorded for any myxomycete. As noted above, Gray (1939b) found that the upper limit for sporulation of *P. polycephalum* was about 32.5° C (provided the substrate had a pH of 3.0 to 4.0), and it can be inferred from Collins' (1959) results that the upper limit for sporulation of *F. cinerea* is somewhat below 30° C. However, neither of these workers established the optimum temperature for sporulation, nor did they attempt to determine the lower temperature limits for sporulation. Skupienski (1920) found that spores of *Didymium nigripes* would not germinate, and hence that there was no plasmodium formation or fructification at a temperature of 1°–2° C, but at 2°–4° fructifications were formed 30 days following the sowing of spores. At 8°–10° sporangia formed 15 days after sowing spores, and at 18°–20° they formed 8 days after sowing. Spores germinated and plasmodia were formed, but no fruiting occurred at 22° (Table 19), and at 25° spores did not germinate and hence there

Table 19. The relation of temperature to germination of spores, formation of plasmodia, and the initiation of sporulation in *Didymium nigripes*. (Based on data of Skupienski, 1920.)

Temperature (° C)	Spore Germination	Plasmodium Formed	Fructification Formed	Time Required For Fruiting
1–2	−	−	−	
2–4	+	+	+	30 days
8–10	+	+	+	15 days
18–20	+	+	+	8 days
22	+	+	−	
25	−	−	−	

were no plasmodia or sporangia formed. One is tempted to set 2° C as the minimum, 18°–20° as optimum, and slightly above 20° as the maximum for sporulation of *D. nigripes*. However, this cannot be done with certainty, since it does not necessarily follow that the cardinal points for spore germination are the same as those for either plasmodium formation or the initiation of sporulation. In fact, it is quite evident that they are not the same, since spores germinated and plasmodia formed at 22°, but sporulation did not occur at this temperature. Further studies of the type conducted by Skupienski should be made, but they should be so designed that the temperature effects on the various processes, such as germination, zygote formation, plasmodial growth, and sporulation can be separated.

Solis (1962) attempted to determine the effect of temperature on sporulation of *Physarum nicaraguense* by culturing this species in mixed culture with *Escherichia coli* on half-strength cornmeal agar and incubating the cultures in continuous light at 15°, 20°, 25°, and 30° C. The cultures were inoculated with spores, and when plasmodia appeared they were fed pulverized rice grains. Plasmodia were formed in 5 days at 20° and 25°, in 27 days at 15°, but no plasmodia were ever formed at 30°. Data from Solis' investigation are presented in Table 20, and from

Table 20. The relation of temperature to plasmodium formation, and sporulation of *Physarum nicaraguense*. (Based on data of Solis, 1962.)

Tempera-ture (° C)	No. of Cultures	Days Required for Plasmodium Formation	Time Required for Fruiting		Total Number of Cultures That Fruited
			No. of Cultures	Days	
15	12	27	5	18	8
			3	20	
20	12	5	10	7	12
			2	9	
25	12	5	12	7	12
30	12	–	–	–	0

these data it is evident that the same criticism levelled against Skupienski's (1920) work is applicable here. Since no plasmodia were formed at 30°, no sporophores could be produced, but this does not necessarily mean that sporulation cannot occur at this temperature—it is possible that at the higher temperature zygotes cannot be formed, assuming, of course, that the organism is homothallic rather than apogamic. As in Gray's (1939b) studies with *P. polycephalum,* the lower temperature limit for sporulation was not determined.

The early work of Cayley (1929) on species of *Didymium* and the work of Seifriz and Russell (1936) on *P. polycephalum* yielded results which led these investigators to suggest that rhythmical fruiting is an innate characteristic of Myxomycetes. Gray (1938) admitted the possibility that fruiting rhythms might well exist in Myxomycetes but demonstrated (principally with *P. polycephalum*) that by proper manipulation of light intensity the assimilative phase of yellow pigmented plasmodia could be lengthened or shortened. Genetic control of sporulation is now being studied, and Rusch (1968) reports that preliminary data indicate that the RNA's necessary for sporulation are probably induced by starvation and light. Such RNA's must be completed about two hours after the illumination period since if actinomycin D is applied at any time after this period it has no effect upon sporulation.

MORPHOGENESIS

Biologists have long known that changes in morphology are always preceded by changes in physiology, and it is (or should be) the ultimate goal of the morphologist to learn the sequence of chemical reactions that lead up to and occur during a specific morphological event. Morphogenesis in a myxomycete is an especially striking phenomenon, since from an active, protoplasmic, assimilative plasmodium there are suddenly formed fructifications wholly different in contents, structure, and appearance from the plasmodium. For this reason, Myxomycetes (especially *P. polycephalum*) have become very popular experimental organisms in studies designed to elucidate the chemical reactions and changes in metabolic patterns during morphogenesis. Most of the interpretations are highly speculative in nature, and as yet we are unable to state exactly what occurs and in what sequence, although there is a growing body of information concerning changes in chemistry, light effects, and so on, prior to and during morphogenesis.

Loss of Cellular Water During Morphogenesis

As early as 1914, in his studies of *Didymium melanospermum,* Harper noted that there was an extrusion of water from the protoplasm. More recently Daniel (1966) has reported that loss of cellular water is one of the striking changes that occurs during sporulation of *P. polycephalum,* since the plasmodium is about 80 per cent water, and the spores only about 20 per cent water. Obviously, this water loss is not a matter of simple evaporation, but rather the forcible extrusion of water often noted in a colloidal gel, and it is probably an indication of major changes in protoplasmic structure. Since, in the transition from plasmodia to fruiting structures, a very considerable quantity of spore wall substance is formed, it is quite probable that much of the extruded water has its origin during the formation of wall substance in much the same way that water is formed when many hexose molecules are condensed into a compound, such as starch or cellulose. This loss of water during morphogenesis is not unique to the Myxomycetes, since spores with lower water content than the assimilative phase from which they were formed are rather common in the Eumycotina.

Changes in Nucleic Acids, Proteins, and Polysaccharides

The amounts of various large molecular components undoubtedly change during sporulation, and Daniel (1966) has noted that when *P.*

polycephalum metabolizes on inorganic salts medium after having been removed from growth medium, there are decreases in RNA, DNA, and protein. When such cultures are incubated with niacin, the RNA level is maintained before and during illumination, there is a rapid drop in alkali-soluble protein after illumination, and there is an approximate doubling of DNA.

Using acrilamide gel electrophoresis, Zeldin and Ward (1963a, b) found distinct differences in protein profiles before and after a plasmodium passes the "commitment to sporulate" point. This protein profile changed before there were any visible evidences of morphogenesis. Particular attention was paid to a specific protein, α-amylase, which mobilizes nutrient polysaccharide, and there was a 60 per cent decrease in activity of this enzyme after the commitment to sporulate. Activity further decreased to undetectable levels as morphological changes became evident.

Changes in amount of polysaccharide and possibly in kind of polysaccharide also occur during morphogenesis. Daniel (1964a) found that when *P. polycephalum* was cultured on growth medium in the dark, it accumulated a glycogen-like polysaccharide. When it was transferred to niacin-salts-$CaCO_3$ medium and incubated in the dark for five days, the polysaccharide content decreased by 90 per cent to a very low level (about 0.6 mg/mg protein). However, when the plasmodium was then illuminated for about four hours, a transient two- to threefold increase in a similar polysaccharide occurred. When niacin (which is essential for sporulation) was omitted from the medium, light-induced polysaccharide synthesis was abortive. Daniel suggested that since this polysaccharide synthesis is light-dependent, differentiation depends upon a shift in energy metabolism pathways.

It seems possible that the polysaccharide synthesized during the period of illumination while on medium lacking an energy source may be different from that synthesized during the dark period on growth medium, although Daniel describes it as similar. Obviously, further work is needed on this point.

Apparently both protein and polysaccharide are utilized for maintenance of the plasmodium when it is deprived of nutrient and not illuminated; however, Daniel states that during this period polysaccharide is used preferentially over protein. Although the possibility exists that there may be some relationship between the α-amylase activity of plasmodia studied by Zeldin and Ward and the polysaccharide utilization and light-induced synthesis studied by Daniel, as yet no attempt has been made to relate these two processes. Since light-induced polysaccharide synthesis on non-nutrient medium is transient in nature, it would be most helpful to know exactly when, in relation to the commitment-to-sporulate point, polysaccharide synthesis begins.

Inhibition of Sporulation by Glucose

Daniel and Rusch (1962a) reported that glucose was a strong inhibitor of sporulation when it was added four days prior to illumination (two-hour period), three hours after illumination, or at intermediate times. Sodium fluoride and iodoacetate did not interfere with this inhibition, so if the effective metabolite of glucose is pyruvic acid it apparently does not arise by way of the Embden-Meyerhof pathway. In a later paper Daniel (1964b) states that glucose inhibits sporulation before but not after illumination, and interprets this in terms of a light-induced alteration of cell permeability, especially to glucose. There is a paucity of analytical data available on this point, and it remains to be determined whether or not glucose is actually inhibitory to sporulation in any way other than that described by Gray (1938), who found that under similar conditions of light intensity, fed cultures of *P. polycephalum* required a much longer period of illumination for sporulation than did starved cultures of the same species. In the early work of Daniel and Rusch (1962a), cultures were exposed for only two hours, but Daniel (1965) stated that a minimum of three hours at 200–400 fc is required for photoinduction and later (Daniel, 1966) reported that a minimum illumination period of two to three hours is necessary to obtain sporulation frequencies of 0.8 or greater. In view of these somewhat conflicting reports from the same investigator, it may well be that the commitment-to-sporulate point had not been reached with the short illumination period. For this reason, it seems necessary to use longer periods of illumination and to determine the exact point at which the apparent inhibitory effect of glucose is manifested in relation to the commitment-to-sporulate point.

Indole-3-acetic Acid and Morphogenesis

Still (1964) and Still and Ward (1963) found indole-3-acetic acid in spores of *P. polycephalum* but were unable to detect this compound in plasmodia or in intermediate stages in morphogenesis. They found that the absence of IAA in plasmodium was due to its enzymatic destruction, but that the enzyme differs from classical IAA oxidase, since it is not inhibited by catechol, chlorogenic acid, caffeic acid, epinephrin, or nor-adrenalin, and its activity is not enhanced by manganous ion or 2,4-dichlorophenol. Evidence of the involvement of pigment(s) as photoreceptors was obtained when Still and Ward freed homogenates of dark-grown plasmodia from pigment, and then placed aliquots in light and dark for one hour. The light exposed homogenate could not enzymatically utilize IAA, but that kept in the dark could. Similar homogenates, still containing pigment, did not demonstrate this dark reversal. In view of the fact that IAA has long been known to be a highly physiologically active compound in higher plants, and also in view of the fact that light has an inhibitory effect upon the IAA binding system in the plasmodium of *P. polycephalum,* it is probable that IAA plays a more significant role in the initiation of sporulation than is presently believed. Further exploration in this area will undoubtedly prove to be most fruitful.

Melanin Production in Spores

Although the plasmodium and immature sporangia are yellow during the early stages of development of *P. polycephalum,* as the spores mature their walls become dark—presumably as a result of the production of melanin. This presupposes the development of some type of phenoloxidase system or the activation of an already existing system. In their investigation of the enzyme systems involved in melanogenesis as spores of *P. polycephalum* are formed, Ward and Havir (1957b) found cresolase activity in *Physarum* extracts. This enzyme differed from classical tyrosinase, which is non-specific, in that it actively oxidized only *p*-cresol from a large number of monophenols and showed very slight activity only to 3:4-dihydroxytoluene from a number of diphenols. Like classical cresolase activity, *Physarum* cresolase activity showed a lag period before oxygen uptake was observed. However, unlike classical cresolase, the lag period could not be eliminated by dihydric phenols nor by 3:4-DHT. The lag period could be eliminated by addition of *p*-chloromercuribenzoate (*p*-CMB), N-ethyl maleimide (NEM), and iodoacetic acid, all of which react with -SH groups. Reduced glutathione and cysteine reversed the effect of these compounds and extended the lag for longer periods.

When reaction mixtures containing *p*-cresol were paper chromatographed, a spot corresponding to 3:4-DHT was found. Subjection of eluted similar undeveloped spots to infrared spectrophotometric analysis gave results consistent with 3:4-DHT. When homogenates were prepared from sporangia which were similar in external appearance to mature sporangia but which were still yellow in color, they easily oxidized *p*-cresol, tyrosine, and other phenolic substances with no period of induction (Ward, 1958a). Ward then suggested that melanin formation is carried into its final stage with another set of enzyme reactions not -SH dependent.

According to Daniel (1966), phenolase activity can be readily detected in NEM-treated plasmodia treated for sporulation. However, it cannot be detected by chronometric assay in untreated plasmodia or their homogenates, except during normal sporangial development.

Changes in ATP Level

Because of the shift from a highly metabolically active plasmodium to a relatively less active structure, such as the spore, it would be anticipated that energy requirements would vary during morphogenesis and that this might be reflected in changes in ATP level. Daniel (1964a, b, 1966) has shown that changes in ATP level do occur, but only if the plasmodium is illuminated and the sporulation medium contains niacin. The effect of light was biphasic causing an initial drop in ATP of 25–50 per cent from the dark level during the first hour of illumination, followed by a rise of 150–200 per cent which peaked at about 2.5 hours. ATP level decreased during the remainder of the four-hour illumination period and continued to decrease during an additional hour in the dark. Daniel (1966) suggests that the ATP peak corresponds to the light-dependent phase of metabolism, since he found that a minimum of two to three hours is required for a sporulation frequency of 0.8 or greater. Thus, light induces a new light-dependent pathway which contributes to the ATP level or stimulates already-existing dark pathways.

Effect of Light on Respiration

Daniel (1965) reported that light strongly inhibits respiration of both sporulating and growing plasmodia. He found that inhibition occurs rapidly—usually within 15 seconds—but that partial or complete recovery of O_2 uptake occurs in the dark. He also reported that respiration of isolated mitochondria was similarly light-sensitive, and later (1966) suggests that mitochondria are the probable sites of the light reaction, the effect then being transmitted to extramitochondrial systems including the yellow pigment. This work was based on few samples, and in view of the long-known similarities between the absorption spectrum of the pigment(s) and the action spectrum, it would seem premature at this time to relegate the pigment to a secondary role until further, more substantial data have been obtained.

Shift in Oxidases During Sporulation

The presence of a cytochrome-oxidase system in P. polycephalum has now been definitely established (see Chapter 7). Ward (1954, 1955, 1956, 1958a, b) has studied the cytochrome c–cytochrome oxidase system in both plasmodia and spores and has measured activity by observing the oxidation of reduced cytochrome spectrophotometrically. There was nearly three times as much cytochrome oxidase activity in spores as in plasmodia. Ward also found that ascorbic acid can be oxidized by homogenates by way of an atypical ascorbic-acid oxidase which forms H_2O_2, is resistant to metallorespiratory inhibitors, and requires the presence of an unknown -SH compound. Plasmodia exhibited six times as much ascorbic acid oxidase activity as spores. Thus, during morphogenesis there are marked shifts in activity of two separate oxidase systems.

The Relation of Sulfhydryl Groups and Iron to Morphogenesis

In a preceding section, brief mention was made of the finding of Ward and Havir (1957a) that the lag period of P. polycephalum cresolase could be eliminated by addition of p-CMB, NEM, or iodoacetate—all of which react with -SH groups. These results led Ward and Havir to suggest that sporulation can be triggered by the inactivation of -SH groups. To test this possibility, they exposed starved plasmodia to dilute solutions of NEM, p-CMB, and iodoacetate. Sporulation of plasmodia so treated occurred in about half the time required by untreated controls. Daniel (1963, 1964a, 1966) has reported that NEM causes a rapid release of yellow pigments from the plasmodium, and that this release is accelerated in light. This seems to suggest that -SH metabolism is not only involved in pigment binding but that light accelerates either formation or turnover of sulfhydryl, and in the process promotes pigment bleaching.

The effect of light on ATP level has been discussed earlier; however, Daniel (1966) has recently reported data that indicate that -SH may also be involved in this phenomenon. Thus, when reduced glutathione was added at the beginning of the illumination period, ATP level rose and peaked at 1–1.5 hours instead of at 2.5 hours when no glutathione was added. In the dark, added glutathione had no effect on ATP level.

The possible importance of iron in sporulation has been suggested by Daniel (1966), who added iron chelating agents, such as a, a'-Dipyridyl (AAP) and o-phenanthroline. Addition of either of these agents in a concentration of 10^{-3} M to medium 15 minutes before illumination completely inhibited sporulation. However, in his Table VIII, Daniel presents data that show that 25 per cent of his cultures (to which no chelating agents were added) sporulated on supposedly iron-free medium, compared to 80 per cent fruiting on medium containing 3×10^{-4} M F^{++}. That one-fourth of the cultures fruited indicates that (1) the iron-free medium was not in fact iron-free, or (2) an iron requirement for sporulation is questionable. In an earlier investigation, Daniel (1946c) reported that a light-dependent reduction of Fe^{++} was indicated, since AAP allowed the light-specific accumulation of $AAP.Fe^{++}$ complex in both medium and plasmodia of illuminated cultures. He also reported that photoreduction of Fe^{++} is stimulated by non-enzymatic preparations of

P. polycephalum pigment, *especially in the presence of sulfhydryl compounds.* The pigment was then bleached in the dark, presumably by the Fe^{++} produced during photoreduction.

The importance of -SH in the sporulation process is also reflected in the finding of Ward (1958a, b) that the activity of atypical ascorbic acid oxidase, *which requires the presence of unknown -SH compounds,* was six times greater in plasmodia than in spores.

Thus, more and more evidence is accumulating that indicates the active participation of -SH in sporulation. The fact that melanin production occurs late in morphogenesis suggests that the phenol oxidase(s) involved in the early stages of its formation are suppressed by -SH groups and do not become active until such groups have disappeared. Also it seems possible that the much decreased ascorbic acid oxidase activity observed by Ward in spores may have been due to the fact that the unknown -SH compound required by this enzyme was in much reduced amounts in the spores. Daniel *et al.* (1963) have shown that *P. polycephalum* requires methionine for growth, and more recently Daniel and Babcock (1966) have reported that this amino acid can serve as the sole source of sulphur. Thus far, no attempt seems to have been made to conduct a thorough study of sulphur metabolism, although, in view of the increasing evidence implicating sulfhydryl in sporulation, this should prove a most profitable study.

The Photochemical Synthesis of a Compound(s) That Triggers Sporulation

Straub's (1954) finding that the length of the period of illumination required for fruiting of *Didymium nigripes* can be reduced by feeding plasmodia on previously illuminated plasmodia leads to the suggestion that some "triggering" compound which can be transmitted through the protoplasm is synthesized photochemically. Rakoczy's (1962) results with *Physarum nudum* point to the same suggestion. This latter worker found an inverse relationship between length of illumination period required for the initiation of sporulation and age of culture, and postulated that a hypothetical photochemically synthesized "Substance B" triggered sporulation when its concentration reached a certain threshold value. According to Rakoczy, Substance B is synthesized from "Substance A," which material is synthesized during vegetative growth in either light or dark:

$$\begin{array}{l} \text{Vegetative Growth} \xrightarrow[\text{or dark}]{\text{light}} \text{Substance A} \\ \qquad\qquad\qquad\qquad\qquad\quad \downarrow \quad \text{light} \\ \qquad\qquad\qquad\qquad\quad \text{Substance B} \xrightarrow{\qquad} \text{Sporulation} \end{array}$$

The synthesis of effective amounts of Substance B is limited by the amount of Substance A at the time of illumination, and hence the relationship between age of culture and length of illumination period required for initiation of sporulation. It is tempting to postulate (1) that Substance A is produced from a metabolite of niacin or a metabolite synthesized through the mediation of niacin, (2) that Substance B is produced by a photochemical reaction involving Substance A and the photoreceptor, and (3) that once formed, Substance B brings about inactivation of -SH groups which appear to prevent sporulation. This hypothesis is a very attractive and logical one, but its acceptance will depend upon isolation and identification of Substance A and Substance B, proof that Substance A is converted to Substance B in a light reaction, and proof that Substance B does in fact trigger sporulation.

SUMMATION

From the above varied accounts, it is quite evident that profound changes occur in a variety of biochemical systems as the organism passes from the plasmodial to the spore-bearing stage, but as yet it is not possible to define morphogenesis biochemically even in P. polycephalum, the only myxomycete in which this phenomenon has been studied to any extent. The role of light may be far more complex than it appeared initially, since it has now been reported to affect nucleic acids, protein and polysaccharide contents, plasmodial ATP level, respiration, the reduction of inorganic iron, the formation of -SH groups, bleaching of pigment, and melanogenesis. Whether or not these effects are separate (which seems highly improbable) or whether they are all linked and in what sequence is presently not known. An even more complicated situation has arisen in connection with light effects with the finding that at least one myxomycete (Physarum gyrosum) does not become pigmented unless exposed to light, and sporulation does not occur unless the plasmodium is pigmented (Koevenig, 1963; Fergus and Schein, 1963).

From a great welter of publications four fairly clear ideas seem to emerge: (1) light is necessary for the induction of sporulation in yellow-pigmented plasmodia, (2) niacin is essential for the induction of light sensitivity, (3) the nutritional history of the plasmodium is of considerable importance in determining whether or not a plasmodium will sporulate and also in determining the time required for sporulation, and (4) the presence of -SH prevents a plasmodium from entering the reproductive stage. Daniel (1966) has suggested that "light appears to act by inhibiting mitochondrial respiration thereby strongly reorienting energy metabolism," which suggestion may be correct in a very general way. However, such an explanation leaves much to be desired, since the sequence of biochemical reactions that occurs is still unknown and probably will remain so until a much greater amount of research has been performed in this area. Even less is known regarding the factors that initiate and influence morphogenesis in non-pigmented plasmodial types, and for this reason any additional speculation seems pointless until we possess a much greater amount of analytical data (both quantitative and qualitative) than we do now.

It seems highly improbable that the sequence of chemical reactions will be established until the initial light reaction is identified beyond question. Once this has been established and the exact point in time (in relation to the commitment-to-sporulate point) has been determined, it may then be possible to describe the step-by-step chemical changes that occur in this transition from highly active plasmodium to stationary fructification containing spores with low levels of metabolic activity. Unfortunately, much of the published work has been conducted with a small number of samples, and hence it seems unwise to draw too-sweeping conclusions from data obtained from a few cultures, since exceptional cases are frequently encountered, and the behavior of two or three cultures may not reflect the typical behavior of a species.

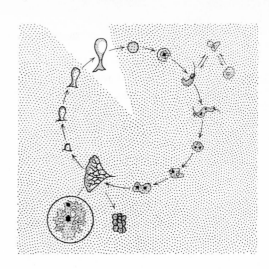

10

The Sporophore

Under favorable conditions—which have not been determined for the majority of species—each myxomycete forms characteristic sporophores by which it may be readily recognized. As already mentioned, it is on the sporophore and spore characters that our system of classification is primarily based.

TYPES OF SPOROPHORES

In addition to the exosporous fructification of *Ceratiomyxa,* four major types of sporophores are recognized in the Myxomycetes:

1. The sporangium
2. The plasmodiocarp
3. The aethalium
4. The pseudoaethalium (Baker, 1933).

The sporangial fructification is the one most commonly encountered and may be regarded as the basic form. It may be sessile or stalked (Fig. 55A, B). It may have a persistent peridium, or it may lose its peridium soon after it is formed. Indeed, Macbride and Martin (1934) questioned whether a peridium is ever formed in at least some species of *Stemonitis.* Typically, a characteristic capillitial system in which the spores are enmeshed is present in the sporangium, and its character has been used as an important taxonomic criterion. In many species, however, capillitium is totally lacking.

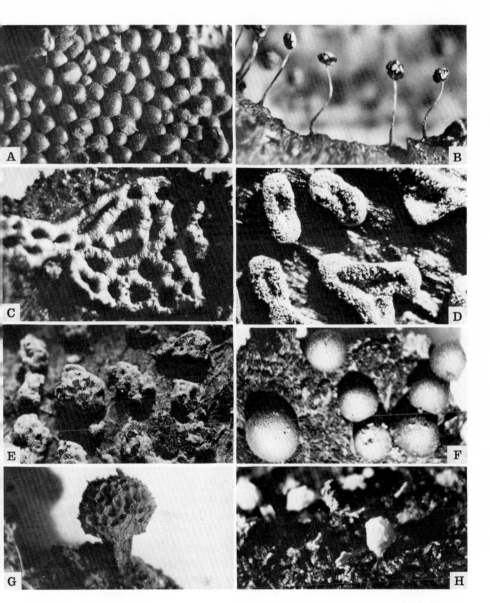

Fig. 55. Various types of fruiting bodies. A. Sessile sporangia of *Trichia varia*. × 10. B. Stipitate sporangia of *Physarum viride*. × 15. C. Reticulate plasmodiocarp of *Hemitrichia serpula*. × 10. D. Short plasmodiocarps of *Didymium annelus*. × 20. E. Aethalia of *Fuligo cinerea*. × 10. F. Aethalia of *Lycogala epidendrum*. × 2. G. Pseudoaethalium of *Tubifera microsperma*. × 6. H. Exosporous fructification of *Ceratiomyxa morchella*. × 12.

One or many sporangia develop from a single plasmodium. In species in which the assimilative stage is a protoplasmodium, only one sporangium usually develops from each plasmodium. There are some exceptions to this. In *Licea biforis*, for example, the protoplasmodium may divide and give rise to two sporangia (Wollman and Alexopoulos, 1967). In the majority of Myxomycetes, however, a well-developed plasmodium produces many, sometimes thousands, of sporangia. These may be crowded as in *Trichia favoginea* or even heaped as in *Oligonema schwein-itzii*, or may be distinct and more or less evenly spaced as in *Craterium leucocephalum*, or may be produced in clusters or tufts as in *Stemonitis smithii*. Sporangia produced from a single plasmodium under favorable conditions are usually quite uniform in character. On occasion, however, some variation is encountered both in nature and in artificial culture. Such variation may take the form of a difference in color or shape. A collection of *Physarum viride*, for example, may consist of both yellow and gray—almost white—sporangia, all presumably developed from a single plasmodium. Whether such a collection represents the fruiting of a heterokaryotic plasmodium or the influence of minute differences in the microenvironment would be interesting to determine. In the tropics the sporangia of *Physarum polycephalum* are often discoid rather than gyrose. Were it not for the presence of some gyrose sporangia among the discoid, an inexperienced collector might not recognize the discoid sporangia as belonging to the same species. Indeed, on occasion, such fruitings consist entirely of uniformly well-developed discoid sporangia which can be positively identified only through artificial culture, starting with spores. Such cultures usually yield the typical gyrose form (Alexopoulos and Henney, unpubl. 1967). Short- and long-stalked sporangia may be intermingled with sessile sporangia in the same collection of some physaraceous species.

A plasmodiocarp is much like a sessile sporangium but is usually elongated and quite often assumes the form of a network which lies flat on the substratum. It is formed along the major strands of the plasmodium that produced it. Because of the method of its formation—the production of a peridium around the main plasmodial veins in situ—a plasmodiocarp is often an extensive, net-like fruiting body (Fig. 55C). A discontinuous series of short, elongated or curved sporangium-like fruiting bodies, however, is often formed, if the protoplasm of the plasmodial vein condenses into short separate sections (Fig. 55D). It follows that the dividing line between plasmodiocarps and sporangia is sometimes very tenuous, and in some species, such as *Physarella oblonga*, both types of sporocarps are formed (Gray 1939a, 1949).

An aethalium is a more or less large fruiting body which is thought by some to represent a mass of completely fused sporangia (Fig. 55E, F).

In some species, the aethalia contain pseudocapillitia in the form of membranous expansions which may represent wall remnants of fused sporangia, although, as Baker (1933) points out, there is no evidence to support such an assumption. In other species, the pseudocapillitium is a system of long, branching tubes and closely resembles a true capillitium. In still other species, both capillitium and pseudocapillitium may be found in a single aethalium.

Intermediate between the sporangium and the aethalium is the pseudoaethalium (Fig. 55G), which is a closely compacted mass of sporangia forming a single fructification in which, however, the individual sporangia are clearly discernible.

The exosporous fructification consists of a spongy matrix in the form of pillars, arboreal branches, polyporous or morcheloid structures (Fig. 55H) on which spores are borne on erect hair-like stalks.

THE ENDOSPOROUS FRUCTIFICATION

Development of the Sporophore

Development of the sporophore of the endosporous species has been studied chiefly in the Physarales and the Stemonitales. Less information is available for the Liceales, Trichiales, and Echinosteliales. This discussion will of necessity, therefore, concentrate on the first two orders.

The Physarales.   When the biochemical changes prerequisite to sporophore formation have been completed, the protoplast of the phaneroplasmodium, typical of members of the Order Physarales, becomes concentrated in certain areas by flowing into the already fleshy fans and forming a continuous layer, or concentrating in portions of the main strands where the sporangial initials develop. In axenic culture, the plasmodial strands of Physarum polycephalum become undulated and the protoplasm accumulates in small nodules which become separated and function as the sporangial primordia (Guttes, et al., 1961). These elongate perpendicularly to the substratum, exhibiting no geotropism, and develop into pillars the central axes of which are filled with pigment and other types of granules. As the pillars elongate, they become more slender throughout their length; the bulk of the protoplasm migrates internally toward the tip and forms a globose head; thus, the whole structure becomes differentiated into a stalked fruiting body.

The stalk is composed of three more or less distinct layers: (1) a fairly thick, tough, lamellate wall which is continuous with the hypothallus [1] and

---

[1] The hypothallus is a thin, often transparent deposit at the base of the fructifications of some Myxomycetes.

with the peridium; this is derived from the outer plasmodial membrane which forms a covering of the entire fruiting body and which has a tendency to thicken somewhat as the sporocarps develop; (2) a cylinder of protoplasm with a foamy structure; (3) a central core of granular consistency which functions as a skeleton and gives strength to the stalk. The type of substratum on which fruiting occurs governs to a considerable extent the rigidity of the stalk (Howard, 1931a).

As the protoplasmic pillar which forms the stalk reaches its full length, the apical portion becomes constricted and begins to differentiate into a sporangium. Virtually all the protoplasm on the stalk below the outer membrane migrates into the sporangial initial, which expands laterally and, in some species, also downward, enveloping the tip of the stalk and thus converting it into a columella (Welden, 1955). The outer membrane together with a layer of condensed protoplasm immediately adjacent to it form the peridium. At this stage, this encloses the frothy reticulum which will produce the spores and in which the capillitium will form.

Information on plasmodiocarpous species is lacking, but judging from the appearance of the fruiting bodies it is obvious that the protoplasm becomes concentrated in the main strands at the time of fruiting. In some species, such as *P. cinereum*, the strands break at intervals, and the separate portions become converted into fruiting bodies. In other species, exemplified by *Didymium perforatum*, the plasmodium is held together in a network and fruits as a unit.

According to deBary (1887), aethalial formation in *Fuligo*, as well as in *Lycogala, Reticularia, Lindbladia*, and so on, begins with the fusion of numerous plasmodia which pool their protoplasm to form a cushion-shaped mass. Though plasmodial fusion may very well take place, it is doubtful whether this is a prerequisite to sporulation. In the initial stages of the aethalium of *Fuligo*, the plasmodial strands are said to be quite thick and the meshes of the reticulum relatively small (Harper, 1900). The solid particles in the protoplasm are extruded, the water containing salts in solution is excreted, and the protoplasmic reticulum condenses. As the water evaporates, the salts are deposited on the surface of the reticulum. As this continues to condense, it withdraws from the excreted waste products, which thus form the limy surface characteristic of the fructifications of *Fuligo*. The yellow pigment in the plasmodium sometimes finds its way to the surface and is incorporated in the friable crust, which is then yellow or brownish and which has given this ubiquitous species the common name of "flowers of tan."

A number of cavities or lacunae in the developing aethalium were demonstrated by Harper (1900) who stated they were all lined with a thin homogeneous membrane in which lime crystals are often embedded.

If the aethalium is indeed a mass of sporangia in which differentiation has stopped short of completion, these membrane-lined cavities are probably the component sporangia.

The Stemonitales. Because of its only slightly granular nature, the aphanoplasmodium, characteristic of this order, is flat, transparent, and difficult to see. As it approaches the fruiting stage, it becomes opaque, its strands thicken, and its protoplast becomes condensed into conspicuous coralloid masses (Alexopoulos, 1959, 1960a) from which the sporangial initials begin to form.

Contrary to the situation in the Physarales, the hypothallus in the Stemonitaceae is deposited directly on the substratum below the plasmodium (Ross, 1957a). From the investigation of five species of *Stemonitis*, four of *Comatricha*, and two of *Lamproderma* (Jahn, 1931; Gray, 1936, 1937; Ross, 1957a, 1960; Goodwin, 1961), it appears that stalk formation in the Stemonitaceae, in general, is essentially similar, differing only in detail. In *Comatricha* and *Lamproderma*, the protoplasmic droplet which represents the sporangial initial begins to deposit internally on the hypothallus below it, a system of fibrous strands which form the base of the stalk. The protoplasm now begins its slow ascent on the stalk, constantly adding more material to its tip which remains internal until the total height of the fructification is reached. The stalk in the species of *Comatricha* and *Lamproderma* that have been investigated thus consists of a system of parallel fibers which, according to Ross (1957a, 1960), are tubular. In *Stemonitis*, the stalk is described as consisting of a single tube, the base of which is deposited internally by the plasmodial droplet on the hypothallus on which it rests. In all species of the Stemonitaceae investigated, after the total height of the stalk is reached, deposition of material continues internally and results in the formation of the columella from which the capillitium wholly or partially originates.

Although no developmental studies have been undertaken in *Macbrideola*, the stalk in this genus appears to be typically stemonitaceous (Alexopoulos, 1967), consisting of a single slender tube which continues into the sporangium as a columella which gives rise to the capillitium. In *Clastoderma*, on the other hand, the development of the stalk, as described by McManus (1961b) appears to be physaraceous rather than stemonitaceous. The inclusion of *Clastoderma* in the Stemonitales should, therefore, be reexamined.

The Peridium

The structure and chemical composition of the peridium remain virtually unknown. Non-cellular in form, the peridium of the Physarales varies in thickness and consistency in different species. In some, such as

Physarum didermoides and *P. bitectum,* it consists of two distinct and widely separated membranes. The inner one, thin, transparent, and often iridescent, is appressed against the spore mass; the outer one, thicker and lightly or heavily covered with lime, is the protective covering of the sporangium. The way the lime is deposited is often characteristic. In some Didermas, for example, the peridium is described as cartilaginous, and the lime appears to be evenly distributed and enmeshed within the peridial layer. In *Diderma testaceum, Physarum dictyosporum,* and other similar species, the lime forms a smooth, porcelain-like cover, and the entire outer peridium appears shell-like. In the Lepidodermas, the lime is deposited in distinct, large, flat, scale-like particles. In *Physarum, Fuligo, Badhamia,* and related genera, the lime is described as amorphous. In *Didymium* it is crystalline, the whole peridium, in most species, being covered with a powder of stellate crystals which, as in *D. leoninum,* may be very large. In all cases, the lime is said to be $CaCO_3$ and, according to Pobequin (1954), in the Didymiaceae it is in the form of calcite.

The peridium of the Stemonitaceae develops from the outer membrane of the plasmodial bleb which initiates the fructification, but is not continuous with the hypothallus which is deposited below the plasmodium nor with the stalk which is produced internally. In most species of *Stemonitis* and *Comatricha* this delicate membrane is the only peridium that develops. When the mature sporangium dries, the membrane disintegrates and the spore ball is without a cover. In *Lamproderma* and in a few species of *Comatricha,* as well as some other genera now placed in the Stemonitaceae (*Macbrideola, Barbeyella, Clastoderma,* and so on), a thicker and sometimes tough peridium is developed which may persist for a long time.

In the Trichiales and Liceales, there is no lime on the peridium except in rare instances. In these forms, the peridial layer is usually tough and has a papery or leathery consistency. In the Echinosteliales, the peridium is no more than a delicate protoplasmic membrane very much like that encountered in most of the Stemonitaceae, which only rarely persists in the mature fructification (Alexopoulos, 1958). In *Cribraria* and *Dictydium,* the peridium is composed of a network of veins running through a delicate membrane which soon evanesces in part or in its entirety.

The Capillitium

As in a number of other organisms that bear spores in sporangia, there is inside the fructification of many Myxomycetes a system of threads which form the capillitium. These threads are intermingled with the spores but are in no way connected to them, having been formed separately by an entirely independent developmental system.

The fructifications of the Liceales are devoid of capillitium, but a pseudocapillitium is present in the sporocarps of some species (Fig. 56A). In the Physarales, characterized by the accumulation of lime in various parts of the fructifications, the capillitium usually forms a network of delicate threads which may be attached to the base of the peridium. In *Diderma, Didymium,* and other members of the Didymiaceae, the threads may be somewhat flattened and are typically free of lime or of any ornamentation (Fig. 56B). Exceptionally, as in *Didymium trachysporum,* the capillitial threads possess, at irregular intervals, swellings which enclose crystals of lime. Not rarely knot- or bead-like structures are present on the capillitial threads. The threads themselves may be straight or undulating, sparingly branched, sometimes with short threads connecting two branches in the acute angle formed near their origin. Whether or not the capillitial threads of the Didymiaceae are solid or tubular is still an unsettled question. DeBary (1887) states they are solid or "with an indication of a cavity. . . ." The lime-enclosing cavities of *D. trachysporum* may indeed be enlargements of an otherwise very slender capillitial tube. Schuster's (1964a) electron micrograph of a capillitial thread of *D. nigripes* (Kerr's strain) in cross-section shows no lumen but clearly indicates that the periphery is much denser than the co̅r̅e̅ Electron microscope studies of many species are needed to give us a broader picture of capillitial structure.

In *Physarum,* very delicate hyaline threads connect the lime nodes characteristic of this and some other genera in the Physaraceae (Fig. 56C). The threads may originate separately at the base of the sporangium, as in *Physarum rigidum* and related species, and form a system of sparingly branched, rigid, ascending columns partially covered with lime; or they may form a complete network bearing lime nodes at the joints. The lime nodes may be large and rounded, as in *P. bogoriense;* small and inconspicuous, as in *P. tenerum;* or characteristically angular or elongate as in *P. javanicum* and *P. viride.* The capillitial lime may be pure white, cream, yellow, or orange. In rare instances reddish tints are present. In *Physarum lateritium* and some other species, a layer of white lime encloses a core of red lime.

The capillitial network of *Badhamia,* described as tubular by Macbride (1899), is completely limy. Whether it actually consists of limy tubules or solid rods has not been determined with certainty.

Several types of capillitia are found in the Trichiales. That of the Dianemaceae consists of extremely slender branched or unbranched threads not exceeding 1–2 microns in diameter, which are said to be solid (Fig. 56D). These are usually attached at both ends to the inner

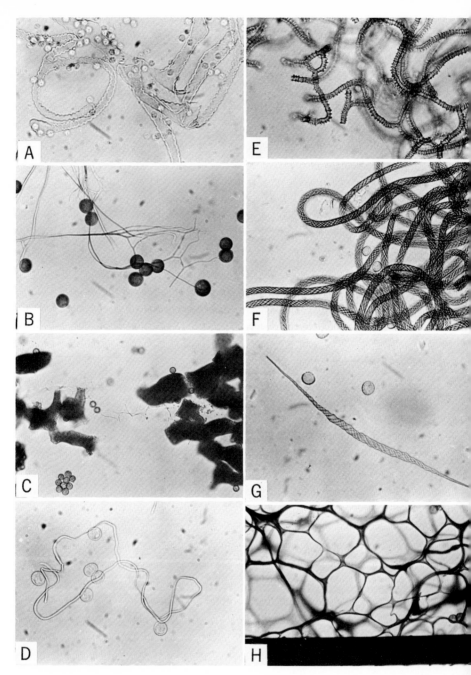

Fig. 56. Various types of capillitia. A. Pseudocapillitium of *Lycogala*. B. Capillitium of *Didymium*. C. *Physarum*. D. *Calomyxa*. E. *Arcyria*. F. *Hemitrichia*. G. Capillitial elater of *Trichia*. H. *Stemonitis*. B and D × 450; all others × 300.

side of the peridium. In the Trichiaceae, coarse, tubular threads, branching and anastomosing and with variously ornamented surfaces are united to form a rather dense network. In *Arcyria* their outer surfaces bear spines, warts, cogs, or half-rings or, more frequently, various combinations of these elements (Fig. 56E). In *A. leiocarpa*, exceptionally, the capillitium bears very faint spiral bands. In *A. nutans* and closely allied species, the capillitium is highly elastic and, upon the evanescence of the delicate peridium that originally holds it in place, expands greatly and droops, carrying masses of spores enmeshed in its network. In the common *A. denudata* and related forms, the capillitial network is strongly attached to the rim of the well-formed, vase-like calyculus which persists after the upper portion of the peridium disappears (Fig. 57A). In other species, of which *A. incarnata* is the most common example, the capillitium is very tenuously attached by one or two free ends deep in the center of the calycular funnel among the spore-like cells that fill the stalk of which the calyculus is a continuation (Fig. 57B).

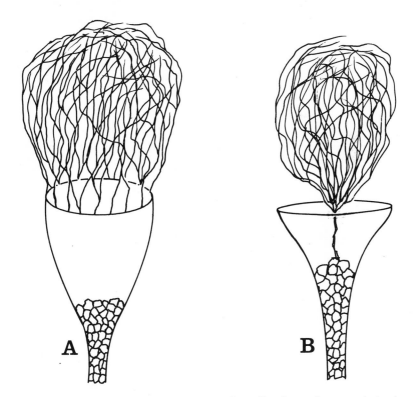

Fig. 57. Diagrammatic representation of capillitial attachment. A. In *Arcyria denudata* (peripheral). B. In *Arcyria incarnata* (central).

The tubular threads that make up the capillitial network of *Hemitrichia* bear characteristic, spirally arranged ridges or bands which are smooth, rough, or spiny (Fig. 56F). The same characteristic is found in *Trichia*, a related genus. Here, the capillitium consists of short or long, free threads, the elaters, which taper gradually or abruptly into pointed ends (Fig. 56G). In an earlier chapter, reference was made to the hygroscopicity of these elaters and the role they play in disseminating the spores.

In the Echinosteliales, the capillitium, when present, appears to be made of solid threads. It originates from the tip of the columella and either branches sparsely as in *Echinostelium minutum* or forms a complete but open network as in *E. cribrarioides*.

In the Stemonitales, the capillitium varies from the few simple threads of *Macbrideola* to the intricate network of *Stemonitis* (Fig. 56H) or the dense mass of threads in *Lamproderma*.

The chemical composition of the capillitium, as of the peridium and stalk of the Myxomycetes, remains largely unknown. Cihlar (cf. Goodwin, 1961) reported the presence of chitin in the capillitium of *Stemonitis fusca*, and von Wettstein (1921) found cellulose in the "membranes" of *Comatricha* and *Stemonitis*. Goodwin's (1961) microchemical tests in three species of *Comatricha* indicate that cellulose is present in the late but not the early stages of capillitium development, and that it develops, therefore, after the main skeleton of the capillitium has been formed. Whether chemical changes take place in the capillitium or whether a cellulose layer is deposited on the surface of the young strands is not known. According to Goodwin, cellulose appears simultaneously with the brown pigment characteristic of the capillitium of *Comatricha*. Goodwin also obtained a cellulose reaction with the stalk, but not with the hypothallus or the peridium. She found no indication of the presence of chitin in any of the structures she investigated.

In two brief papers, Locquin (1947, 1948) reported that in *Hemitrichia serpula* the capillitium consists chiefly of chitin and that the capillitium of *Calomyxa* (*Margarita*) *metallica* exhibits strongly dichroic and birefringent inclusions with a spiral structure.

Only X-ray diffraction studies and chemical isolation can provide the much needed information on the chemical composition of the myxomycete fructification.

Capillitium Development

The development of the myxomycetous capillitium was first studied by Strasburger (1884) in *Trichia pusilla*. This remained a unique study until Kranzlin (1907), working in Jahn's laboratory, undertook an investigation of sporangial development in the Trichiaceae. The work of

Harper and Dodge (1914) and of Bisby (1914) closed what might be termed the early era of capillitial investigation. In more recent times Cadman (1931), Howard (1931a), Welden (1955), Ross (1957a, 1960), Goodwin (1961), and Schuster (1964a) have all added some information to our knowledge of capillitium development and structure.

The Physarales. When the peridium is formed in the Physarales, exemplified by *Badhamia gracilis*, tubular invaginations begin to form at the base and the periphery of the sporangium; they originate from the inner peridial layer and extend inward. Soon the sporangial protoplasm begins to condense progressively from the periphery toward the center, and a gradual transition takes place from a frothy, reticulate structure to a homogenous structure (Howard, 1931a; Welden, 1955). During this transition, vacuoles appear which are bounded by peripheral membranes. In *B. gracilis*, these are large and conspicuous; in *Didymium iridis*, they are much smaller and relatively few, according to Welden.

In *B. gracilis* and *P. polycephalum*, the vacuoles elongate and soon coalesce and form an anastomosing vesicular network. In *B. gracilis*, this network meets and unites with the tubular invaginations. Howard (1931a) reported no tubular invaginations in *P. polycephalum*. Welden, however, states that inasmuch as they stain only slightly darker than the surrounding protoplasm they are difficult to see. In *Physarella oblonga*, Bisby (1914) reported the formation of such invaginations and declared them to be the precursors of capillitial formation.

This network of tubules thus formed acts as a conducting system (Welden, 1955) through which calcium carbonate and other "excretory products" move toward the peridium and are deposited there. In *Didymium*, all the calcium is thus eliminated, and the capillitium is completely devoid of lime. In *Badhamia* and presumably in other genera of the Physaraceae, considerable lime remains in the tubes and becomes a part of the capillitial system either covering the threads, as in *Badhamia*, or becoming deposited as lime nodes in the junctions of the network, as in *Physarum, Craterium*, and so on. As the sporangium matures, the membranes which form the walls of the tubular system dry and collapse, forming the threads of the capillitium.

If Welden's explanation is correct, the capillitial threads are actually tubular, but their finally appressed walls give them the appearance of solid threads. Schuster's (1964a) electron micrograph of a cross-section of a capillitial thread of *D. nigripes*, however, shows a solid rod, the interior of which is lamellate. No membranes are discernible to indicate a tubular structure.

The Trichiales. In *Hemitrichia* and *Trichia*, capillitium formation begins with the formation of vacuoles in the cytoplasm. These coalesce and form either an anastomosing system of tubules or individual elongated vacuoles, depending on the type of capillitium to be formed. According to Harper and Dodge (1914), the nuclei migrate toward the vacuolar system and form a definite layer around the developing capillitial threads. Deeply staining granules, from which fibrils radiate in a manner suggesting astral rays, are abundant on the surface of the developing threads. It is suggested that the fibrils represent streams in the cytoplasm through which material is brought to the vacuoles for the formation of the capillitium.

The vacuolar system thus forms a tubular thread onto which the cytoplasm deposits thickenings in the form of spirals, which appear at first to be distinctly granular. These findings agree essentially with Strasburger's (1884) earlier account.

The Stemonitales. Whereas in both the Physarales and Trichiales the formation of a special system of vacuolar tubes precedes the formation of capillitial threads, in the Stemonitales the situation is more uncertain. Bisby (1914), in his study of *Stemonitis fusca,* described the formation of tubular invaginations originating from the peridial membrane and from the columella. He believed that the capillitium was formed by "the deposition of hollow threads by plasma membranes lining tubular capillary spaces." His study was based on microtome sections. It will be remembered that Bisby described essentially the same method for *Physarella oblonga* and that Welden's results with *Badhamia* and *Didymium* were in general agreement with Bisby's description, differing only in some details. Later workers present a somewhat different picture of capillitial development in the Stemonitales.

Ross (1957a, 1960) studied capillitial development in *Stemonitis, Comatricha,* and *Lamproderma* by squashing sporangia at various stages of development in aceto-orcein or mounting them whole in Hoyer's medium. He agreed that in *Stemonitis* the capillitium originates both from the columella and from the periphery of the sporangium, but he found no evidence of invaginations or vacuoles connected with capillitium formation. Although he admits that his technique may have destroyed such structures, he states that "the ends of the capillitial threads of *Stemonitis, Comatricha,* and *Lamproderma* all appear to blend gradually into the cytoplasm surrounding them." This would seem to indicate that no vacuolar membrane was present. Goodwin (1961), studying three species of *Comatricha* by mounting in Hoyer's medium whole sporangia at various stages of development, also failed to find "the slightest indication of the presence of infolded or invaginated membranes in or around the stalk, columella, or capillitium." Nor did she detect capillitial vacuoles in the cytoplasm. Both Ross and Goodwin are of the opinion that the capillitium in the Stemonitaceae is formed by intraprotoplasmic secretions.

In *Comatricha,* the capillitium originates entirely from the columella. As the columella grows the strands or tubes that compose it (see page 197) bend out to form the main branches of the capillitium. The cytoplasm in which they are forming continues to deposit material on their tips, causing them to elongate. Branching also occurs, but it is not known whether this is due to a separation of strands in a bundle that bends out from the columella or to other causes. When the capillitial system has reached the peridium, its growth stops. In *Stemonitis* two capillitial systems are formed, one originating near the periphery of the sporangium, the other as a series of branches from the tip or sides of the columella. The two meet near the periphery and anastomose, the first forming the surface net, the second the main structural system.

Pseudocapillitium

The difference between true capillitium and pseudocapillitium is not always easy to describe. Pseudocapillitium may consist of long, branching strands, which often resemble capillitial threads to a remarkable extent, or of thin, perforated membranes variously arranged within an aethalium. Where capillitium-like strands are present, as in *Lycogala* (Fig. 56A), these are generally irregular in shape, diameter, and ornamentation, whereas true capillitial strands tend to be much more uniform. In *Dictydiaethalium,* in which the fructification consists of a large number of closely appressed sporangia, the pseudocapillitium is formed from the thickened parts of the walls at the corners formed where four sporangia are pressed together, and which persist after the thinner walls have disintegrated.

Wilson and Cadman (1928) concluded that in *Reticularia lycoperdon* the pseudocapillitium represents degenerated and condensed protoplasmic strands. If this is so, it would constitute a good cytological criterion for differentiating between true capillitia and certain types of pseudocapillitia.

Spore Formation

A few hours after the sporangial primordium has developed, one or two synchronous divisions occur (see Chapter 4), and the protoplasm begins to cleave. Many nuclei seem to degenerate at this point (Harper and Dodge, 1914; Howard, 1931a; Wilson and Ross, 1955; Guttes, *et al.,* 1961). In *Didymium melanospermum* (Harper, 1914), the protoplasm of the sporangium condenses and withdraws from the capillitial threads already formed, thus forming cavities between the surface of the threads and the plasma membrane. These cavities become connected and form radially oriented canals in which the extruded water flows to the outside. Cleavage furrows originate from these canals. They anastomose and divide the sporoplasm into multinucleate sections, which by further cleavage are divided into the uninucleate portions that finally develop into the spores. In *Badhamia gracilis* cleavage furrows begin at the periphery and develop progressively toward the center. In *Didymium iridis* they begin not only at the periphery but also at the surface of the space above the columella (Welden, 1955). In *Physarum polycephalum*, cleavage furrows first become evident along the already formed capillitial threads. Later, they also develop from the periphery toward the center (Howard, 1931a).

Schuster (1964a) and Aldrich (1966) have studied the ultrastructural features of the sporangia during cleavage in *Didymium nigripes* (Kerr's strain) and *Physarum flavicomum*, respectively (Fig. 58). The cleavage

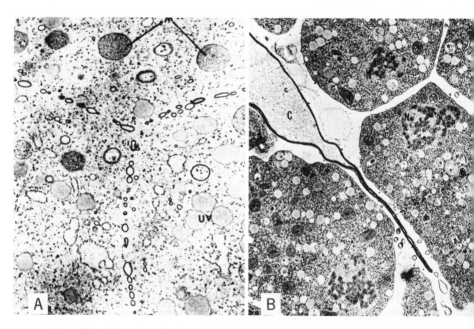

Fig. 58. *Physarum flavicomum.* Early stage (A) × 15,000 and late stage (B) × 6000 in spore cleavage. (Aldrich, 1966. Courtesy Henry Aldrich and Cell Research Institute, University of Texas at Austin.)

furrows are formed by the fusion of cisternae. Aldrich describes this process as follows:

Numerous vesicles line up along the cleavage planes, and as these vesicles coalesce, their membranes form the plasma membrane of the presumptive spores. At this stage, expanded rough endoplasmic reticulum is present in the cytoplasm. Since no Golgi apparatus has been found in the sporangial mass at this stage, it seems likely that the vesicles forming the cleavage furrows may be a product of this rough endoplasmic reticulum.

Multinucleate masses first formed are further cleaved into uninucleate spheres. When these are formed, dense osmiophilic granules appear along the furrows under the plasma membrane. Schuster (1964a) suggests they may be of polysaccharide or mucopolysaccharide consistency. Evenly spaced projections of a granular nature are now formed at the periphery of the protoplasmic spheres. These projections become the spines of the mature spore which is invested by two walls (see Chapter 2).

THE EXOSPOROUS FRUCTIFICATION

Famintzin and Woronin (1873) gave us the first account of the development of the sporophore of *Ceratiomyxa fruticulosa,* the only one of the three exosporous species that has been studied. Olive (1907a, b) and Jahn (1908) also published cytological studies on this species, but it is Gilbert's (1935) account of the life history of *Ceratiomyxa* that is generally accepted today. Five forms of fructification may be recognized according to Gilbert. These are the "simple pillar," the "fruticulus," the "arbuscula," the "filiforme," and the "porioides." The development is similar in all forms. As the plasmodium emerges from the wood it inhabits, it begins to form papillae in which large quantities of matrix are manufactured. As the plasmodium continues to flow into the papillae and more matrix is formed, the papillae elongate into pillars. At maturity, the pillars consist of the highly vacuolated matrix which bears a thin layer of protoplasm on its surface. A simple mitosis occurs, and this is followed by a cleavage of the protoplasmic layer into uninucleate segments. In view of the homologies proposed by Gilbert, it is important to quote directly from his article at this point:

The process of cleavage is in no way related to the mitosis just being completed except that it follows as the next step in development. Where the nucleated reticulum is scattered and attenuated, cleavage is accomplished by constriction of the strands between the nuclei and aggregation of the protoplasm around the nuclei. No cleavage furrows need be formed. This is one of the conditions that clearly marks the homology of the matrix with the hypothallus and of the spore with the endosporous sporangium. The process is identical with the segmentation of a large plasmodium into units for sporangial development. In *Ceratiomyxa* the units are very small and uninucleate. In the Endosporeae the units are larger and multinucleate. The pillars are but elaborate developments of a hypothallus.

After cleavage, the protospores become spherical, and each surrounds itself with a "delicate plastic wall." At about this time stalks are formed eccentrically, but the spores creep up on the stalks so that when the process is completed each spore is perched at the tip of its stalk.

The exosporous fructification has been variously interpreted, but the most widely accepted explanation is that it represents a modified, extensive, specialized hypothallus on which the spores are borne (Gilbert, 1935). This interpretation was strengthened by Gilbert's further proposal that homologized the spore of *Ceratiomyxa* with the sporangium of the endosporous species, using *Lamproderma* as his example (Fig. 59). This proposal was, in turn, partially based on Gilbert's belief that whereas meiosis in *Ceratiomyxa* typically occurs in the spore, in the endosporous species it occurs typically in the sporangium at the time of cleavage. After von Stosch's (1935, 1937, 1964) work with several endosporous species, which places meiosis in the spores, and Aldrich's (1967) electron microscope studies, which largely support and expand von Stosch's conclusions, the supposed homology of the *Ceratiomyxa* spore to the sporangium of the endosporous species loses some of its support. However, from the information now available (see Chapter 4), it appears that in some endosporous species meiosis does take place in the sporangium at the time of cleavage but that in others it occurs in the maturing spore. Homologies, therefore, are not clear. On the basis of the newer findings Martin and Alexopoulos (1969) consider "the basal portions of the fruiting structures as well as the branches, when present . . . as constituting the fructification" of *Ceratiomyxa*.

STABILITY OF CHARACTERS

A very delicate balance of largely unknown factors seems to govern the characters of the sporophore, which are much more plastic than the characters of the spores. Aberrant sporophores which are difficult or impossible to place in a known taxon often produce spores typical of the species to which the organism belongs. *Comatricha typhoides* is a case in point. Unless the substratum is devoid of free water, sporangia produced in the laboratory are so aberrant as to be unrecognizable (Wollman, 1966). Nevertheless, the majority of the spores they contain may be perfectly formed and characteristically ornamented. This is not to deny that giant or grotesque spores are very often produced by improperly matured sporophores in many species.

Gray (1939a, 1949) has noted that *Physarella oblonga* produces plasmodiocarps, as well as sporangia, both in nature and in culture. The sporophores of *Physarum gyrosum*, when well formed, are so chararacter-

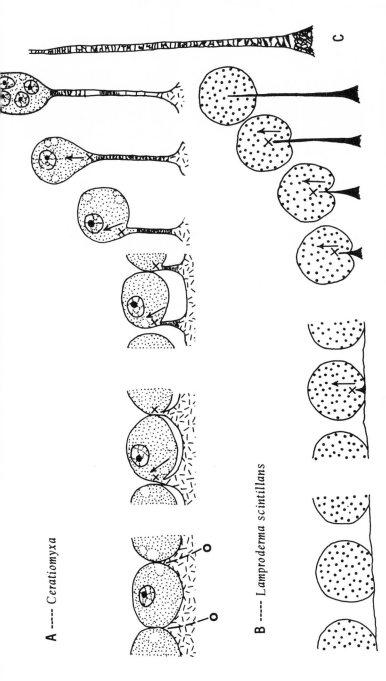

A ---- *Ceratiomyxa*

B ---- *Lamproderma scintillans*

C

Fig. 59. A comparison of spore elevation in *Ceratiomyxa* with sporangial elevation in *Lamproderma scintillans*. X indicates the points of activity in stalk formation. The arrows indicate the direction of movement of the protoplast. O indicates the small cones of matrix between the rounded protospores. C is a single *Ceratiomyxa* spore stalk magnified about × 1000. (Redrawn from Gilbert, 1935.)

istic that they cannot be confused with those of any other species. Yet, under certain culture conditions, the fruiting bodies that develop may resemble those of *P. compressum, P. cinereum,* and *Physarella oblonga* (Koevenig, 1961c). Koevenig believes that the amount of moisture in the substratum and the humidity in the surrounding air may be—more than any other factor—responsible for the shape of the sporophore. Gilbert (1929a), too, proposed that humidity has a great effect on the "normal" development of the sporangia, particularly the spores of *Didymium iridis,* but he had little to say about the effect of this factor on the character of the sporangia except to point out that those that failed to develop properly were smaller. On the basis of his observations on the variability of the sporocarps of *Didymium squamulosum, Physarum polycephalum,* and *Badhamia foliicola,* Cohen (1942) theorized that a difference in surface tension of the plasmodium governs the shape of the fructification, a low surface tension favoring the production of plasmodiocarps and a high surface tension the production of sessile spheres. "If the material is secreted preferentially at the substrate-protoplasm interface, we should expect a stiped form" of fructification. This explanation has considerable merit, especially for species that usually produce stipitate fructifications. As Alexopoulos (1963) pointed out, however, some forms, such as *Hemitrichia serpula,* always produce plasmodiocarps regardless, it seems, of the conditions under which sporulation takes place. Also, although the sporangia of many of the Stemonitaceae sometimes fail to mature properly, seldom in our experience do typically stipitate forms produce completely sessile sporangia, and never plasmodiocarpous fructifications. Composition of the substratum also influences the form and structure of the fructification. Skupienski (1953) reported that on beer-wort agar the sporangia of *Didymium nigripes* measured 1 mm in diameter and had very short stalks, whereas on plain agar they were smaller and had a "normal," i.e., considerably longer, stalk.

In this connection may also be mentioned the abundance or lack of lime on the sporangia of species in which lime is characteristically present on the peridium. Again, according to Skupienski, on plain agar the sporangia of *Didymium nigripes* display an abundance of lime crystals, on Knop's agar a moderate amount, and on beer-wort agar none at all. Gray (1961) reported that sporangia of *Physarum flavicomum* that develop under dry conditions tend to have a limy peridium whereas those that develop in a humid environment have a limeless peridium. This difference in quantity of lime both in the peridium and the capillitium of the Physarales has been carefully recorded by monographers. Thus, Macbride and Martin (1934), discussing *Physarum pusillum,* state that "the capillitium in some sporangia is strongly calcareous, suggesting Badhamia, but in most sporangia the physarum characters are sufficiently clear."

As might be expected, species that are common and widely distributed vary considerably from locality to locality. *Didymium squamulosum,* for example, "is remarkable for the variations which it presents in the fruiting phase" (Macbride and Martin, 1934). *Arcyria cinerea* is another species in which the fructifications vary considerably in color, size, and sometimes appearance of the stalk. Some of these variations are undoubtedly stable and genetically controlled. Others may be due to variations in environment. Of particular interest in this connection are some dwarf forms that occur on leaves rather than on dead wood, which is the more usual habitat for this species. The sporangia of these minute forms are of such uniform size in single collections that one might be inclined to conclude that they represent a distinct variety. Culture work by Keefer and by Alexopoulos (unpublished, 1966), however, shows that sporangia varying in size from that of typical *A. cinerea* to that approaching *Echinostelium minutum,* one of the smallest of Myxomycetes, are developed on the same agar plate in cultures initiated by sowing spores from one of several dwarf sporangia in a single collection.

Brandza (1926a, b) performed some field experiments from which he concluded that environment has a profound effect on the color and structure of the fructifications of several species. Sporangia that formed on house roofs in full sunlight were very different from those formed from plasmodia of the same species that he had transferred to a ravine in a forest near by. These experiments were among the first to call attention to the effect of the environment on the characters of the fructification. Somewhat better controlled experiments were set up by Cayley (1929), Skupienski (1928, 1933), and, more recently, Solis (1962) to study these phenomena. When Cayley (1929) sowed on Knop's agar spores from a sessile form of *Didymium squamulosum* collected on dead leaves, she obtained the stalked form. She also found that *Didymium iridis* produces larger-than-normal stalked or sessile sporangia on Knop's agar. Stalk color in this species, used among others as a taxonomic character, was also found to vary considerably when the plasmodia fruited on different media.

Studying the effect of environmental factors on the fructification of Myxomycetes, Skupienski (1930, 1933) found that the morphology of the sporangia of *Didymium nigripes* was profoundly affected by temperature, as was the color of the stipe and the columella. The latter characters are used to differentiate between *D. nigripes* and *D. iridis,* and their stability under different environmental conditions is, therefore, of interest taxonomically as well as physiologically. The substratum also affected the sporangial characters, a medium rich in carbohydrates tending to produce unusually large sporangia on thick stalks. The spores in these sporangia varied considerably in size and shape, indicating that the fructifications were aberrant. On media with a low pH (5.5), the sporangia were well formed but smaller than usual. On media with a high pH (7.8), they were larger and much more calcareous. Skupienski also reported that on carrot-juice agar *Didymium difforme* formed only ramose plasmodiocarps, whereas on horse-dung agar it produced globose fructifications.

Solis studied the effect of temperature and type of substratum on the morphology of 300 fructifications of *Physarum nicaraguense*. She found that the number of lobes on each sporangium increased as the temperature increased, as follows:

Number of Lobes per Sporangium

	Minimum	Median	Maximum	Average
15°	1	4	6	3.72
20°	4	5	8	5.38
25°	4	6	12	6.28

The number of lobes was also affected by the substratum, but the effect was not so great as that of the temperature factor. Height and color of stalk were also affected by temperature and substratum. In contrast to the above characters, the presence of pseudocolumella and the character of capillitium were not affected by the environmental factors that were studied. It is obvious, therefore, that some sporangial characters are more stable than others. It is also important to note that whereas a certain character may be stable under different conditions in one species, the same character may be very variable in other species, thus rendering futile any attempt at generalization.

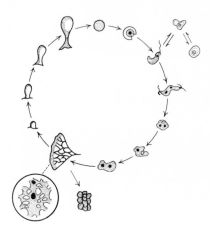

11

Laboratory Culture and Nutrition

Until comparatively recent times, most of the information relating to the laboratory cultivation and nutrition of Myxomycetes was obtained entirely by trial and error. In many instances, the primary objective was merely to be able to maintain a plasmodium in culture, and if a particular food material were found suitable, no attempt was made to determine what was in the substrate that made it an acceptable food for the plasmodium in question. The development of a precise method for culturing plasmodia of *Physarum polycephalum* under sterile conditions in liquid medium (Daniel and Rusch, 1961) has now opened the way for critical studies of the nutritive requirements of this species. However, for Myxomycetes in general there is still very little precise information in this area.

PLASMODIAL FEEDING

Almost as soon as the importance of the plasmodium in the myxomycete life cycle had been established, the ability of this free-living, protoplasmic, assimilative body to engulf and digest solid food was recognized. Earlier investigators observed bacteria, spores of fungi, myxamoebae, and other small particulates being engulfed by plasmodia, but no evidence that would indicate that plasmodia have the capability of utilizing food in solution was provided until Daniel and Rusch (1961) developed means of culturing *P. polycephalum* in pure culture in liquid medium in which all components were dissolved. Even now, this evidence applies to a few species only and is still open to question. With the discovery of Guttes and Guttes (1960) that *P. polycephalum* plasmodium can engulf droplets of liquid medium by pinocytosis, the question can again be raised as to whether or not plasmodia ever obtain their material requisites by means other than ingestion.

Because of the structure of the plasmodium, and in the face of our knowledge of plasma membranes, it seems highly improbable that ingestion would be the only means of obtaining nutrients and other requisites, but the fact remains that until now the absorption of nutrients through the slime layer and the plasma membrane of the plasmodium has not been demonstrated with certainty.

M. Ward (1884) reported that he had observed a form of *Didymium difforme* that was truly aquatic in that it has passed its entire life cycle under water. This observation has never been verified by other investigators, but Parker (1946) reported culturing three Myxomycetes "close to or identical with *Physarum gyrosum, Physarum nutans,* and *Fuligo cinerea*" submerged in water until the fruiting stages began. On this basis Parker refers to them as aquatic Myxomycetes—a term apparently not adopted by other investigators. Although, according to our own experience, the plasmodia of some members of the Physarales, including those of *P. gyrosum* and *F. cinerea,* can indeed be grown under water, they much prefer an exposed but moist substratum. On the other hand, most members of the Stemonitaceae and the Trichiaceae that have been cultured thrive in an aquatic environment and some seem to require it, at least in the early stages of plasmodial development (see page 89).

In their natural habitats, and because of the nature of these habitats, it is likely that plasmodia obtain most of their nutrients by the ingestion of solid food particles. Cienkowski (1863b) and deBary (1858, 1864, 1884) both observed such ingestion, and Lister (1888) showed that the plasmodia of *Badhamia utricularis* could live wholly on ingested pieces of basidiocarps of seven different Basidiomycetes. Howard and Currie (1932a, b) observed that plasmodia would destroy both sporophores of hymenomycetes and fungous mycelia and referred to this activity as parasitism; however, Cohen (1939) suggested that this might better be termed "preying." Neither Lister nor Howard and Currie made any attempt to eliminate bacterial contaminants, and hence it is impossible to know whether the sporophores were digested by plasmodia or by bacteria that probably were present.

Sobels (1950) attempted to obtain plasmodia of various species in pure culture, and from her studies concluded that some species are both parasitic and saprobic, and hence can be easily purified and maintained in pure culture. Others are parasitic, and when their plasmodia are purified, they always decline. If this view is correct, then there are both obligate and facultative parasites in the Myxomycetes just as there are in other classes of fungi. Čelakovský (1893) observed ingestion of egg white, starch, green algae, and vegetable cells, and Harshberger (1901) fed portions of four species of agarics, boiled egg white, and beefsteak to *Fuligo septica*. Various investigators have fed bacteria and other microorganisms to plasmodia as is evidenced by the reports of Henneberg (1901), Pinoy (1902, 1907), Vouk (1913a), Cohen (1939), and others. In fact, because of the difficulty encountered by various workers in their attempts to obtain plasmodia in axenic culture it has been a rather common practice to maintain cultures by feeding them bacterial or yeast cells of known organisms. For example, Pinoy (1902, 1907) successfully cultured *Didymium difforme* and *D. effusum* with a bacterium, *Bacillus luteus;* von Stosch (1935) cultured *D. nigripes* with a false yeast (*Torula* sp.), as well as molds, bacteria, and true yeast; and Cohen (1939) cultured plasmodia of several species with the wine yeast *Saccharomyces ellipsoideus.*

That plasmodia exercise a certain amount of selectivity in their feeding is evidenced by the first report on their mycophagy (Lister, 1888). The plasmodium of *Badhamia utricularis* ingested bits of basidiocarps of *Agaricus campestris, A. melleus, A. rubescens, A. fascicularis, Boletus flavus, Corticium puteanum, and Stereum hirsutum,* but of all these species *S. hirsutum* was utilized most readily. Again it must be emphasized that bacteria were probably present together with the fungi in all these cultures. Apparently encouraged by the fact that the plasmodium of *F. septica* engulfed bits of beefsteak, Harshberger offered it bits of butter but this material was not ingested. It is to be expected that plasmodia of different species would have different feeding habits, and this is exemplified by Howard's (1931a) observation that *P. polycephalum* would not engulf *Alternaria* spores, while Kambly (1939a) found that plasmodia of *P. bivalve* would. However, this difference in feeding habits is best shown by the failures encountered by many investigators in their attempts to successfully culture plasmodia of a wide variety of species other than *P. polycephalum* on rolled oats, using the moist chamber method developed by Camp (1936).

While Čelakovský had established much earlier that plasmodia would engulf green algae, Lazo (1961) performed some extremely interesting experiments in which pure cultures of green algae were fed to plasmodia of several species. He used ten different species of algae and found that only three species (*Chlorella protothecoides, C. xanthella,* and *C. ellipsoides*) were able to enter into full association with bacterium-free plasmodia of *Physarum didermoides* and *Fuligo cinerea.* Lazo did not claim that a true symbiotic relationship had been established, but he noted that plasmodium containing algae grew much better than plasmodium alone and was much more resistant to acidity.

Whereas it is beyond question that plasmodia engulf solid food particles, positive proof, as we have said, has not as yet been provided that food in solution may also enter through the plasma membrane. Such proof will be difficult to obtain, but unless the intake of droplets of liquid through pinocytosis can be demonstrated to be far more prevalent than present evidence would indicate, it can be assumed that food in solution can be utilized—at least by plasmodia cultured in liquid medium in which all components are dissolved.

LABORATORY CULTIVATION

As we shall see presently, about 10–15 per cent of the known species of Myxomycetes have been cultivated in the laboratory on artificial media from spore to spore. In the majority of cases, no attempt appears to have been made to exclude other organisms. In addition to the myxomycete, therefore, such crude cultures often contain bacteria, fungi, protozoa, and even nematodes. Nevertheless, it is usually true that if a myxomycete completes its life cycle from spore to spore in crude culture, it can be induced to do so in monoxenic culture with a known bacterium. Axenic cultures present an entirely different problem.

Plasmodia or sclerotia brought in from the field can be easily cultured either directly on the substratum on which they were found by placing it in a moist chamber, or on artificial media by placing on agar the material on which the plasmodium was found and allowing it to migrate onto the agar surface. For life-history studies, however, it is desirable to induce the organism to complete its life cycle from spore to spore on artificial media. This has proved extremely difficult with some species and impossible, up to now, with others. The authors, for example, have repeatedly attempted the cultivation from spores of various species of *Ceratiomyxa, Cribraria, Lycogala, Tubifera,* and *Trichia,* always with negative results, and it is probable that other researchers have had the same experience; yet seldom are such failures recorded in the literature, except, in passing, while discussing the successful cultivation of other species. It is possible that more successes might be encountered in this area if investigators would bear in mind that spore germination, zygote formation, and plasmodium formation are different and distinct processes, and that the set of conditions that is optimum for one process may not necessarily be optimum for the others.

Cultivation of Myxomycetes from spores was early recorded by Lister (1901) for *Badhamia utricularis.* Since then, a number of species have been cultivated by various investigators. It is not the purpose of this treatise to give a complete historical account of the laboratory culture of Myxomycetes, but rather to discuss the situation as it stands at present and to point out areas in which success might be expected and others in which failure is virtually certain with present methods.

For a review of the literature on laboratory culture of the Myxomycetes, the reader is referred to Martin (1940), Hawker (1952), and Alexopoulos (1963). The work of Howard (1931b) deserves special attention, since it represents the first instance in which a simple and sure method of culturing a myxomycete was devised. Much of the very fine and varied research that has been performed with *Physarum polycephalum* was made possible by Howard's work.

CRUDE CULTURES

Cultivation of Plasmodia

Unless otherwise noted, the following remarks apply to phaneroplasmodia only. Phaneroplasmodia found growing in the field or developed in moist chamber (Timnick, 1947) may be cultured and often induced to sporulate. Unfortunately, this does not guarantee that the organism can be cultivated from the spores so produced, viable though these may be.

Wood- or bark-bearing plasmodia should be placed in a plastic bag or other moisture-proof container and brought into the laboratory as soon as possible. Either of two methods may be used to cultivate the plasmodium.

Timnick's Method. A thin slice of the substratum with a portion of the plasmodium may be placed on Knop's agar (Timnick, 1947) or CM/2 agar [1] in a Petri dish, incubated at 20°–25° C, and allowed to spread on the agar. The substratum may then be removed and the plasmodium fed by sprinkling over it sterile, pulverized rolled oats. Agar blocks bearing vigorous plasmodium fans free of fungi may be cut and transferred to new Petri dishes to maintain or propagate the culture. Vigorous plasmodia of some species may be obtained by growing them on oat flake agar.[2]

Camp's Method. Absorbent paper (filter paper, toweling paper, and so on) is wrapped over the top or the bottom part of a Petri dish which is then placed in a large finger bowl (Camp, 1936). Enough water is poured into the container to keep the paper moist at all times through

---

[1] See Appendix.
[2] *Ibid.*

wick action. Material bearing a plasmodial fan or sclerotium is then placed on the paper, and a few, preferably sterile, oat flakes are arranged around the inoculum or pulverized flakes are sprinkled over the paper. The finger bowl is then covered with a glass plate or a second finger bowl, and the culture is allowed to develop. Oat flakes are added as needed and the old ones removed as they mold. Not infrequently those using this method for the first time have a tendency to overfeed. Hence, it should be borne in mind that better results may often be obtained if oat flakes are added sparingly. Whereas some species like *P. polycephalum* do well in moist chamber culture, there are many that will move about over the oats, but the plasmodium will not increase in size. Whether or not a species can be successfully cultured by this method can be determined only by trial.

Cultivation from Spores

Fewer than 15 per cent of the known species of Myxomycetes have been induced to complete their life cycles in crude agar culture from spore to spore. Table 21 lists 55 species the cultivation of which on

Table 21.   List of Myxomycetes cultivated in crude agar culture from spore to spore.   Names of species are those accepted by Martin and Alexopoulos (1969)

Physarales
  Physaraceae
    Badhamia utricularis (Lister, 1901)
    Badhamia gracilis (Alexopoulos, unpubl.)
    Fuligo cinerea (Collins, 1961)
    Fuligo septica (Scholes, 1962)
    Physarella oblonga (Gilbert, 1931)
    Cienkowskia reticulata (Therrien, unpubl.)
    Physarum aeneum (Aldrich, unpubl.)
    Physarum auriscalpium (Wollman, unpubl.)
    Physarum bilgramii (Henney, unpubl.)
    Physarum cinereum (von Stosch, 1935)
    Physarum compressum (Gray, 1938)
    Physarum didermoides (Gray, 1949)
    Physarum flavicomum (Gray, 1961)
    Physarum globuliferum (Henney, unpubl.)
    Physarum gyrosum (Koevenig, 1964)
    Physarum leucophaeum (Garjeanne, 1953)
    Physarum leucopus (Schünemann, 1930)
    Physarum melleum (Alexopoulos, unpubl.)
    Physarum nicaraguense (Solis, 1962)
    Physarum nucleatum (Alexopoulos, unpubl.)

---

* Sporulation was not obtained on agar but only when the plasmodia were transferred to moist, porous flower pots.

Table 21. Continued.

Physarum nudum (Rakoczy, 1962)
Physarum oblatum (Alexopoulos, unpubl.)
Physarum polycephalum (Howard, 1931a)
Physarum pusillum (Collins, *et al.*, 1964).
Physarum rigidum (Henney and Henney, 1968)
Physarum serpula (Indira, 1965)
Physarum tenerum (Gray, 1938)
Physarum vernum (Indira, 1965)
Didymiaceae
    Physarina echinospora (Alexopoulos and Blackwell, 1968)
    Diderma effusum (Constantineanu, 1907)
    Diderma hemisphaericum (Henney, unpubl.)
    Mucilago crustacea (Schure, 1949) °
    Didymium difforme (Lister, 1901)
    Didymium iridis (Cayley, 1929)
    Didymium nigripes (Skupienski, 1920)
    Didymium ovoideum (Taylor, unpubl.)
    Didymium squamulosum (Constantineanu, 1907)
    Didymium trachysporum (Henney, unpubl.)

Stemonitales
  Stemonitaceae
    Diachea splendens (Indira, 1965)
    Lamproderma scintillans (Alexopoulos, unpubl.)
    Clastoderma debaryanum (McManus, 1961b)
    Stemonitis flavogenita (Alexopoulos, 1959)
    Stemonitis fusca (McManus and Richmond, 1961)
    Stemonitis herbatica (Indira and Kalyanasundaram, 1963)
    Stemonitis hyperopta (Alexopoulos, unpubl.)
    Comatricha laxa (Wollman and Alexopoulos, 1964)
    Comatricha nodulifera (Wollman and Alexopoulos, 1968)
    Comatricha typhoides (Wollman, 1966)

Trichiales
  Dianemaceae
    Calomyxa metallica (Wollman, 1966)
  Trichiaceae
    Perichaena depressa (Wollman and Alexopoulos, 1964)
    Perichaena vermicularis (Ross, 1967b)
    Arcyria cinerea (Alexopoulos, 1960a)
    Arcyria denudata (Gilbert, 1929b)
    Metatrichia vesparium (Gray, 1938)

Liceales
  Liceaceae
    Licea biforis (Wollman and Alexopoulos, 1964)

Echinosteliales
  Echinosteliaceae
    Echinostelium cribrarioides (Alexopoulos, 1961)
    Echinostelium minutum (Alexopoulos, 1960b)

agar, starting with spores, has been described in the literature or has been accomplished in the authors' laboratories and has therefore been authenticated by at least one of them. An attempt has been made to cite the first report of the cultivation of a species from spores, but some references may have been missed. Some authors do not make clear whether the culture described originated from spores, and their work is not, therefore, cited in this connection.

It must be emphasized here that even with species that are relatively easy to cultivate, culture from spores is not always successful, and it may be necessary to try several times, using spores from different field collections, before success is achieved. What has been said about spore germination on pages 14–25 is pertinent here.

Criteria for Myxomycete Culture

Claims of having grown a myxomycete in culture from spores cannot be accepted as authentic unless spores are sown on sterile media, and fruiting bodies that closely resemble those from which spores were taken are produced. The mere appearance of a plasmodium in a culture does not constitute evidence that a particular species has been cultivated. Contaminant spores of easy-to-grow species frequently gain entrance to laboratory cultures and give rise to myxamoebal populations that produce plasmodia. There is no known way to identify a myxomycete from plasmodial characters alone.

Vouchers of fruiting bodies produced on artificial media should be deposited in well-known myxomycete collections. Such vouchers may be easily prepared by smearing a 22 × 40 mm cover-slip with white glue, placing on it a block of agar bearing mature, well-formed characteristic fruiting bodies, and allowing the preparation to stand until the agar dries. The cover-slip may then be glued in a box on which the following data should appear: (1) collecting data or herbarium number of original deigma [3] from which the spores were taken, (2) medium, (3) date of planting spores, (4) date of germination, (5) date of plasmodium formation, (6) date of fruiting, and (7) name of experimenter. Inasmuch as Myxomycetes in artificial culture often fruit on the side of the container, it is desirable to use 60 × 20 mm plastic Petri dishes for such cultures. If the fruiting bodies to serve as vouchers are produced on the sides of the dish, either the entire dish may be deposited as a voucher, or pieces on which the fruiting bodies are formed may be cut and glued in boxes. Plastic dishes are advantageous in that the agar usually does not adhere to them after it dries. Thus, cultures in which fruiting bodies

---

[3] A particular specimen consisting of one or more fruiting bodies bearing an identifying number by means of which it may be located by subsequent workers.

have been formed may be allowed to dry in the dish by removing the cover; the whole agar disk is then easily lifted out with a pair of forceps.

Spore-to-Spore Culture of Physarales

A number of physaraceous species can be cultured from spores with relative ease. The spores are spread on the surface of CM/2 agar, and the surface is flooded with a thin film of sterile distilled water. When a large population of myxamoebae has developed, the water is poured off, if it has not already dried. If a good bacterial population is present, nothing more need be done until plasmodia become evident under the microscope in from three to six days, at 20°–25° C, depending on the species. If the bacterial population is small, a milliliter of a suspension of *Escherichia coli, Aerobacter aerogenes,* or *Flavobacterium* sp. may be poured over the myxamoebae. When plasmodia have been formed, a small amount of sterile, pulverized oats should be sprinkled over the cultures.

When the plasmodia have grown to a large size they should be freed from fungi (see page 224), fed oats until they become vigorous, and then transferred to non-nutrient agar to fruit. With species such as *Fuligo cinerea, Didymium squamulosum, D. iridis, D. nigripes, Physarum pusillum,* and *P. didermoides* this appears to be sufficient. Usually they fruit easily. Yellow plasmodia, such as those of *P. polycephalum, P. flavicomum,* and *Physarella oblonga,* must be illuminated in order to sporulate (see Chapter 9).

Unfortunately, we do not know the factors that govern sporulation in most species. With *P. polycephalum* in pure culture a procedure has been worked out by Daniel and Rusch (see page 172). Aldrich (1966) was able to induce at will sporulation of fungus-free plasmodia of *P. flavicomum* by using the following method:

1. Grow a vigorous plasmodium and allow to migrate on oat-flake agar plates for a week.
2. Transfer 2–3-cm agar squares bearing plasmodium to standard size Petri dishes containing plain agar and incubate them in the dark for four hours or until the plasmodium has covered the agar surface.
3. Arrange plates under electric lights. Aldrich used 40-watt fluorescent tubes 6 inches from the plates and found that fruiting began 12 hours after the cultures were placed under the lights.

Sporangia developed in this way were typical of the species and contained viable spores. Unfortunately the results are not as predictable when this method is used for other species, such as *P. polycephalum* or *Didymium nigripes.*

Culture of Non-physaraceous Species

Whereas physaraceous species prefer a relatively dry medium, most non-physaraceous species require a film of water under which they develop their plasmodia (Alexopoulos, 1960a). Also, bark-extract agar appears to be more favorable than other types for the cultivation of the Stemonitaceae, the Liceaceae, and, to a lesser extent, the Trichiaceae (Wollman, 1966). At the University of Texas, we have used bark-extract–cornmeal agar [4] for the cultivation of non-physaraceous species with good results. Noble's agar also has proved to be excellent for some species.

After the sterile agar has solidified in the Petri dishes to be used, spores are spread on its surface and enough sterile distilled water is poured over the agar to form a thin film of liquid. If the small Petri dishes (60 × 20 mm) are used, 3 ml is sufficient. Three drops of a moderately heavy suspension of *Flavobacterium* are added. The cultures are incubated in the dark at 20° C. Sterile water is added to the cultures as needed to keep the agar surface constantly submerged.

When plasmodia are formed—this to be ascertained by examination under the compound microscope, as aphanoplasmodia are all but invisible to the unaided eye and very difficult to see under the stereomicroscope—sterile, pulverized, rolled oats are lightly sprinkled over the cultures. When the plasmodia have become vigorous, the cultures are transferred to a lighted incubator and water is withheld. This is a critical stage in the life of the cultures, and they should be examined rather frequently until fruiting begins. If the plasmodia have not reached the fruiting stage, they will often sclerotize as soon as the surface of the agar is permitted to dry. The film of water should then be restored as soon as possible. If the plasmodia continue to migrate on the dry surface and appear healthy, fruiting is about to take place and nothing more need be done. If the cultures are too wet at the time of fruiting, the fructifications will be aberrant.

Perichaena depressa and *Arcyria cinerea*, among the non-physaraceous species, will generally grow quite readily on various media, such as CM/2. The former species is quite tolerant of great variations in moisture at any stage of development after plasmodia have been formed. It thrives best on a moderately dry agar surface but will form perfect fruiting bodies even under water. In our experience, the young plasmodia of *A. cinerea* sclerotize very quickly if the agar surface dries, but once they become well established they will grow and spread on the agar even after the surface dries. Indira and Kalyanasundaram (1963) report having induced that organism to develop its entire life cycle on a dry

[4] See Appendix.

agar surface. We have been unable, in repeated attempts, to confirm their results.

Monoxenic Cultures

Monoxenic cultures of Myxomycetes starting from spores are relatively easy to obtain with species that produce large, actively migrating myxamoebae (Ross, 1964). The following procedure developed by Henney (1966) has been in use at the University of Texas for several years.

1. Prepare a spore suspension by crushing one or more sporangia in a sterile screw-cap tube containing 10 ml sterile distilled water, and shake vigorously to facilitate dispersal of spores.
2. Place three drops of the spore suspension near the edge of a standard-size Petri dish containing 3 per cent CM/2 and tilt plate, allowing the suspension to run in a straight line across the center of the dish. Incubate at 25° C.
3. Examine periodically for the formation of a myxamoebal population which should migrate away from the bacteria growing along the inoculation streak.
4. Using a stereomicroscope with a magnification of at least 90×, search the agar surface for places where the myxamoebae appear to be far from any bacterial colony and, using a flamed, fine entomological needle, cut out a small agar block bearing several myxamoebae.
5. Transfer to a Petri dish containing sterile CM/2 and add 0.5 ml of a suspension of *Escherichia coli*.
6. Cut five additional blocks all in the immediate vicinity of the first, and place one in each of five tubes containing the following media: [5]
   a. Nutrient broth
   b. Difco AC broth
   c. Yeast extract broth
   d. Thioglycolate broth
   e. Glucose broth
7. Incubate broth cultures at 25° C and examine for turbidity periodically. If bacterial growth develops in any of the media within 30 days, discard the cultures and repeat the entire procedure. If all five test media remain clear, it is safe to assume that a monoxenic culture has been established.
8. During the 30-day test period, the agar culture established (instruction 5) should be watched for formation of plasmodia and these fed with sterile, pulverized oats. The culture should at all times be protected from contamination. When fruiting occurs,

[5] See Appendix.

new monoxenic cultures may be started from the spores, always using the same bacterium. The culture should be tested periodically by streaking a loopful of myxamoebal/bacterial association or bits of the plasmodium formed on Eosin Methylene Blue agar. If bacterial colonies other than those of *E. coli* develop, the culture should be discarded.

AXENIC CULTURES

Purification of Phaneroplasmodia

Some plasmodia collected in nature or developed from sclerotia or from spores in culture may be purified and grown in axenic or monoxenic culture. Unfortunately, this is true of the plasmodia of certain species only. Usually a large, vigorous, rapidly migrating plasmodium can be purified much more easily than a small, weak, slow-moving one. This implies that not all plasmodia can be induced to grow to a large size. This, in the authors' experience, is true. The plasmodia of certain species, *Physarina echinospora,* for example, could not be induced to grow larger than 1–2 cm in diameter in a large number of attempts over a period of two years. The plasmodia either disintegrated or sporulated but never grew large.

Two methods have been found to be efficient in purifying plasmodia: migration and enrichment (Cohen, 1939). The first method, as employed at the University of Texas laboratory, is as follows:

1. Rid the plasmodium of fungi by allowing it to migrate on plain or CM/2 agar and transferring a fungus-free fan to oat-flake agar.
2. Grow the plasmodium on oat-flake agar until large, vigorous fans develop. Three to seven days are usually required for this step.
3. Transfer a block of agar, about 2 cm square and bearing a vigorous plasmodial fan, to 2 per cent agar containing 1,000,000 units potassium penicillin G and 1 gr streptomycin sulfate per 500 ml agar, and allow to migrate. Six hours is usually long enough for rapidly migrating plasmodia.
4. Transfer to oat-flake penicillin/streptomycin agar [6] as many times as necessary to purify.[7]

The first of these steps is sometimes very difficult to accomplish. Plasmodia of some species migrate too slowly to get away from the constantly growing fungal hyphae. Plasmodia of other species cannot be induced to leave a fungal colony once they have spread over it. As the fungus grows, the plasmodium remains on it at the periphery of the

---

[6] See Appendix.
[7] For criteria of axenism see p. 226.

colony, probably feeding on the hyphae, and must be watched constantly in the hope of finding a plasmodial lobe or fan protruding beyond the margin of the fungus colony so that it may be cut and transferred. This requires a steady hand and considerable skill in order not to transfer any part of the fungus.

The enrichment method as described by Cohen (1939) is as follows:

1. Washed agar plates [8] are streaked along a diameter for 5 cm with a suspension of *Saccharomyces ellipsoideus*.
2. A bit of plasmodium is placed at one end of the streak.
3. After reaching the end of the streak on which it migrates, the plasmodium is transferred to a second streak in another plate.
4. Small portions of the plasmodium are inoculated in the test media to test for presence of bacteria.
5. Bacterium-free plasmodia are then allowed to migrate over non-nutrient agar once or twice to free them from yeast.

Until 1963, axenic plasmodial cultures of 11 species had been reported in the literature (Alexopoulos, 1963) as follows: *Badhamia foliicola, B. utricularis, Physarum polycephalum, P. didermoides, P. gyrosum, Fuligo septica, F. cinerea, Didymium squamulosum, D. nigripes, Stemonitis axifera,* and *Licea variabilis.* Since that time Ross (1964) has reported axenic cultures of *Physarum flavicomum* and *Physarella oblonga,* and Henney and Henney (1968) of *Physarum rigidum.* It is important to emphasize, as Alexopoulos (1963) has pointed out, that many of the axenic cultures reported were maintained on killed bacteria or yeasts. To our knowledge, bacterium- and yeast-free cultures of myxomycete plasmodia have been maintained for a relatively long time only by Sobels (1950), Daniel and Rusch (1961), Lazo (1961), Ross (1964 and personal communication), H. Henney (personal communication) and in the laboratory of one of the authors (C.J.A.).

We have found that among several species, the plasmodial purification of which has been attempted in our laboratories, *Physarum polycephalum, P. flavicomum, P. gyrosum,* and *Physarella oblonga* are easiest to purify and to maintain in axenic culture. Plasmodia of many species are so weakened by the third or fourth transfer that they die unless fed bacteria. *Escherichia coli* serves well as food for such plasmodia, and a presumably monoxenic culture can be established. However, unless one is certain that the plasmodium is growing axenically before *E. coli* is added, he cannot be certain that he has indeed established a monoxenic culture. The literature abounds in claims of axenic and monoxenic cul-

---

[8] Plain agar washed for five days in frequent changes of distilled water, squeezed dry in cheesecloth and used to prepare 2 per cent agar. Difco Noble's agar is essentially prepared in this way. It is used exclusively at the University of Texas for this purpose.

tures which, when critically examined, fall short of presenting absolute proof of the claimed status.

Because most aphanoplasmodia, in the authors' experience, require a liquid environment while they are growing and are apt to sclerotize if allowed to stand for any length of time on a dry agar surface, their purification is extremely difficult. Except for Cohen's (1939) claim for *Stemonitis axifera*, plasmodia of no stemonitaceous species have been obtained in axenic culture. Parenthetically it may be said that relatively few of the Stemonitales have been grown in culture under any conditions (Table 21).

Criteria of Axenism

Skupienski (1928) was the first to claim he had obtained axenic cultures of Myxomycetes. He sowed spores from four-year-old sporangia of *Didymium difforme* and obtained feeble plasmodia which could not be induced to fruit unless grown with bacteria or molds. He assumed that the bacteria normally carried on spores had died when he initiated the cultures. In view of the experience of subsequent investigators with other species (Parker, 1946; Alexopoulos, 1963), Skupienski's claim of axenic cultures cannot be accepted unequivocally. Dangeard (1947) claimed to have purified the plasmodia of *Didymium clavus*, but he offered no proof of the absence of bacteria in his cultures.

It was Cohen who in 1939 first subjected myxomycete cultures to critical tests that failed to reveal the presence of bacterial contaminants and proposed the following two criteria that must be met before the axenism of a culture is accepted:

1. There must be no growth of micro-organisms in nutrient media inoculated from the cultures. The media should include at least one comparable in composition with the media used for pure culture of plasmodia, of approximately the same pH, and incubated at the same temperature for a sufficiently long time.
2. The cultures must be carried through several transfers without decline in vigor, and strictly should grow indefinitely on the pure culture media without a permanent loss of vigor.

Daniel and Baldwin (1964) are of the opinion that plasmodia should be tested for the presence of organisms under a wide range of temperature, pH, aeration conditions, and types of media, and that they must be examined with the light and the electron microscope for the presence of bacterial cells.

Although it cannot be denied that very strict criteria of axenism are desirable, it is also true that one may carry on tests *ad absurdum* without ever being able to prove a negative proposition, *i.e.*, the complete absence of all bacterial cells from a culture. We believe, therefore, that if five carefully selected liquid media of varied composition are inoculated with the presumed axenic culture and remain bacterium-free, as evidenced by absence of turbidity for 30 days, any organisms that may be present are of a kind that will not multiply under conditions favorable for the myxomycete and their presence is, therefore, unlikely to influence experimental results.

We propose, therefore, that the media listed on page 223 be established as the test media, and that the cultures be incubated at 25° C for a month. An added precaution might be adopted by incubating a second set of cultures at 37° C. If on the thirtieth day the test cultures are as limpid as a similarly incubated set of uninoculated controls, it would be safe to assume that axenic culture has been accomplished.

Axenic Cultures from Spores

It is probable that many of the species that have been cultivated in monoxenic culture, as described in a previous section, may also be cultivated in axenic culture with dead bacterial or yeast cells, but this has not been reported in the literature. The only published reports of spore-to-spore axenic culture in the absence of living or dead bacterial cells are those of Daniel and Baldwin (1964) and Daniel (personal communication) for *Physarum polycephalum* and those of Ross and Sunshine (1965) for *Physarum flavicomum*. Purified plasmodia were induced to sporulate in axenic culture. The spores so produced germinated and yielded amoebae which developed into plasmodia without, however, multiplying to form a myxamoebal population. According to Ross and Sunshine, such "plasmodia may be subsequently cultured to complete the life cycle in pure culture." The medium on which *P. flavicomum* spores germinated would not support plasmodial growth, and on none of the media tried did the amoebae multiply.

Kerr (1963) and later Schuster (1964b) reported success in cultivating amoebae of *Didymium nigripes* (Kerr's strain), the first with formalin-killed bacteria, the second with heat-killed bacteria. Kerr does not state whether his myxamoebal cultures formed plasmodia. Schuster reports that his cultures remained in the myxamoebal stage throughout. With *Physarum cinereum*, however, Schuster reports success in obtaining plasmodia from myxamoebae grown on heat-killed bacteria. The plasmodia did not sporulate. Axenic cultures of myxamoebae, in the absence of bacterial cells, was achieved by Ross (1964) as stated in Chapter 3. These gave rise to minute plasmodia only when subjected to centrifugation, but the plasmodia thus formed did not grow further.

MAINTENANCE AND STORAGE OF CULTURES

The following remarks about clonal and plasmodial cultures apply to species in the order Physarales. We have had no experience in storing cultures of species in other orders, and there appears to be no literature on the subject.

Clonal Cultures

Myxamoebal clones may be stored on CM/2 agar slants, with a few milliliters bacterial suspension, in screw-cap or cotton-plugged tubes at 10°–15° C. Such clones have been stored, with occasional transferring, for at least three years in one of our laboratories. More frequent transferring maintains the clones in greater vigor but increases the danger of contamination. For longer storage that will insure maintenance of the genotype, lyophilization or liquid-nitrogen storage is recommended (Davis, 1965). Genetic stocks should be deposited in the American Type Culture Collection or another internationally known organization.

Plasmodial Cultures

Plasmodia in monoxenic or, in some instances, axenic culture may be maintained for many years on oatmeal agar in Petri dishes or flasks at 10°–15° C in the dark. They should be transferred once a month to maintain them in vigorous condition. Axenic cultures that have a tendency to deteriorate under these conditions may have to be grown at intervals with a bacterial associate to reinvigorate them and then re-purified.

Plasmodia may also be induced to sclerotize according to the method of Lonert (1965) where applicable (see page 152), or that of Hemphill, described by Daniel and Baldwin (1964). The sclerotia may then be stored at 10°–15° C for one or two years, often longer, and placed on moist agar to reconstitute the plasmodia when desired.

Spores

Spores are usually stored dry in the sporangia in which they were formed. If these were collected in the field, some insecticide, such as paradichlorobenzene (PDB), should be kept in the herbarium case or drawer in which the specimens are stored; otherwise insects and mites will destroy them. It should be borne in mind, however, that the effect of PDB fumes on the viability of the spores has not been determined. Also, in spite of what was said in Chapter 2 about longevity of myxomycete spores, in our own experience spores stored in a herbarium for more than three or four years are often extremely difficult or impossible to germinate. Spores may also be lyophilized. Kerr (1965b) reports the successful storage for more than five years of myxomycete spores which he lyophilized by a rather simple method he describes.

NUTRITION

Early investigators (Skupienski, 1928; Pinoy, 1903) believed that a symbiosis exists between myxomycete plasmodia and certain kinds of bacteria, but there is no evidence that this is true. Nor is there any evidence that some bacteria are better than others for the nutrition of a plasmodium, although admittedly very little work has been done with undoubted monoxenic cultures utilizing various types of bacteria. Indeed, it would be desirable to establish monoxenic and polyxenic cultures with known bacteria and on different substrata to determine this point. Such knowledge would be very useful in experimental work until we discover how to induce Myxomycetes to complete their entire life cycle from spore to spore in axenic culture on chemically defined media.

For culturing Myxomycetes with bacteria, cornmeal agar and Knop's agar remain the best of the various media that have been employed for carrying the organism through from spore to spore. Oat flakes or oat-flake agar appear to be best for growing plasmodia to a vigorous state, but not for fruiting. A rich, oatmeal-agar medium tends to produce bizarre and aberrant fructifications as compared to a weaker medium.

Various other media have been employed with good results. Notable among these is the SM/5 medium [9] on which Kerr and Sussman (1958) grew *Didymium nigripes* (Kerr's strain) with *Aerobacter aerogenes*. In general, it may be said that any medium that will support a moderate growth of bacteria is fairly satisfactory for growing a number of physaraceous species. Much less is known about species belonging to other orders, and there are indications that at least some of those that have been grown in culture have special nutrient requirements which many media cannot supply, in spite of the fact that they support bacterial growth.

In their first report of the pure culture of *P. polycephalum*, in a partially defined soluble medium, Daniel and Rusch (1961) found that growth occurred only in the presence of an unknown growth factor which is present in chick-embryo extract, foetal-calf serum, and foetal-calf-erythrocyte haemolysate. Further analysis of the chick-embryo extract requirement of the plasmodium showed that it could be met with hematin or by certain hemo-proteins (Kelley, *et al.*, 1960; Daniel, *et al.*, 1962). Thus, *P. polycephalum* was shown to have an absolute requirement for hematin. In a subsequent paper, Daniel, *et al.* (1963) reported that they

[9] See Appendix.

Table 22. Composition of synthetic media A, AV-40, and OV-40.
(Daniel, et al., 1963.)

Component I	Conc (mg/liter)	Component II	Conc (mg/liter)	Component III	Conc (mg/liter)
Citric acid·H_2O	2,850	Inositol	11.9	DL-*Methionine*	252
Glucose	10,250	Choline hydrochloride	8.57	*Glycine*	454
NH_4Cl	2,020	*Biotin*	0.158†	L-*Arginine hydrochloride*	605
KH_2PO_4	656	*Thiamine hydrochloride*	0.424†	L-Cysteine hydrochloride·H_2O	502
K_2HPO_4·$3H_2O$	875	Pyridoxal hydrochloride	60.9	L-Histidine hydrochloride·H_2O	268
$FeCl_3$·$4H_2O$	46.5	Pyridoxine hydrochloride	8.72	L-Leucine	524
$MnCl$·$4H_2O$	65	Niacin	4.22	L-Lysine hydrochloride	630
$ZnSO_4$·$7H_2O$	33.6	Calcium pantothenate	4.5	DL-*Isoleucine*	348
Na_2SO_4	300	p-Aminobenzoic acid	0.816	DL-*Phenylalanine*	434
$CuCl_2$·$2H_2O$	2.56	Folic acid	0.407	DL-*Tryptophan*	177
$CoCl_2$·$6H_2O$	0.36	Vitamin B_{12}	0.0049	DL-*Serine*	470
$MgSO_4$·$7H_2O$	232	Riboflavine	4.36	DL-*Threonine*	376
$CaCl_2$·$2H_2O$	933			DL-*Valine*	432
				(DL-Alanine) ‡	2,437

* Columns I and II comprise the constituents for the 4× Basal for medium A. Column I comprises the constituents of the 4× Basal for media AV-40 and OV-40. Only the italicized vitamins (column II) are used in the AV-40 and OV-40 media. Column III gives the amino acid composition of the A and AV-40 media. Only the italicized amino acids (column III) appear in the OV-40 medium.

† For AV-40 and OV-40 media; × 100 for A medium.

‡ DL-Alanine appears only in the OV-40 medium.

Table 23.   Volumes of stock solutions used to prepare media.
(Daniel, et al., 1963.)

Medium	4 × Basal with Vitamins (ml)	4 × Basal no Vitamins (ml)	Thiamine (ml)	Biotin (ml)	Amino Acids (ml)	Water (ml)
A	252	—	—	—	260	581
AV-40	—	252	20	20	260	541
OV-40	—	252	20	20	120	680

were able to culture *P. polycephalum* in a chemically defined medium. In this later work, this same species was also shown to have absolute requirements for biotin, thiamine, and either D- or L-methionine. The composition of stock solutions utilized in the preparation of three media by Daniel and his coworkers are presented in Table 22; volumes of the stock solutions used to prepare media A, AV-40, and OV-40 are listed in Table 23. For exact details of the preparation of these media, the reader should consult the original research report, and the excellent review of Rusch (1968).

Thus, specific growth requirements of the plasmodium are known only for *Physarum polycephalum*.[10]   The organism is either kept in continuous culture or permitted to sclerotize on sterile filter paper, and new cultures are begun from sclerotial fragments.

It must be noted here that although these media support plasmodial growth they apparently cannot be utilized to culture the myxamoebae. Thus, the multiplication of the myxamoebae is dependent on nutritional factors or other conditions as yet unknown. As mentioned in Chapter 9, the sporulation medium for *P. polycephalum* differs from the growth medium in several respects, notable among which is the necessity for niacin, niacinamide, or tryptophan in the former.

The results obtained by Rusch and his coworkers, which demonstrated that *P. polycephalum* has four biosynthetic deficiencies, are highly suggestive. It seems quite possible that many of the failures encountered by various investigators in their attempts to culture other species may have been due to a lack of knowledge concerning the inability of the species to synthesize one or more of the organic compounds that they require. Similar work on other species obviously is necessary, but again it should be remembered that establishment of the optimum chemical and physical factors for growth of a plasmodium may not necessarily mean that these conditions will be optimum for spore germination, plasmodial formation, and sporulation.

[10] H. Henney and his co-workers (personal communication) now have a chemically defined liquid medium on which the plasmodia of *P. flavicomum* and *P. rigidum* grow vigorously.

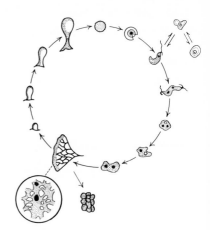

12

Geographic Distribution
and Ecology

It is axiomatic that the known distribution of many groups of organisms coincides with the distribution and/or the interests of the biologists who hunt them! Thus, it is understandable that we know very much more about the Myxomycetes of New York, Iowa, and Colorado than we do of any other part of the United States because of the field work in those areas of Hagelstein, Macbride and Martin, and Sturgis, respectively, over a large number of years; that we have a good knowledge of the slime molds of the Jura Mountains in Switzerland and the Carpathians of Rumania because of Meylan's collecting in the former and Brandza's in the latter; but that we have no knowledge of the Myxomycetes of the Albanian mountains; that we are well acquainted with the Myxomycetes of Japan which have been studied by Emoto, Hattori, and others, but very little with those of Thailand or Burma. So it is also with our knowledge of the ecology of these organisms. In spite of the fact that field collections of Myxomycetes have been made by dozens of naturalists in many parts of the world for more than a century, there is surprisingly little knowledge concerning the ecology of these organisms. The little there is has been gleaned for the most part from the collecting data recorded rather than from systematic, ecologically oriented studies. Thus, experience has taught us that certain species are partial to certain substrates; that a few well-known species are strictly tropical and that a few are confined to the temperate zones; that some are predominantly alpine; that some fruit early in the season and others not until later—but for none do we have sufficient data to enable us to reach definite conclusions regarding the factors that govern its fruiting habits and its geographical distribution.

Are the tropical species absent from the temperate zones because of winter temperatures, or are there other factors that confine them to the tropics? Do the alpine species, which fruit at the edge of or under the melting snows, require a prolonged period of exposure to low temperatures? Are they perhaps unable to endure the summer heat of lower altitudes? Is it ultraviolet light that is important? Why do certain species fruit usually on dead leaves, others usually on dead wood, still others preferably on bark, whereas a great many seem to be widely tolerant and independent of the substratum? Inasmuch as the spores of most species are airborne they are presumably present on most substrata in the field. Is the distribution of the fruiting bodies governed by conditions that favor spore germination, plasmodial formation, or sporulation? These are questions for which as yet we have no answers.

GEOGRAPHIC DISTRIBUTION

Cosmopolitan Species

It is perhaps safe to say that the majority of Myxomycetes are worldwide in their distribution. Of the 425 or so known species, about one-third have been found in so many widely scattered localities that they are unhesitatingly classed as cosmopolitan by monographers. Many of these are extremely common. There are few published lists of Myxomycetes, regardless of the region they treat, that do not include *Ceratiomyxa fruticulosa, Lycogala epidendrum, Dictydium cancellatum, Metatrichia vesparium, Hemitrichia stipitata, Fuligo septica, Physarum nutans, P. viride, Didymium squamulosum, D. nigripes, D. iridis, Arcyria cinerea, A. denudata, Stemonitis fusca, Comatricha typhoides,* and many others.

Another 50 or more species have been found frequently enough in many scattered localities to make it highly probable that they are also cosmopolitan in their distribution. For one reason or another, however, they are not as plentiful in all regions as those in the first group and are therefore less often encountered. This group includes, among others, *Lycogala conicum, Arcyria ferruginea, A. oerstedtii, Trichia botrytis, T. floriformis, T. verrucosa, Stemonitis flavogenita, S. smithii, Badhamia macrocarpa, B. obovata, Physarum aeneum, P. flavicomum, P. leucophaeum,* and so on.

A third group comprises some species that have been encountered rarely but which appear to be widely distributed. Because of the minute size of their fructifications, they are easily overlooked in the field, but many of them can be detected by the moist chamber technique of Gilbert and Martin (1933). This consists of collecting bark from living trees (or, by extension of this method, of plant debris such as dead leaves, twigs, etc.); placing it on a sterile filter paper disk in a sterile Petri dish; pouring sterile distilled water over the material; and allowing the material to soak overnight. The water is then poured off and the cultures incubated in the light for a week or more. Species which may be expected to develop include *Licea biforis, L. pedicellata, L. operculata, Echinostelium minutum, Comatricha fimbriata, C. laxa, Macbrideola decapillata, Clastoderma debaryanum,* and many other minute species as well as some more common ones as *Arcyria cinerea* and *Perichaena chrysosperma.*

Temperate Zone Species

Whether some species are strictly confined to the temperate zones, as it appears presently, is a question that cannot be answered until the tropics are much more thoroughly explored for Myxomycetes. There are, of course, many species that have not as yet been reported from the tropics and some that have been reported from tropical regions because of misidentification. *Hemitrichia clavata* is a case in point. This name appears in tropical lists of Myxomycetes now and then, but tropical collections so named have invariably proved to be *H. stipitata* after careful study. To be sure, the two species resemble one another closely, and some authors (Hagelstein, 1944) do not recognize them as distinct, but the sporangium-stalk relationship, the chief distinguishing feature, is clear in most collections and, whereas both *H. clavata* and *H. stipitata* are common in temperate climates, only the latter species seems to be present in the tropics.

Tropical Species

A few species of Myxomycetes seem to be predominantly tropical but are occasionally found in temperate regions. *Physarum bogoriense,* for example, is abundant in the tropics, less so in the warmer regions of the temperate zone, and relatively rare but present in some colder climates. The same may be said of *P. pezizoideum.* A few species have been found only in tropical and subtropical areas. *Craterium paraguayense, Perichaena microspora, Physarum javanicum, P. nicaraguense, P. rigidum,* and *Didymium leoninum* are examples. Six of the well-known species are strictly tropical: *Ceratiomyxa morchella, Tubifera bombarda,*

Arcyria virescens, Physarina echinocephala, Physarum echinosporum, and *Diderma subdictyospermum. Ceratiomyxa sphaerosperma* could be added to this list were it not for one report of its occurrence in Spain.

Far Eastern Species

Six of the better known species seem to be confined to the Far East. These are: *Arcyria glauca, A. virescens, Erionema aureum, Craterium rubronodum, Physarina echinocephala,* and *Didymium leoninum.* However, *A. virescens* and *E. aureum* are included by Parris (1940) in his list of Myxomycetes from Hawaii.

Rare Species

A few undoubtedly good species appear to be truly rare. Among them are such distinctive forms as *Listerella paradoxa,* known only from North Germany, the British Isles, and Sweden; *Dianema harveyi* and *Elaeomyxa cerifera,* both rarely collected; *Barbeyella minutissima*—which, however, may have been missed because of its size—known from Switzerland, Poland, Sweden, Japan, and Oregon; *Physarina echinocephala* which has been collected only two or three times known only from Java and Thailand; and *P. echinospora* known only from India and Mexico.

The above discussion on geographic distribution is based only on well-known species that have been found more than once and—except for *Physarina echinocephala*—in more than one area. The lists could be augmented somewhat in each category if species known only from their type collections were included, but it was felt that not enough is known about such species to enable us to categorize them. Some of these species are possibly rare; others may simply be variations of well-known species that will eventually be properly placed where they belong.

ECOLOGY

Martin (1940) and Alexopoulos (1963) have summarized what little knowledge we have concerning the ecology of the Myxomycetes. Little has been added since these reviews were published, and there is complete lack of experimental data to substantiate general conclusions that have been drawn from field observations.

Moisture and availability of decaying plant material are two important requirements for the completion of the life cycle of Myxomycetes and therefore affect the distribution and abundance of fruiting bodies in nature. As Smith (1931) pointed out, however, adequate rainfall by itself does not necessarily furnish the right conditions for the growth and fruiting of these organisms. What is required is a continuous supply of moisture over a period of time sufficient to enable the slime molds to complete their life cycles. In addition, an optimum range of temperature must prevail during the periods in which adequate moisture is available.

Seasonal Distribution

Temperature and moisture seem to be the primary factors that affect seasonal distribution of Myxomycetes in general. In the northern United States, for example, in years with adequate rainfall, June, July, and August are the most favorable months for collecting Myxomycetes; in central Texas, spring and fall are usually better for field collecting in an average year; whereas in Jamaica year-round collecting is possible and profitable. But even during the relatively short fruiting season in the north, there is a noticeable difference in the species that appear at the beginning of the season and those that appear later on. *Ceratiomyxa fruticulosa* and *Lycogala epidendrum* are almost invariably the first species to appear in the spring, whereas *Physarella oblonga*, for example, is rarely encountered before the middle of July. The factors that determine such limited seasonal fruiting are unknown.

Of interest in this connection is Farr's (1957b) summary of her collections in Jamaica from January 1954 through April 1955, which indicates that myxomycete fruiting bodies were found throughout the year. Farr also summarizes the monthly distribution of her collections by species without claiming that this summary is of any ecological significance. Indeed, the experience of one of us (C. J. A.) indicates that some of Farr's seasonal records could be augmented considerably. Alexopoulos (unpublished), collecting in January 1966 on the island, found, among other species, *Ceratiomyxa sphaerosperma, Lycogala epidendrum, Physarum bogoriense, Didymium squamulosum,* and *Dictydium cancellatum* which Farr had collected during June to July, April to October, June, April, and May to October respectively.

The seasonal distribution of Myxomycetes in the Swietokrzyskie Mountains, in the Western Carpathians, and in Lower Silesia was summarized by Krzemieniewska (1957) for 1955–56. Most species fruit most abundantly in July and August. There are, however, some that begin fruiting in August or September and reach their climax in October. These are: *Cribraria rufa, Trichia pusilla, T. scabra,* and *T. varia.*

Although of considerable interest, seasonal distribution records are of little value unless they are correlated with data on environmental factors operating at the time and place the Myxomycetes are fruiting. Such data are completely lacking.

Habitat and Substratum

The first comprehensive discussion of myxomycete habitats was presented by Gulielma Lister (1918) who brought together the information available up to that time on the ecology of the Myxomycetes. Lister lists a large number of species that she found or that others had reported on various substrata in several types of habitats, and generalizes on the occurrence of these organisms in nature.

Field observations by various collectors indicate that some species show a decided preference for certain types of substrata for sporulation. It is well known, for example, that many of the Cribrarias and *Dictydium cancellatum* are much more common on coniferous wood than on other substrata. A notable exception is *C. laxa* which almost always fruits on leaves and may be tentatively identified in the field by its fruiting habit alone. The Diacheas almost always fruit on leaves and forest debris; they are seldom found on rotting wood or on the bark of decaying logs where so many other species abound. The list of leaf-inhabiting species is considerable and includes, besides the Diacheas, *Craterium aureum*, *C. paraguayense*, *Physarum bivalve*, *P. braunianum*, *P. cinereum*, *P. luteolum*, *Didymium megalosporum*, *D. nigripes*, *D. serpula*, and many others.

In contrast, there are many species that are rarely found on leaves but almost always fruit on wood or bark. Examples are the Enerthenemas, most species of *Stemonitis*, *Physarum tenerum*, and *P. viride*, the Lycogalas, and, as mentioned above, the Cribrarias.

A number of species seem to be associated with bryophytes. *Elaeomyxa cerifera*, *Barbeyella minutissima*, *Comatricha caespitosa*, *Physarum diderma*, *Diderma sauteri*, *D. ochraceum* and *Lepidoderma tigrinum* are among them.

None of these associations is, of course, absolute, but they are too frequent to be attributed to chance. Of interest is a note by Buchet (1939) reporting that he collected *Physarum pezizoideum* on *Auricularia mesenterica* and recalling that at least five other collections, including the type collection in Java, have also been found in association with jelly fungi. He believes that such an association is more than accidental. Nevertheless, the literature and the herbaria reveal many fruitings of *P. pezizoideum* on other substrata, such as dead wood, leaves, and litter.

From her studies of the Myxomycetes of the Swietokrzyskie Mountains, referred to before, Krzemieniewska (1957) drew the following conclusions with reference to the relationship of substratum and the fruiting of Myxomycetes:

1. Most species are independent of the substratum on which they fruit. Among species that show "remarkable ability of adaptation" in this respect are *Physarum bivalve, P. virescens, Leocarpus fragilis, Diachea leucopodia, Mucilago spongiosa,* and *Didymium melanospermum.*
2. Among species that fruit most often on wood from broadleaved trees rather than on conifer wood are *Fuligo rufa, Physarum psittacinum, Comatricha typhoides, Lycogala conicum, Arcyria ferruginea, A. denudata, Trichia persimilis, T. scabra,* and *Metatrichia vesparium.*
3. *Cribraria* and *Dictydium* are more often found on conifer wood.

In the main, these conclusions substantiate those of other workers, except for that concerning *Diachea leucopodia* which is usually considered to fruit on dead leaves and litter rather than on wood or bark.

A number of myxomycete species appear to be decidedly coprophilous. Those known only from dung are *Licea fimicola, L. scintillans* and *Comatricha mirabilis.* Others that often develop on dung but which are also known from other substrata include *Licea tenera, Echinostelium minutum, Perichaena corticalis, Arcyria cinerea, A. leiocarpa, Lamproderma scintillans, Badhamia ovispora, Fuligo cinerea, Diderma effusum, Didymium difforme, D. iridis, D. ochroideum, D. squamulosum,* and *D. trachysporum.*

Myxomycetes in the Soil

The fruiting of Myxomycetes on forest litter (many species), on lawns (*Physarum cinereum*), and on the soil itself (*Fuligo septica*) indicates that myxomycete spores and possibly myxamoebae may form a significant part of the soil biota. Krzemieniewska (1929, 1933) and Krzemieniewska and Badura (1954) isolated nine species from the soil or litter of a beech forest of Muszkowice in Poland; Thom and Raper (1930) found two species in their cultures of soil and litter; and Warcup (1950) reported myxomycete plasmodia developing in his plates when soil was dispersed in Chapek-Dox agar with 0.5 per cent yeast extract acidified with phosphoric acid to pH 4.0. In our own experience, forest litter placed in moist chamber or directly on CM/2 in plates often yields fructifications of various species, such as *Perichaena corticalis, Clastoderma debaryanum,* and *Didymium iridis.* The discovery of *Physarina echinospora* for the first time in the western hemisphere, which constitutes the second world "collection," came about in this way (Alexopoulos and Blackwell, 1968).

Calcareous Species

Some attention has been given to the distribution of calcareous versus non-calcareous species, and some authors (R. E. Fries, 1903) have concluded that the calcareous species predominate in the tropics. As Martin (1940), however, points out, there are many tropical collections in which the opposite is true, and the deciding factor in such distribution cannot be climatic. Macbride (1914) wrote that the Colorado mountains are remarkable for their wealth of calcareous species which are scare in the mountains around Puget Sound, and that the latter are rich in non-calcareous forms such as Trichias and Lamprodermas. Jarocki (1931), investigating the Myxomycetes of the Czarnohora Mountains in the Polish Eastern Carpathians, also remarks on the relative scarcity of calcareous species and attributes this to the low calcium content of the Flysh strata forming those mountains, which consist chiefly of sandstone. Carr (1939a) compared the species in a sandstone region and a limestone region in August County, Virginia, and he found that "lime loving genera are abundant in limestone regions, while in others they are lacking or are not prolific over wide areas." Conversely, non-calcareous species "appear in abundance in localities where lime content of the soil is low."

Alpine and Subalpine Species

The preponderance of certain species in alpine environments poses another question concerning factors that affect distribution. Relatively few collectors have worked extensively in mountain areas, and many of the predominantly alpine species that are considered rare may be cosmopolitan and common in the proper environment. Brandza, Meylan, Karsen, and Jarocki in Europe; Sturgis, Bethel, and Macbride in the United States have collected Myxomycetes in alpine regions and have included them in their published lists.

Karsen (1943) collecting Myxomycetes in Norway, recorded the following species to be alpine or subalpine: *Trichia alpina, Lamproderma carestiae, L. cribrarioides, L. sauteri, Diderma alpinum, D. niveum,* and *Lepidoderma granuliferum.* To these may be added *Dianema nivale, Hemitrichia montana, Enerthenema melanospermum, Lamproderma gulielmae, L. robustum, Comatricha suksdorfii, Physarum alpinum, P. auripigmentum, Diderma lyallii, Didymium quitense,* and *Lepidoderma carestianum.* Some of these, to be sure, have occasionally been found at lower altitudes (Ing, 1968), but in general they all seem to be much more common in mountainous regions.

Meylan (1908–1937), who collected extensively in the Jura Mountains of Switzerland, described many new species, varieties, and forms of *Lamproderma* from that area. Although many of his new taxa have not been accepted by monographers, they do, nevertheless, indicate the variability of the genus as it occurs in the Jura Mountains. Of particular interest, therefore, is Kowalski's experience with *Lamproderma* in the montane regions of California where the genus is also abundant. In less than two years, Kowalski (personal communication, 1967) has made over 500 collections of *Lamproderma,* many of which exhibit exceptional intraspecific variations. Kowalski reports that the only Lamprodermas he has found in lowland areas are *L. scintillans* and *L. muscorum.* Macbride (1914), on the other hand, collecting around Puget Sound commented on the abundance of "lamprodermas at sea level and comatrichas on the mountains." [1] Strangely enough, Jarocki (1931) found no alpine forms of what Meylan has called *"espèces nivales"* in the Eastern Carpathians of Poland. As Martin (1940) states, this is a rather specialized group of species which fruit near the edge of the snow banks as the snow melts. Jarocki made a special search for these forms but found none, possibly because he was not collecting at the right season, i.e., in the spring. Kowalski reports that these species abound above 4000 feet in California. He believes they fruit under the snow rather than at the edge of the snow banks (Kowalski, 1967).

Miscellaneous Ecological Studies

A few papers have been published that purport to be ecological studies on Myxomycetes, but most are not extensive enough to warrant serious conclusions. These are reviewed by Alexopoulos (1963), and the reader is referred to that paper for further details.

As has already been noted, there are few data available from experimental ecology either in a natural or a controlled environment, and this field of investigation, which richly deserves attention, awaits the researcher with a fresh approach to solve the enigma of species distribution.

---

[1] This may have been an inadvertent error in writing as Lamprodermas are well known for their abundance in mountainous regions.

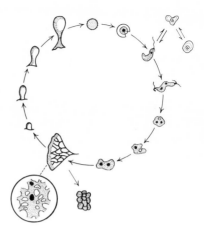

13

Conclusions—
Future Directions

From the foregoing chapters it is quite evident that not only has there been a tremendous upsurge of interest in the Myxomycetes since the popular review of Fry and Fry (1899), but also that a very great amount of information concerning these anomalous organisms has been amassed. Nonetheless, all of the questions have not been answered.

As is usual when the biology of an organism is probed deeply, when a question is answered at least one still more perplexing question rises in its stead. For example, if it is proved beyond question that the streaming of the protoplasm is due to the transformation of the chemical energy of ATP into mechanical work through a contractile protein fibrillar system, there still remains the more perplexing question concerning the nature of the coordinating mechanism by which streaming in different directions in different parts of a plasmodium is prevented from pulling the plasmodium apart or causing it to flow into a single large heap.

The Myxomycetes are a fairly homogenous group of organisms which appear to have no close living relatives, unless they be the Protostelida which Olive (1967) suggests may represent an ancestral line. In the past, the Myxomycetes have not uncommonly been considered to be related to the Plasmodiophorales, but unless much more evidence is produced to support this view, we must at present consider them to have had a different origin. Whether or not the Myxomycetes are fungi can still be debated; however, at the present state of our knowledge it seems advisable to follow tradition and include them in the Mycota.

The general taxonomy of the Myxomycetes is in a presently usable state, although the situation can by no means be described as perfect. The artificial system presently in use is workable and will probably be adequate until such time as it becomes possible to culture the majority of the presently recognized species under controlled conditions in the laboratory. It does not, however, always reflect relationships. Sufficient collections have been made to provide us with a reasonable concept of the variations that occur in a great many species, but the complete range of variations, and knowledge concerning the specific set of environmental conditions that result in a specific variation can be obtained only by studying each species under carefully controlled conditions.

The development of methods for the artificial cultivation of a great number of species under controlled conditions constitutes the major problem of myxomycete study today. Although several species may be readily grown in crude culture, and obtaining two-membered (myxomycete plasmodium and bacterium or yeast) cultures is not difficult, pure cultures have not been easily obtainable. Even though Cohen obtained pure cultures nearly thirty years ago, and though Rusch and his associates have succeeded in growing plasmodia of the ubiquitous *Physarum polycephalum* in agitated cultures in chemically defined, liquid medium containing no other organisms, the fact remains that to date the completion of the myxomycete life cycle in its entirety, in the absence of living or dead bacterial cells, has not yet been achieved with any one species. While the accomplishment of Rusch and his coworkers represents a major advance and provides the opportunity to conduct studies that would otherwise be impossible, the truly significant contribution will be made by the investigator who devises a method that will enable us to induce a myxomycete to complete repeatedly its entire life cycle in pure culture on chemically defined medium. Only then will exact biochemical, physiological, and morphogenetic studies be possible.

Sufficient collections have been made in various areas of the world to give us a reasonable idea of the geographic distribution of Myxomycetes. Most species are cosmopolitan, but a few seem to be confined either to the tropics or to the temperate zones. A few species have been reported only from alpine habitats. Some species are seasonal in appearance, and others may be found whenever temperature and moisture conditions permit, regardless of season. The nature of the substrate appears to be important with some species, but others may be found on a wide variety of substrates. In general, it must be stated that there is a great paucity of information concerning the ecology of Myxomycetes, and if we are to glean an ecological picture of the distribution of Myxomycetes from specimens collected in their natural habitats, collectors must take and record other data besides substrate and date.

Myxomycete spores, which are usually uninucleate and contain haploid nuclei, may germinate by means of a wedge-shaped rupture or an irregularly shaped pore which is suggestive of enzyme action from within. Although exactly what initiates the germination process is not known, moisture (not necessarily liquid water) is a requisite. We will probably be in a better position to understand the germination process when the exact nature of the cell wall has been established. While there is some evidence that the cell wall contains cellulose, this has not been established with certainty, and the exact composition of the spore wall will probably not be determined until further, more critical, ultrastructural and cytochemical studies have been made.

Spores of some species have a remarkable longevity and thus have the capacity to germinate after many years of storage. However, the rates and percentage of germination are adversely affected by age. Although it has been reported that spores of one species are capable of germinating after 75 years of storage, such great longevity is probably exceptional.

Upon germination, one or two and occasionally four myxamoebae or swarm cells emerge from the spore. In free water, myxamoebae form two anterior flagella and thus become swarm cells. In the absence of free water, swarm cells retract their flagella and become myxamoebae. Typically, one flagellum is long and active, the other short and recurved against the protoplast. If a myxamoeba is subjected to further drying it will assume a spherical shape and encyst, forming a microcyst. When wetted, the microcyst will excyst and again form a myxamoeba. Under suitable conditions of environment myxamoebae will divide and form great numbers of haploid cells—a rather unusual situation since myxamoebae are gametes or potential gametes. In some species the myxamoebal stage can be prolonged for long periods by adding brucine to the medium.

In all species that have been studied critically, syngamy must occur prior to plasmodium formation, but there is some evidence for the occurrence of apogamy in some species. Whereas heterothallism is known to occur in the Myxomycetes, the existence of homothallism has not been proved and so-called homothallic species may prove to be apogamic. Interspecific hybrids have not yet been produced in the laboratory, but hybridization between different intraspecific genotypes has been accomplished with at least two species. Although heterokaryosis is known to occur in the Myxomycetes, the extent of its occurrence is still not known.

Immediately after plasmogamy, karyogamy occurs in the zygote. Although meiosis may occur in the fruiting bodies when the spores are delimited, it seems possible that in most species we will find that meiosis occurs in the young spores, as von Stosch has said. If this proves to be true for most species, then the occurrence of meiosis in spores of *Ceratiomyxa* no longer will appear exceptional, and Gilbert's view that the "spore" of *Ceratiomyxa* is homologous to the sporangium of the Myxogastromycetidae (Myxogastres) will no longer be valid on this basis.

It has been demonstrated by cinephotomicrography that a plasmodium may be formed by growth of a zygote, and that it may be enlarged by successive coalescence with other zygotes. It is still not known whether any species forms plasmodia by an active aggregation and simultaneous multiple fusion of many zygotes.

As in the Eumycotina, the chromosomes of the Myxomycetes are typically quite small, and in many species large chromosome numbers ($n = 25$ to $n = 90$) have been reported. The exception is *Ceratiomyxa fruticulosa* in which species $n = 8$.

Three distinct types of plasmodia are now recognized:

1. The protoplasmodium, which is minute, is formed by members of the Echinosteliales and some other small species, and is considered the most primitive type.
2. The aphanoplasmodium is characteristic of the Stemonitaceae. Although typically much larger than the protoplasmodium, it is difficult to see because it is greatly flattened and often colorless.
3. The phaneroplasmodium is the largest and most familiar type and is characteristic of members of the order Physarales.

In addition to these three distinct plasmodial types, plasmodia that are intermediate in their characteristics are being discovered, so it may be that as our knowledge increases, additional types will be added to our present list of three.

Because of the ease with which it can be cultured and the fact that its phaneroplasmodium is quite large, *Physarum polycephalum* has been widely used as an experimental organism in a great variety of biochemical and biophysical studies. While unquestionably of importance, many such studies are not concerned with Myxomycetes *per se* and hence for the most part have not been included in the present discussion. For example, while the effects of various snake venoms upon protoplasm (Lepow, 1938) is undoubtedly of great importance to the toxicologist or pharmacologist, it is of negligible significance in the life of a myxomycete, since to date none has been reported to have been bitten by venomous snakes!

Much of the cytological and physiological work on Myxomycetes still continues to be conducted with *Physarum polycephalum*, although in the past several years there has been an encouraging increase in the number of other species that have been used in such studies. Increasing numbers of electron microscope studies are appearing in the literature, and it seems possible that in a few years the fine structure of Myxomycetes will be as well known as that of other organisms. As in all such work, caution must be exercised in interpretation, and much careful work yet remains to be done before our knowledge of fine structure is complete.

Synchronous mitosis in the plasmodium of *P. polycephalum* was reported over thirty years ago, but it is now possible to synchronize mitosis in this species with such precision that various syntheses can be studied with relation to their occurrence in time with respect to mitosis. Thus, since it has been found that DNA synthesis begins immediately after mitosis and occurs over a one- to two-hour period, DNA cannot trigger mitosis.

Many of the fine structure studies on Myxomycetes have been concerned with whether or not fibrils occur in the plasmodium. The preponderance of evidence to date indicates that fibrils do occur. Also, there is good evidence that these fibrils may be a high molecular weight contractile protein (myxomyosin) which by its interaction with ATP may provide the motive force for the vigorous shuttle streaming so characteristic of the protoplasm of plasmodia. Even if this is proved beyond question, the still more complex problem of how streaming is coordinated in a large plasmodium remains to be solved.

While not essential for life-cycle completion, the sclerotium probably plays an important role in survival of a myxomycete during periods of adverse conditions of temperature and moisture. The sclerotium is not simply a dried plasmodium, since it has been shown that during the sclerotization process many multinucleate, sphaeroidal macrocysts (10–25 microns) are formed. Although greater longevity of sclerotia has been reported, these structures usually remain viable for one to three years.

The factor or factors that initiate sporulation of species with non-pigmented plasmodia are not known. In at least one non-pigmented species, light has been reported to be necessary for initiation of sporulation, but this report has not yet been verified. In species with yellow-pigmented plasmodia, light is necessary for the initiation of sporulation, but the actual reaction that triggers sporulation as well as the sequence of biochemical reactions that follow have not been identified. It has been shown that niacin is necessary for light sensitization, that a shift in oxidases occurs during sporulation, that age of plasmodium at time of illumination is important, and that effectiveness of light in initiating the process varies with wavelength. Since light is a requisite for sporulation in yellow-pigmented plasmodia, many investigators have suggested that the pigment(s) is the photoreceptor. While this is a good possibility, it has never been proved, and there is much disagreement about the chemical nature of the pigment. Some investigators have reported the isolation of several pigments from the same species.

From the foregoing brief account and the more comprehensive treatment in the chapters that precede it, it is evident that we possess a considerable body of information about the Myxomycetes. But from the same account it is evident that there are a great many questions yet to be answered. Let us say that at this time we have a good working knowledge of the Myxomycetes, but that there is a great amount of exacting research to be conducted and a great amount of exciting information yet to be gained by future workers. We hope that this volume will assist in giving the student access to knowledge already gained and that this, coupled with his access to existing sophisticated modern techniques (as well as those that will be developed), will lead to the accumulation of more complete information about this fascinating group of organisms.

Appendix

FORMULAE FOR PREPARING VARIOUS MEDIA

1. Bark-Extract Cornmeal Agar (BECM)

Tree bark	50 g
Bacto agar	17.5 g
Cornmeal agar	8.5 g
Distilled water	1000 g

Quercus fusiformis outer bark is used at the University of Texas, but bark from other trees may serve equally well or better for many species of Myxomycetes.

Cut the bark in small pieces, place in a large Erlenmeyer flask with the water, and steam for one hour. Allow flask to stand for one week at room temperature. Filter through filter paper to obtain a clear liquid. Add water to bring volume to 1000 ml. Add agar and autoclave at 15 pounds for 15 minutes.

2. Difco Nutrient Broth

Bacto nutrient broth	8 g
Distilled water	1000 g

3. Half-Strength Cornmeal Agar (CM/2)

Cornmeal agar	8.5 g
Bacto agar	12.5 g
Distilled water	1000.0 g

4. Half-Strength Cornmeal Agar with Three Per Cent Agar (3% CM/2)

Cornmeal agar	8.5 g
Bacto agar	22.5 g
Distilled water	1000.0 g

5. Penicillin-Streptomycin Agar

Bacto agar	20.0 g
Potassium penicillin G	2 million units
Streptomycin sulfate	1.0 g
Distilled water	1000.0 g

Melt the agar in the water by steaming. Add the antibiotics and autoclave at 15 pounds for 15 minutes.

6. Knop's Solution Agar

$Ca(NO_3)_2 \cdot 4H_2O$	0.8 g
KNO_3	0.2 g
KH_2PO_4	0.2 g
$MgSO_4 \cdot 7H_2O$	0.2 g
$FeSO_4$ or $FePO_4$	trace
Bacto agar	20.0 g
Distilled water	1000.0 g

7. Difco AC Broth

Bacto-AC medium	34.0 g
Distilled water	1000.0 g

8. Yeast-Extract Broth

Yeast extract	1.0 g
Distilled water	1000.0 g

9. Thioglycollate Broth

Bacto-Thioglycollate medium	24.0 g
Distilled water	1000.0 g

10. Glucose Broth

Glucose	1.0 g
Bacto peptone	1.0 g
Distilled water	1000.0 g

11. Eosin Methylene Blue Agar

Bacto EMB agar	36.0 g
Distilled water	1000.0 g

12. SM/5 Medium (Kerr and Sussman, 1958)

Bacto peptone	2.0 g
Glucose	2.0 g
Yeast extract	0.2 g
K_2HPO_4	0.2 g
KH_2PO_4	0.3 g
$MgSO_4 \cdot 7H_2O$	0.2 g
Bacto agar	20.0 g
Distilled water	1000.0 g

13. Oat-Flake Agar

Place enough oat flakes (rolled oats), preferably the slow-cooking type, in 100×20 mm Petri dishes to form a layer about 5 mm deep in each dish. Pour enough melted, hot, 2 per cent Bacto agar in each dish just to cover the oat flakes. Autoclave for one hour or more at 15 pounds.

14. Oat Flake–Penicillin/Streptomycin Agar

Follow instructions for preceding method, but use penicillin-strepto-mycin agar instead of plain Bacto agar.

15. Noble's Agar

Difco Special Agar (Noble)	2.0 g
Distilled water	1000.0 g

Bibliography

ABE, S. 1934. On the syngamy of some Myxomycetes. Sci. Rpts. Tokyo Bunrika Daigaku 1: 193–202.

———. 1941. Über die physiologischen Untersuchungen der Sporenkeimung bei Myxomyceten II. Der Einfluss des pH- Wertes der Lösungen auf die Sporenkeimung. Bot. Mag. Tokyo 55: 139–149. (Japanese with German summary).

ALDRICH, H. C. 1966. A study of the ultrastructural details of morphogenesis in the myxomycete *Physarum flavicomum*. Ph.D Dissertation, Univ. of Texas at Austin.

———. 1967. The ultrastructure of meiosis in three species of *Physarum*. Mycologia 59: 127–148.

———. 1968. The development of flagella in swarm cells of the myxomycete *Physarum flavicomum*. Jour. Gen. Microbiol. 50: 217–222.

ALEXOPOULOS, C. J. 1958. Three new species of Myxomycetes from Greece. Mycologia 50: 52–56.

———. 1959. The laboratory cultivation of *Stemonitis*. Am. Jour. Bot. 46: 140–142.

———. 1960a. Gross morphology of the plasmodium and its possible significance in the relationships among the Myxomycetes. Mycologia 52: 1–20.

———. 1960b. Morphology and laboratory cultivation of *Echinostelium minutum* deBary. Am. Jour. Bot. 47: 37–43.

———. 1961. A new species of *Echinostelium* from Greece. Am. Midl. Natural. 66: 391–394.

———. 1962. Introductory Mycology. 2nd ed.; John Wiley & Sons, Inc., New York.

———. 1963. The Myxomycetes II. Bot. Rev. 29: 1–78.

———. 1964a. The rapid sporulation of some Myxomycetes in moist chamber. Southwest. Natural. 9: 155–159.

———. 1964b. The white form of *Physarella oblonga*. Mycologia 56: 550–554.

———. 1966. Morphogenesis in the Myxomycetes. In The Fungi (Ainsworth & Sussman, eds.) Volume II, Chapter 8, pp. 211–234. Academic Press, New York.

———. 1967. Taxonomic studies in the Myxomycetes. I. The genus *Macbrideola*. Mycologia 59: 103–116.

ALEXOPOULOS, C. J., and BLACKWELL, MEREDITH. 1968. Taxonomic studies in the Myxomycetes. II. *Physarina*. Jour. El. Mitch. Sci. Soc. 84: 48–51.

ALEXOPOULOS, C. J., and ZABKA, G. G. 1962. Production of hybrids between physiological races of the true slime mould *Didymium iridis*. Nature (London) 193: 598–599.

ALLEN, P. J., and PRICE, W. H. 1950. The relation between respiration and protoplasmic flow in the slime mold, *Physarum polycephalum*. Am. Jour. Bot. 37: 393–402.

ALLMAN, W. T. 1955. Methods for the quantification of myxomycete plasmodia. Ph.D. Dissertation, Vanderbilt University, Nashville, Tenn. (also Diss. Abst. 15: 1297).

ALSTON, R. E., and TURNER, B. L. 1963. Biochemical Systematics. Prentice Hall, Englewood Cliffs, N. J.

ANDERSON, J. D. 1951. Galvanotaxis of slime mold. Jour. Gen. Physiol. 35: 1–16.

———. 1962. Potassium loss during galvanotaxis of slime mold. Jour. Gen. Physiol. 45: 567–574.

ANDERSON, J. D. 1964. Regional differences in ion concentration in migrating plasmodia, in "Primitive Motile Systems in Cell Biology" (Allen and Kamiya, eds.), pp. 125–134. Academic Press, New York.

ANDRESEN, N. 1942. Cytoplasmic components in the amoeba *Chaos chaos* Linne. Compt. Rend., Lab. Carlsberg, Ser. Chim. *24*: 140 (cf. Andresen & Pollock).

ANDRESEN, N., and POLLOCK, B. M. 1952. A comparison between the cytoplasmic components in the myxomycete, *Physarum polycephalum*, and in the amoeba, *Chaos chaos*. Compt. Rend., Lab. Carlsberg. Ser. Chim. *28*: 247–264.

BAKER, GLADYS E. 1933. A comparative morphological study of the myxomycete fructification. Univ. Iowa St. Nat. Hist. *14*: 1–35.

BARANETZKI, J. 1876. Influence de la lumière sur les plasmodia des Myxomycètes. Mem. Soc. Sci. Nat. Cherbourg *19*: 321–360 (cf. Hawker, 1952).

BARY, A. de. 1854. Euglenaartige Gebilde aus Sporen von *Trichia rubiformis*. Flora *12*: 648.

———. 1858. Ueber die Myxomyceten. Bot. Zeit. *16*: 357–358, 361–364, 365–369.

———. 1859. Die Mycetozoen. Ein Beitrag zur Kenntnis der niedersten Thiere. Zeit. Wiss. Zool. *10*: 88–175.

———. 1864. Die Mycetozoen (Schleimpilze). Ein Beitrag zur Kenntnis der niedersten Organismen (2nd ed.). Leipzig. W. Engelman.

———. 1866. Morphologie und Physiologie der Pilze, Flechten, und Myxomyceten. Leipzig.

———. 1884. Vergleichende Morphologie und Biologie der Pilze, Mycetozoen, und Bacterien. Leipzig.

———. 1887. Comparative morphology and biology of the fungi, Mycetozoa and bacteria. (Eng. trans.), Clarendon Press, London.

BENEDICT, W. G. 1962. Haplophase activity in *Stemonitis fusca* Roth. Can. Jour. Bot. *40*: 71–76.

———. 1965. Plasmodial activity in *Stemonitis fusca* Roth. Can. Jour. Bot. *43*: 355–359.

BESSEY, E. A. 1950. Morphology and taxonomy of fungi. Blakiston Co., Philadelphia.

BISBY, G. R. 1914. Some observations on the formation of the capillitium and the development of *Physarella mirabilis* Peck and *Stemonitis fusca* Roth. Amer. Jour. Bot. *1*: 274–288.

BISHOP, D. W. 1964. Introduction, in "Primitive Motile Systems in Cell Biology" (Allen and Kamiya, eds.), pp. 469–470, Academic Press, New York.

BLICKLE, A. H. 1943. Sulfhydryl and cell increase in number in the Myxomycetes. Growth 7: 291–297.

BOIC, D. 1925. Über den chemischen Character der Peridie, des Kapillitiums und der Sporenmembranen bei Myxomyzeten. Acta Botanica Inst. Bot. Univ. Zagreb. *1*: 44–63.

BRANDZA, M. 1926a. Sur l'influence de la chaleur et de l'évaporation rapide sur les Myxomycètes calcarées vivant en plein soleil. C. R. Acad. Sci. Paris. *182*: 488–489.

———. 1926b. Sur la polychromie des Myxomycètes vivant en plein soleil. C. R. Acad. Sci. Paris *182*: 987–989.

———. 1928. Observations sur quelques sclérotes de Myxomycètes calcarées. Le Botaniste *20*: 117–145.

BRAUN, R., MITTERMAYER, C., and RUSCH, H. P. 1965. Sequential temporal replication of DNA in *Physarum polycephalum*. Proc. Nat. Acad. Sci. 53: 924–931.

———. 1966. Ribonucleic acid synthesis *in vivo* in the synchronously dividing *Physarum polycephalum* studied by cell fractionation. Biochim. Biophys. Acta *114*: 527–535.

BREWER, E. N. 1965. Culture and chemical composition of the slime mold, *Phy-*

sarum polycephalum. Ph.D. Dissertation, Univ. of Wisconsin, Madison. (Diss. Abst. *25*: 6190–6191, 1965.)

BREWER, E. N., and RUSCH, H. P. 1965. DNA synthesis by isolated nuclei of *Physarum polycephalum.* Biochem. and Biophys. Res. Commun. *21*: 235–241.

BRODIE, H. J., and GREGORY, P. H. 1953. The action of wind in the dispersal of spores from cup-shaped plant structures. Can. Jour. Bot. *31*: 402–410.

BROWN, R. M., LARSON, D. A., and BOLD, H. C. 1964. Airborne algae: their abundance and heterogeneity. Science *143*: 583–585.

BUCHET, S. 1939. Nouvelle récolte en France de *Trichamphora pezizoidea* Jungh. Bull. Soc. Mycol. Fr. *55*: 114–117.

CADMAN, E. J. 1931. The life history and cytology of *Didymium nigripes* Fr. Trans. Roy. Soc. Edinburgh *57*: 93–142.

CAMP, W. G. 1936. A method of cultivating myxomycete plasmodia. Bull. Torrey Bot. Club *63*: 205–210.

―――. 1937a. The fruiting of *Physarum polycephalum* in relation to nutrition. Am. Jour. Bot. *24*: 300–303.

―――. 1937b. The structure and activities of the myxomycete plasmodia. Bull. Torrey Bot. Club *64*: 307–335.

CARLILE, M. J., and DEE, JENNIFER. 1967. Plasmodial fusion and lethal interaction between strains in a myxomycete. Nature (London) *215*: 832–834.

CARR, L. G. 1939a. A comparison of Mycetozoa fauna in sandstone and limestone regions of Augusta County, Virginia. Mycologia *31*: 157–160.

―――. 1939b. The plasmodium of *Hemitrichia vesparium* (Batsch) Macbr. Science *90*: 329.

CARROLL, G. C. and DYKSTRA, R. 1966. Synaptinemal complexes in *Didymium iridis.* Mycologia *58*: 166–169.

CAYLEY, D. M. 1929. Some observations on mycetozoa of the genus *Didymium.* Trans. Brit. Mycol. Soc. *14*: 227–248.

ČELAKOVSKY, L. 1893. Ueber die Aufnahme lebender und todter verdaulicher Körper in die Plasmodien der Myxomyceten. Flora *76*: 182–244.

CIENKOWSKI, L. 1863a. Zur Entwickelungsgeschichte der Myxomyceten. Jahr. Wiss. Bot. *3*: 325–337.

―――. 1863b. Das Plasmodium. Jahr. Wiss. Bot. *3*: 400–441.

CIHLAR, C. 1916. Mikrokemijska istrazivan johitin ublinskim membranama Bot. Centr. *131*: 524 (cf. Goodwin, 1961).

CLARK, J. 1888. Über den Einfluss niederer Sauerstoffpressungen auf die Bewegungen des Protoplasmas. Ber. d. deutsch. Bot. Ges. *6*: 273–280.

CLEVELAND, L. R., and SANDERS, E. P. 1930. Encystation, multiple fission without encystment, encystation, metacystic development, and variation in a pure line and nine strains of *Entamoeba histolytica.* Arch. Protist. *70*: 223–266.

COHEN, A. L. 1939. Nutrition of the Myxomycetes. I. Pure culture and two-membered culture of myxomycete plasmodia. Bot. Gaz. *101*: 243–275.

―――. 1942. The organization of protoplasm. A possible experimental approach. Growth *6*: 259–272.

―――. 1959. An electron microscope study of flagellation in the myxomycete swarm cell. Proc. IXth Internat. Bot. Congr. Montreal. *11*: 77.

COLLINS, O. R. 1959. Some effects of temperature and pH on the life cycle of *Fuligo cinerea* (Schw.) Morgan in laboratory culture. Master's Thesis Univ. of Iowa, Iowa City.

―――. 1961. Heterothallism and homothallism in two Myxomycetes. Am. Jour. Bot. *48*: 674–683.

―――. 1963. Multiple alleles at the incompatibility locus in the myxomycete *Didymium iridis.* Am. Jour. Bot. *50*: 477–480.

―――. 1965. Homothallic behavior in two Costa Rican isolates of the slime mold *Didymium iridis.* (Abstr.) Am. Jour. Bot. *52*: 634.

COLLINS, O. R. 1966. Plasmodial compatibility in heterothallic and homothallic isolates of *Didymium iridis*. Mycologia 58: 362–372.

COLLINS, O. R., and CLARK, J. 1966a. Inheritance of the brown plasmodial pigment in *Didymium iridis*. Mycologia 58: 743–751.

––––––. 1966b. On the genetic basis of plasmodial compatibility in *Didymium iridis*. (Abstr.) Am. Jour. Bot. 53: 625.

––––––. 1968. Genetics of plasmodial compatibility and heterokaryosis in *Didymium iridis*. Mycologia 60: 90–103.

COLLINS, O. R., and LING, H. 1963. Further studies on heterothallism in *Didymium iridis*. (Abstr.) Am. Jour. Bot. 50: 625.

––––––. 1968. Clonally produced plasmodia in heterothallic isolates of *Didymium iridis*. Mycologia 60.

COLLINS, O. R., ALEXOPOULOS, C. J., and HENNEY, MARY. 1964. Heterothallism in three isolates of the slime mold *Physarum pusillum*. (Abstr.) Am. Jour. Bot. 51: 679.

CONRAD, H. S. 1910. Spore formation in *Lycogala exiguum*. Proc. Iowa Acad. Sci. 17: 83–84.

CONSTANTINEANU, J. C. 1907. Uber die Entwicklungsbedigungen der Myxomyceten. Annal. Mycol. 4: 495–540.

COOKE, W. R. I., and HOLT, E. M. 1928. Some observations on the germination of the spores of some species of Mycetozoa. Mycologia 20: 340–352.

COWDRY, N. H. 1918. The cytology of the Myxomycetes with special reference to mitochondria. Biol. Bull. 35: 71–94.

CUMMINS, J. E., BREWER, E. N., and RUSCH, H. P. 1965. The effect of actidione on mitosis in the slime mold, *Physarum polycephalum*. Jour. Cell Biol. 27: 337–341.

DALLEUX, G. 1940. Recherches sur les plasmodes de deux Myxomycètes. Rev. Cytol. Cytophysiol. Veget. 4: 123–182.

DANGEARD, P. 1947. Notes biologiques et cytologiques sur un Myxomycète (*Didymium clavus*). Botaniste 33: 39–57.

DANIEL, J. W. 1963. Metabolism of the phenolic precursor of a myxomycète spore pigment. Jour. Cell Biol. 19: 18A–19A.

––––––. 1964a. Photo induced polysaccharide synthesis during differentiation of a myxomycete. Fed. Proc. 23: 320.

––––––. 1964b. Changes in glucose permeability as an early event in the light-induced morphogenesis of a myxomycete. Bact. Proc., 1964, p. 144.

––––––. 1964c. The light-dependent reaction inducing sporulation of the myxomycete, *Physarum polycephalum*. Jour. Cell Biol. 23: 23A.

––––––. 1965. Control of respiration by light during the sporulation and growth of a myxomycete. Jour. Cell Biol. 27: 23A–24A.

––––––. 1966. Light-induced synchronous sporulation of a myxomycete—the relation of initial metabolic changes to the establishment of a new cell state, in "Cell Synchrony" (Cameron and Padilla, eds.), pp. 117–152. Academic Press, New York.

DANIEL, J. W., and BABCOCK, K. 1966. Methionine metabolism of the myxomycete *Physarum polycephalum*. Jour. Bact. 92: 1028–1035.

DANIEL, J. W., BABCOCK, K. L., SIEVERT, A. H., and RUSCH, H. P. 1963. Organic requirements and synthetic media for growth of the myxomycete, *Physarum polycephalum*. Jour. Bact. 86: 324–331.

DANIEL, J. W., and BALDWIN, HELEN H. 1964. Methods of culture for plasmodial Myxomycetes, in Methods in Cell Physiology 1: 9–41. (D. M. Prescott ed.), Academic Press, New York.

DANIEL, J. W., KELLEY, J., and RUSCH, H. P. 1962. Hematin-requiring plasmodial myxomycete. Jour. Bact. 84: 1104–1110.

DANIEL, J. W., and RUSCH, H. P. 1958. Control of sporulation in *Physarum polycephalum*. (Abstr.). Fed. Am. Soc. Expt. Biol. Fed. Proc. 17 (1, pt. 1): 434.

————. 1961. The pure culture of *Physarum polycephalum* on a partially defined soluble medium. Jour. Gen. Microbiol. *25*: 47–59.

————. 1962a. Method for inducing sporulation of pure cultures of the myxomycete *Physarum polycephalum*. Jour. Bact. *82*: 234–240.

————. 1962b. Niacin requirement for sporulation of *Physarum polycephalum*. Jour. Bact. *83*: 1244–1250.

DAVIS, E. E. 1965. Preservation of Myxomycetes. Mycologia *57*: 986–988.

DEE, JENNIFER. 1960. A mating-type system in an acellular slime-mould. Nature *185*: 780–781.

————. 1962. Recombination in a myxomycete *Physarum polycephalum* Schw. Gen. Res. (Cambridge) *3*: 11–23.

————. 1966a. Genetic analysis of actidione-resistant mutants in the myxomycete *Physarum polycephalum* Schw. Genet. Res. (Cambridge) *8*: 101–110.

————. 1966b. Multiple alleles and other factors affecting plasmodium formation in the true slime mould *Physarum polycephalum* Schw. Jour. Protozool. *13*: 610–616.

DRESDEN, C. F. 1959. Pigments of *Physarum polycephalum*. (Abst.). Diss. Abst. *20*: 869–870.

DUGAS, D. J., and BATH, J. D. 1962. Electron microscopy of the slime mold *Physarum polycephalum*. Protoplasma *54*: 421–431.

DURAND, E. J. 1894. Some rare Myxomycetes of central New York, with notes on the germination of *Enteridium Rozeanum*. Bot. Gaz. *19*: 89–95.

ELLIOTT, E. W. 1948. The swarm cells of Myxomycetes. Wash. Acad. Sci. Jour. *38*: 133–137.

————. 1949. The swarm-cells of Myxomycetes. Mycologia *41*: 141–170.

ELLISON, B. R. 1945. Flagellar studies on zoospores of some members of the Mycetozoa, Plasmodiophorales, and Chytridiales. Mycologia *37*: 444–459.

EMOTO, Y. 1933a. Studien über die Myxomyceten in Japan. Bot. Mag. Tokyo *47*: 371–383.

————. 1933b. Entwicklung der Sporangien von Myxomyceten. (I). Uber *Ceratiomyxa fruticulosa* und ihre Varietäten. Bot. Mag. Tokyo *47*: 721–729.

————. 1934a. Entwicklung der Sporangien von Myxomyceten. (II). Uber drei Arten von Stemonitaceae. Bot. Mag. Tokyo *48*: 61–67.

————. 1934b. Entwicklung der Sporangien von Myxomyceten. (IV). Uber *Physarella oblonga* und Hemitrichia clavata. Bot. Mag. Tokyo *48*: 934–938.

————. 1935. A list of the literature on the Myxomycetes. III (1931–1934). Bot. Mag. Tokyo *49*: 317–324.

————. 1938. Untersuchungen über die Entwicklung der Myxomyceten auf Faulenden Holzern. Bot. Mag. Tokyo *52*: 253–257.

ENGELHARDT, W. A. 1957. Enzymology and mechanochemistry of tissues and cells. Proc. Intern. Symp. Enzyme Chem. (Tokyo), pp. 34–39.

ERBISCH, F. H. 1964. Myxomycete spore longevity. The Michigan Botanist *3*: 120–121.

FAMINTZIN, A., and WORONIN, M. 1873. Über zwei neue Formen von Schleimpilzen: *Ceratium hydnoides* und *Ceratium poroides*. Mem. Acad. Imp. Sci. St. Petersburg. VII *20*: 1–16.

FARR, M. L. 1957a. Taxonomic studies in the Myxomycetes. Ph.D. Thesis, State Univ. of Iowa, Iowa City.

————. 1957b. A checklist of Jamaican slime-moulds (Myxomycetes). Bull. Inst. Jam. *7*: 1–67.

————. 1958. Taxonomic studies in the Myxomycetes. I. The *Trichia favoginea* complex. Mycologia *50*: 357–369.

FERGUS, C. L., and SCHEIN, R. D. 1963. Light effects on fruiting of *Physarum gyrosum*. Mycologia *55*: 540–548.

FRIES, ELIAS. 1829. Systema mycologicum. III: 67–199.

FRIES, R. E. 1903. Myxomyceten von Argenitien und Bolivia. Ark Bot. *1*: 57–70.

Fry, E., and Fry, A. 1899. The Mycetozoa and Some Questions Which They Suggest. "Knowledge" Office, London.

Garjeanne, A. J. M. 1953. De levengeschiedenis van een slijmzwam (*Physarum nutans* var. *leucophaeum*). Levende Natuur 56: 67–72 (cf. Biol. Abstr. 30: 14479).

Gehenio, P. M. 1944. Longevity of the sclerotia of Mycetozoa. Biodynamica 4: 359–368.

Gehenio, P. M., and Luyet, B. J. 1950. Complete development of mycetozoon from a single spore or a single myxamoeba. Biodynamica 7: 11–23.

―――. 1951. Effect of light in inducing reproductive processes in the mycetozoon *Physarella oblonga*. Biodynamica 7: 85–99.

Gilbert, F. A. 1927. On the occurrence of biflagellate swarm cells in certain Myxomycetes. Mycologia 19: 277–283.

―――. 1928a. Feeding habits of the swarm cells of the myxomycete *Dictydiaethalium plumbeum*. Am. Jour. Bot. 15: 123–131.

―――. 1928b. Observations on the feeding habits of the swarm cells of Myxomycetes. Am. Jour. Bot. 15: 473–484.

―――. 1928c. A study of the method of spore germination in Myxomycetes. Am. Jour. Bot. 15: 345–352.

―――. 1929a. Factors influencing the germination of myxomycetous spores. Am. Jour. Bot. 16: 280–286.

―――. 1929b. Spore germination in the Myxomycetes: a comparative study of spore germination by families. Am. Jour. Bot. 16: 421–432.

―――. 1931. The cultivation of slime moulds for laboratory use. Proc. West Virginia Acad. Sci. 5: 77–79.

Gilbert, H. C. 1935. Critical events in the life history of *Ceratiomyxa*. Am. Jour. Bot. 22: 52–74.

Gilbert, H. C., and Martin, G. W. 1933. Myxomycetes found on the bark of living trees. Univ. Iowa St. Nat. Hist. 15: 3–8.

Goodwin, D. C. 1961. Morphogenesis of the sporangium of *Comatricha*. Am. Jour. Bot. 48: 148–154.

Gottsberger, G. 1966. Die Myxomyceten der Steiermark mit Meitragen zu ihrer Biologie. Nova Hedwigia 12: 203–296.

―――. 1967. Geisseln bei Myxomyceten. Nova Hedwigia 13: 235–243.

Gray, W. D. 1936. Notes on plasmodial behavior of *Stemonitis fusca* Roth. Proc. Ind. Acad. Sci. 45: 74–76.

―――. 1937. Observations on the methods of stipe formation in *Stemonitis* and *Comatricha*. Proc. Ind. Acad. Sci. 46: 81–85.

―――. 1938. The effect of light on the fruiting of Myxomycetes. Am. Jour. Bot. 25: 511–522.

―――. 1939a. Myxomycetes of Clark County, Indiana. I. Proc. Ind. Acad. Sci. 45: (1936): 69–73. II. 48: (1939): 71–73.

―――. 1939b. The relation of pH and temperature to the fruiting of *Physarum polycephalum*. Am. Jour. Bot. 26: 709–714.

―――. 1941. Some effects of heterochromatic ultra-violet radiation on myxomycete plasmodia. Am. Jour. Bot. 28: 212–216.

―――. 1945. The existence of physiological strains in *Physarum polycephalum*. Am. Jour. Bot. 32: 157–160.

―――. 1948. Myxomycetes new or rare in Indiana. Proc. Ind. Acad. Sci. 57: 69–73.

―――. 1949. The laboratory cultivation and development of the myxomycetes *Physarella oblonga* and *Physarum didermoides*. Ohio Jour. Sci. 49: 105–108.

―――. 1953. Further studies on the fruiting of *Physarum polycephalum*. Mycologia 45: 817–824.

―――. 1955. Riboflavin synthesis in cultures of *Physarum polycephalum*. Ohio Jour. Sci. 55: 212–214.

————. 1959. The relation of fungi to human affairs. Henry Holt & Company, New York.

————. 1961. The laboratory cultivation of *Physarum flavicomum*. Am. Jour. Bot. 48: 242–243.

GUTTES, E., and GUTTES, S. · 1960. Pinocytosis in the myxomycete *Physarum Polycephalum*. Exptl. Cell Res. 20: 239–241.

————. 1963. Starvation and cell wall formation in the myxomycete *Physarum polycephalum*. Ann. Bot. N. S. 27: 49–53.

GUTTES, E., GUTTES, S., and RUSCH, H. P. 1959. Synchronization of mitosis by the fusion of the plasmodia of *Physarum polycephalum*. (Abst.). Fed. Am. Soc. Expt. Biol. Fed. Proc. 18: 479.

————. 1961. Morphological observations on growth and differentiation of *Physarum polycephalum* grown in pure culture. Devel. Biol. 3: 588–614.

HAGELSTEIN, R. 1944. The Mycetozoa of North America. Pub. by author. Mineola, New York.

HARPER, R. A. 1900. Cell and nuclear division in *Fuligo varians*. Bot. Gaz. 30: 217–251.

————. 1914. Cleavage in *Didymium melanospermum*. Am. Jour. Bot. 1: 127–144.

HARPER, R. A., and DODGE, B. O. 1914. The formation of capillitium in certain Myxomycetes. Ann. Bot. 28: 1–18.

HARSHBERGER, J. W. 1901. Observations upon the feeding plasmodia of *Fuligo septica*. Bot. Gaz. 31: 198–203.

HATANO, S., and NAKAJIMA, H. 1961. Effect of acetylcholine and acetylcholinesterase inhibitors on the protoplasmic streaming in the myxomycete plasmodium. Ann. Rept. Sci. Works, Fac. Sci. Osaka Univ. 9: 21–28.

HATANO, S., and OOSAWA, F. 1962. Actin-like protein of myxomycete plasmodium. I. Extraction and cross reaction with myosin from muscle. Ann. Rept. of the Res. Group on Biophysics in Japan. II. pp. 29–30.

————. 1963. Actin-like protein of myxomycete plasmodium. II. Isolation and observation of some physico-chemical properties. Ann. Rept. of the Res. Group on Biophysics in Japan. III. pp. 97–98.

————. 1964. Actin-like protein of myxomycete plasmodium. IV. Purification and observations of some physico-chemical properties. Ann. Rept. of the Res. Group on Biophysics in Japan. IV. pp. 25–28.

HATANO, S., and TAKEUCHI, I. 1960. ATP content in myxomycete plasmodium and its levels in relation to some external conditions. Protoplasma 52: 169–183.

HATANO, S., TAZAWA, H., and OOSAWA, F. 1965. Actin and myosin A from myxomycete plasmodium. U.S.–Japan Cooperative Science Program, Sept. 14–17, 1965. Tokyo, Japan.

HAWKER, L. E. 1952. The physiology of Myxomycetes. Trans. Brit. Mycol. Soc. 35: 177–187.

————. 1965. Fine structure of fungi as revealed by electron microscopy. Biol. Rev. 40: 52–92.

HEMPHILL, M. D. 1962. Studies on a resting phase of *Physarum polycephalum* in axenic cultures. M.S. Thesis. University of Wisconsin, Madison.

HENNEBERG, W. 1901. Hefe fressende Amöben eines Schleimpilzes (*Physarum leucophaeum* Fr.) und hefe fressende Thieramöben. Wochenschr. Brauerei. 18: 159–161, 173–175.

HENNEY, MARY R. 1966. The mating type system in the myxomycete *Physarum flavicomum* and the ascomycete *Anixiopsis stercoraria*. Ph.D. Dissertation. Univ. of Texas at Austin.

————. 1967. The mating type system of the myxomycete *Physarum flavicomum*. Mycologia 59: 637–652.

HENNEY, MARY, and HENNEY, H. R., JR. 1968. The mating type systems of the Myxomycetes *Physarum rigidum* and *Physarum flavicomum*. Jour. Gen. Microbiol. (In press).

HODAPP, E. L. 1942. Some factors influencing sclerotization in mycetozoa. Biodynamica *4*: 33–46.

HOFFMANN, H. 1859. Über Pilzkeimungen. Bot. Zeitung *17*: 209–214, 217–219.

HOFMEISTER, W. F. B. 1867. Lehre von der Pflanzenzelle. Leipzig. (cf. Hawker, 1952).

HOITINK, A. W. J. H., and VAN DIJK, G. 1967. The influence of neurohumoral transmitter substances on protoplasmic streaming in the myxomycete *Physarella oblonga*. J. Cell. Physiol. *67*: 133–140.

HOLTER, H., and POLLOCK, B. M. 1952. Distribution of some enzymes in the cytoplasm of the myxomycete, *Physarum polycephalum*. Compt. Rend. Trav. Lab. Carlsberg. Ser. Chim., *28*(5): 221–245.

HOWARD, F. L. 1931a. The life history of *Physarum polycephalum*. Am. Jour. Bot. *18*: 116–133.

———. 1931b. Laboratory cultivation of myxomycete plasmodia. Am. Jour. Bot. *18*: 624–628

———. 1932. Nuclear division in plasmodia of *Physarum*. Ann. Bot. *46*: 461–477.

HOWARD, F. L., and CURRIE, M. E. 1932a. Parasitism of myxomycete plasmodia on the sporophores of hymenomycetes. Jour. Arnold Arb. *13*: 270–284.

———. 1932b. Parasitism of myxomycete plasmodia on fungous mycelia. Jour. Arnold Arb. *13*: 438–447.

INDIRA, P. U. 1964. Swarmer formation from plasmodia of Myxomycetes. Trans. Brit. Mycol. Soc. *47*: 531–533.

———. 1965. In vitro cultivation of *Diachea splendens* Peck. Curr. Sci. *34*: 601–602.

INDIRA, P. U., and KALYANASUNDARAM, R. 1963. Some investigations in culture of some Myxomycetes. Ber. Schweiz. Bot. Ges. *73*: 381–388.

ING, B. 1968. A census catalogue of British Myxomycetes. 24 pp. Br. Mycol. Soc. Foray Committee, Br. Mycol. Soc., Kew.

INGOLD, C. T. 1940. Spore discharge in land plants. Oxford Univ. Press.

JAHN, A. 1934. Über Wachstum, Plasmastromung und vegetative Fusionen bei *Humaria leucoloma*. Hedw. Z. Bot. *27*: 193–250.

JAHN, E. 1899. Zur Kenntniss des Schleimpilzes *Comatricha obtusata* Preuss. Festschrift für Schwendener, 288–300.

———. 1901. Myxomycetenstudien. 1. *Dictydium umbilicatum* Schrader. Ber. deutsch. Bot. Ges. *19*: 97–115.

———. 1905. Myxomycetenstudien. 4: Die Keimung der Sporen. Ber. deutsch. Bot. Ges. *23*: 489–497.

———. 1907. Myxomycetenstudien, 6. Kernverschemlzungen und Reduktion-steilungen. Ber. deutsch. Bot. Ges. *25*: 23–26.

———. 1908. Myxomycetenstudien, 7. *Ceratiomyxa*. Ber. deutsch. Bot. Ges. *26a*: 342–352.

———. 1911. Myxomycetenstudien, 8. Der Sexualakt. Ber. deutsch. Bot. Ges. *29*: 231–247.

———. 1919. Lebensdauer und Alterscheinungen eines Plasmodiums. Ber. deutsch. Bot. Ges. *37*: 18–33.

———. 1931. Myxomycetenstudien. 13. Die Stielbildung bei den Sporangien der Gattung *Comatricha*. Ber. deutsch. Bot. Ges. *49*: 77–82.

———. 1933. Myxomycetenstudien. 15. Somatische und generative Kernteilungen. Ber. deutsch. Bot. Ges. *51*: 377–385.

JAHN, T. L. 1964. Protoplasmic flow in the mycetozoan, *Physarum*—II. The mechanism of flow; a re-evaluation of the contraction-hydraulic theory and of the diffusion drag hypothesis. Biorheology *2*: 133–152.

JAHN, T. L., RINALDI, R. A., and BROWN, M. 1964. Protoplasmic flow in the mycetozoan, *Physarum*—I. Geometry of the plasmodium and the observable facts of flow. Biorheology *2*: 123–131.

JAROCKI, J. 1931. Mycetozoa from the Czarnohora Mountains in the Polish Eastern

Carpathians. Polska akad. umiej. Krakow. Wydzial Math. Przutod. Bull. Intern. S. B.: Sc. Nat. 2: 447–464.

JOHNSON, G. T., and Moos, C. 1956. Succinoxidase activity of mitochondria from myxomycete plasmodia. J. Cell Comp. Physiol. 48: 243–252.

JORGENSEN, C. A. 1925. Sclerotiet hos Badhamia utricularis Berk. Bot. Tidsskrift, 38: 434–437.

JUMP, J. A. 1954. Studies on sclerotization in Physarum polycephalum. Am. Jour. Bot. 41: 561–567.

KAMBLY, P. 1939a. The color of myxomycete plasmodia. Am. Jour. Bot. 26: 386–390.

———. 1939b. Some physiological characteristics of myxomycete swarm cells. Am. Jour. Bot. 26: 88–92.

KAMIYA, N. 1940. Control of protoplasmic streaming. Science 92: 462–463.

———. 1942. Physical aspects of protoplasmic streaming. A symposium on "The Structure of Protoplasm." (W. Seifriz, ed.). Monograph, Am. Soc. Physiol. Ames. Iowa. pp. 199–244.

———. 1943. Motive force of protoplasmic streaming. (I)–(III). Kagaku 13, No. 10–12. (cf. Ohta, 1952).

———. 1950a. The protoplasmic flow in the myxomycete plasmodium as revealed by a volumetric analysis. Protoplasma 39: 344–357.

———. 1950b. The rate of the protoplasmic flow in the myxomycete plasmodium. I. Cytologia 15: 183–193.

———. 1950c. The rate of the protoplasmic flow in the myxomycete plasmodium. II. Cytologia 15: 194–204.

———. 1959. Protoplasmic streaming. Protoplasmologia Vol. 8, Pt. 3a.

KAMIYA, N., and KURODA, K. 1965. Movement of the myxomycete plasmodium. I. A study of glycerinated models. Proc. Jap. Acad. 41: 837–841.

KAMIYA, N., and TAKATA, T. 1967. Movement of the myxomycete plasmodium. V. The motive force of endoplasm-rich and endoplasm-poor plasmodia. Proc. Jap. Acad. 43: 537–540.

KAMIYA, N., and YONEDA, M. 1967. Movement of the myxomycete plasmodium. IV. Dislocation of endoplasm and its effect on motive force production. Proc. Jap. Acad. 43: 531–536.

KAMIYA, N., NAKAJIMA, H., and ABE, S. 1957. Physiology of the motive force of protoplasmic streaming. Protoplasma 48: 94–112.

KAR, A. K. 1962. Investigation on the plasmodial membrane of the Myxomycetes. (Abstr.) Diss. Abst. 1962: 3359–3360.

KARSEN, A. 1943. Studies on Myxomycetes. II. The myxomycete flora of Hardangen. Bergens Mus. Arbok, Naturvid. Rekke 1943: 1–34.

KELLEY, J., DAVID, J. W., and RUSCH, H. P. 1960. A hemin-requiring plasmodial slime mold. Fed. Proc. 19: 243.

KENT, W. SAVILLE. 1880–1881. Manual of Infusoria. Vol. 1. London.

KERR, N. S. 1960. Flagella formation by myxamoebae of the true slime mold Didymium nigripes. Jour. Protozool. 7: 103–108.

———. 1961. A study of plasmodium formation by the true slime mold, Didymium nigripes. Exp. Cell Research 23: 603–611.

———. 1963. The growth of myxamoebae of the true slime mold, Didymium nigripes in axenic culture. Jour. Gen. Microbiol. 32: 409–416.

———. 1965a. Inhibition by streptomycin of flagella formation in a true slime mold. Jour. Protozool. 12: 276–278.

———. 1965b. A simple method of lyophilization for the long-term storage of slime molds and small soil amoebae. Bio-Science 15: 469.

———. 1965c. Disappearance of a genetic marker from a cytoplasmic hybrid plasmodium of a true slime mold. Science 147: 1586–1588.

———. 1967. Plasmodium formation by a minute mutant of the true slime mold, Didymium nigripes. Exp. Cell Res. 45: 646–655.

KERR, N. S., and SUSSMAN, M. 1958. Clonal development of the true slime mold, *Didymium nigripes*. Jour. Gen. Microbiol. *19*: 173–177.

KERR, SYLVIA J. 1967. A comparative study of mitosis in amoebae and plasmodia of the true slime mold, *Didymium nigripes*. Jour. Protozool. *14*: 439–445.

KESSLER, D. 1964. An autoradiographic study of rapidly synthesized ribonucleic acid with reference to the mitotic cycle in the slime mold *Physarum polycephalum*. Ph.D. Thesis. University of Wisconsin, 142 pp. (cf. Koevenig, J. L. and R. C. Jackson, 1966).

KIESEL, A. 1930. Chemie des Protoplasmas. Berlin.

KISHIMOTO, V. 1958. Rhythmicity in the protoplasmic streaming of a slime mold, *Physarum polycephalum*. II. Theoretical treatment of the electric potential rhythm. J. Gen. Physiol. *41*: 1223–1244.

KITCHING, J. A., and PIRENNE, M. A. 1940. The influence of low tensions of oxygen on the protoplasmic streaming of myxomycetes. Jour. Cell. Comp. Physiol, *16*: 131–133.

KLEBS, G. 1900. Zur physiologie der Fortpflanzen einiger Pilze III. Jahr. Wiss. Bot. *35*: 80–203.

KOEVENIG, J. L. 1961a. Slime molds I: Life cycle. U5518, 30 min. sd. color film. Bureau Aud. Vis. Instr., Ext. Div., Univ. of Iowa, Iowa City.

———. (Technical Director.) 1961b. Slime molds II: Collection, cultivation, and use. U-5519, 19 min. sd. color film. Bureau Aud. Vis. Instr., Ext. Div., Univ. of Iowa, Iowa City.

———. 1961c. Three educational films on Myxomycetes with a study of the life cycle of *Physarum gyrosum* Rost. Ph.D. Thesis, University of Iowa, Iowa City.

———. 1963. Effect of the environment on fruiting in the myxomycete *Physarum gyrosum* Rost. Amer. Midland Nat. *69*: 373–375.

———. 1964. Studies on life cycle of *Physarum gyrosum* and other Myxomycetes. Mycologia *56*: 170–184.

KOEVENIG, J. L., and JACKSON, R. C. 1966. Plasmodial mitosis and polyploidy in the myxomycete *Physarum polycephalum*. Mycologia *58*: 662–667.

KORN, E. D., GREENBLATT, C. L., and LEES, A. M. 1965. Synthesis of fatty acids in the slime mold *Physarum polycephalum* and the zooflagellates *Leishmania tarentolae*, *Trypanosoma lewisi* and *Crithia* sp.: a comparative study. Jour. Lipid Res. *6*: 43–50.

KOWALSKI, D. T. 1967. New records of Myxomycetes from California II. Madrono *19*: 43–45.

KRANZLIN, H. 1907. Zur Entwicklungsgeschichte der Sporangien bei den Trichien und Arcyrien. Arch. Protistenk. *9*: 170–194.

KRZEMIENIEWSKA, H. 1929. Ein Beitrag zur Biologie der Schleimplize. Acta Soc. Bot. Polon. *6*: 121–145.

———. 1933. Contribution à la connaissance des Myxobactéries et des Myxomycètes d'une forêt de pins. Spraw. Kom. fizjogr. Polskiej Akad. Urniej. *67*: 121–145.

———. 1957. A list of Myxomycetes collected in the years 1955–56. Acta Soc. Bot. Polon. *26*: 785–811. (Polish with English Summary.)

KRZEMIENIEWSKA, H., and BADURA, L. 1954. A contribution to the knowledge of the microorganisms from litter and soil of the beechwood. Acta Soc. Bot. Poloniae *23*: 545–587, 727–781.

KURAISHI, S., GARVER, J. C., and STRONG, F. M. 1961. Mass culture of *Physarum polycephalum* plasmodium and purification of its pigments. (Abst.). Pl. Physiol. *36* (suppl.): XLVI–XLVII.

LAZO, W. A. 1961. Growth of green algae with myxomycete plasmodia. Am. Midl. Nat. *65*: 381–383.

LEPESCHKIN, W. W. 1923. Über die chemische Zusammensetzung des Protoplasmas des Plasmodiums. Ber. d. deutsch. Bot. Ges. *41*: 179–187.

LEPOW, S. S. 1938. Some reactions of slime mold protoplasm in certain alkaloids and snake venoms. Protoplasma *31*: 161–179.

Léville, J. H. 1843. Mémoire sur le genre *Sclerotium*. Ann. Sci. Nat. Bot. II, 20: 218–248.

Lewis, W. H. 1942. The relation of the viscosity changes in protoplasm to amoeboid locomotion and cell division, in The structure of protoplasm. Iowa State Coll. Press, pp. 163–197.

Lieth, H. 1954. Die pigmente von *Didymium eunigripes* und ihre Beziehungen zur Lichtabsorbtien. Ber. d. deutsch. Bot. Ges. 67: 323–325.

———. 1956. Die Wirkung des Grünlichtes auf die Fruchtkorperbildung bei *Didymium eunigripes*. Arch. Mikrobiologie 24: 91–104.

Lieth, H., and Meyer, G. F. 1957. Über den Bau der Pigmentgranula bei den Myxomyceten. Naturwiss. 44: 449.

Link, J. H. F. 1833. Handbuch zur Erkennung der nutzbarsten und am häufigsten vorkommenden Gewächse. 3.

Lister, A. 1888. Notes on the plasmodium of *Badhamia utricularis* and *Brefeldia maxima*. Ann. Bot. 2: 1–24.

———. 1890. Notes on the ingestion of food material by the swarm-cells of Mycetozoa. Jour. Linn. Soc. (Bot.) 25: 435–441.

———. 1893. On the division of nuclei in the Mycetozoa. Jour. Linn. Soc. Bot. 29: 529–542.

———. 1894. A monograph of the mycetozoa. 1st. ed. London.

———. 1901. On the cultivation of Mycetozoa from spores. Jour. Bot. 39: 5–8.

———. 1906. Presidential Address. Trans. Brit. Mycol. Soc. 2: 142–149.

———. 1925. A monograph of the Mycetozoa. 3rd ed. (revised by G. Lister). British Museum (Nat. Hist.), London.

Lister, Gulielma. 1912. The past students of Mycetozoa and their work. Trans. Br. Mycol. Soc. 4: 44–46.

———. 1918. The Mycetozoa: A short history of their study in Britain; an account of their habitats generally; and a list of species from Essex. Essex Field Club Special Memoirs 6:1–56.

Lister, J. J. 1909. Mycetozoa. A treatise on Zoology. E. R. Lankester, London.

Locquin, M. 1947. Structure du capillitium d'*Hemitrichia serpula*. C. R. Acad. Sci. Paris. 224: 1442–1443.

———. 1948. Structure du capillitium de *Margarita metallica*. Bull. Soc. Linn. Lyon 17: 135–137.

———. 1949a. Recherches sur les simblospores de Myxomycètes. Bull. Soc. Linn. Lyon 18: 43–46.

———. 1949b. Analyse microcinématographique et en contraste de phase du comportement des noyaux quiescents dans les plasmodes du myxomycète "*Licea biforis*." Bull. Soc. Linn. Lyon 18: 75–76.

Loewy, A. G. 1950. Protoplasmic streaming under anaerobic conditions in a myxomycete. Jour. Cell. Comp. Physiol. 35: 151–153.

———. 1952. An actomyosin-like substance from the plasmodium of a myxomycete. J. Cell. Comp. Physiol. 40: 127–156.

Lonert, A. C. 1965. A high-yield method for inducing sclerotization in *Physarum polycephalum*. Turtox News 43: 98–102.

Luyet, B. J. 1950. Evidence and lack of evidence of sexuality in Myxomycetes. VIIth Internat. Bot. Congr. Stockholm, pp. 433–434.

Luyet, B. J., and Gehenio, P. M. 1944. The lethal action of desiccation on the sclerotia of mycetozoa. Biodynamica 4: 369–375.

———. 1945. The role of water in the lethal action of heat on dormant protoplasm. Biodynamica 5: 339–352.

Macbride, T. H. 1899. The North American slime moulds. Macmillan Co., New York.

———. 1914. Mountain Myxomycetes. Mycologia 6: 146–149.

———. 1922. The North American Slime Molds. Macmillan Co., New York.

Macbride, T. H., and Martin, G. W. 1934. The Myxomycetes. Macmillan Co., New York.

MANGENOT, G. 1932. Sur le pigment et le calcaire chez *Fuligo septica* Gmel. C. R. Soc. Biol. *111*: 936–940.

———. 1933. Le plasmode d'*Hemitrichia vesparium* Macbr. C. R. Soc. Biol. *112*: 236–240.

———. 1934. Recherches cytologiques sur les plasmodes de quelques Myxomycètes. Rev. Cytol. Cytophysiol. Veg. *1*: 19–66.

MARTIN, G. W. 1940. The Myxomycetes. Bot. Rev. *6*: 356–388.

———. 1949. The Myxomycetes. N. Am. Flora, 1. Pt. 1: 1–190. N. Y. Bot. Gard., New York.

———. 1958. The contribution of de Bary to our knowledge of Myxomycetes. Proc. Iowa Acad. Sci. *65*: 122–127.

———. 1959. Are fungi plants? Mycologia *47*: 779–792.

———. 1960. The systematic position of the Myxomycetes. Mycologia *52*: 119–129.

———. 1966. The genera of Myxomycetes. Univ. Iowa St. Nat. Hist. *20* (8).

MARTIN, G. W., and ALEXOPOULOS, C. J. 1969. Monograph of the Myxomycetes. Univ. of Iowa Press, Iowa City.

MCCLATCHIE, A. J. 1894. Notes on germinating myxomycetous spores. Bot. Gaz. *19*: 245–246.

MCMANUS, SISTER M. A. 1958. In vivo studies of plasmogamy in *Ceratiomyxa*. Bull. Torrey Bot. Club *85*: 28–37.

———. 1961a. Culture of *Stemonitis fusca* on glass. Am. Jour. Bot. *48*: 582–588.

———. 1961b. Laboratory cultivation of *Clastoderma debaryanum*. Am. Jour. Bot. *48*: 884–888.

———. 1962. Some observations on plasmodia of the Trichiales. Mycologia *54*: 78–90.

———. 1965. Ultrastructure of myxomycete plasmodia of various types. Am. Jour. Bot. *52*: 15–25.

———. 1966. Cultivation on agar of the plasmodia of *Licea biforis, Licea variabilis,* and *Cribaria violacea*. Mycologia *58*: 479–483.

MCMANUS, SISTER M. A., and RICHMOND, SISTER M. V. 1961. Spore to spore culture on agar of *Stemonitis fusca*. Am. Midl. Nat. *65*: 246.

MCMANUS, SISTER M. A., and ROTH, L. E. 1968. Ultrastructure of the somatic nuclear division in the plasmodium of the myxomycete *Clastoderma debaryanum*. Mycologia *60*: 426–436.

MENZEL, M. Y., and PRICE, J. M. 1966. Fine structure of synapsed chromosomes in F_1 *Lycopersicon esculentum–Solanum lycopersicoides* and its parents. Am. Jour. Bot. *53*: 1079–1086.

MEYLAN, C. 1908–1937. Contributions à la connaissance des Myxomycètes du Jura. (Title varies) Bull. Soc. Vaud. Sci. Nat. *44*: 285–302, 1908; *46*: 49–57, 1910; *50*: 1–14, 1914; *51*: 259–269, 1917; *52*: 95–97, 1918; *52*: 447–450, 1919; *53*: 451–463, 1921; *55*: 237–244, 1924; *56*: 65–74, 1925; *56*: 319–328, 1927; *57*: 39–47, 1929; *57*: 147–149, 1930; *57*: 301–307, 1931a; *57*: 359–373, 1931b; *58*: 81–90, 1933; *58*: 319–320, 1935; *59*: 479–486, 1937; Ann. Conserv. Jard. Bot. Genève 1913: 309–321, 1913; Bull. Soc. Bot. Gen. 2me ser. *2*: 261–267, 1910; *6*: 86–90, 1914.

MICHELI, P. A. 1729. Nova plantarum genera. Florence.

MILLER, C. O. 1898. The aseptic cultivation of Mycetozoa. Quart. Jour. Micro. Sci. *41*: 43–71.

MITTERMAYER, C., BRAUN, R., and RUSCH, H. P. 1964. RNA synthesis in the mitotic cycle of *Physarum polycephalum*. Biochim. Biophys. Acta *91*: 399–405.

———. 1965. The effect of actinomycin D on the timing of mitosis in *Physarum polycephalum*. Expt. Cell Res. *38*: 33–41.

———. 1966a. Ribonucleic acid synthesis in vitro in nuclei isolated from the synchronously dividing *Physarum polycephalum*. Biochim. Biophys. Acta *114*: 536–546.

MITTERMAYER, C., BRAUN, R., CHAYKA, T. G., and RUSCH, H. P. 1966b. Polysome patterns and protein synthesis during the mitotic cycle of *Physarum polycephalum*. Nature *210*: 1133–1137.

MOORE, A. R. 1933. On the cytoplasmic framework of the plasmodium, *Physarum polycephalum*. Sci. Rept. Tohoku Imper. Univ., 4th Ser., Biol. *8*: 189–192.

————. 1934. Relation of cytoplasmic structure to growth and respiration in plasmodium. Proc. Soc. Expt. Biol. and Med. *32*: 174–176.

————. 1935. On the significance of cytoplasmic structure in plasmodium. Jour. Cell and Comp. Physiol. *7*: 113–129.

MOSES, M. J., and COLEMAN, J. R. 1964. Structural patterns and the functional organization of chromosomes, in The role of chromosomes in development. (M. Locke, ed.) 2nd Symp. Soc. Study Devel. Gr. Acad. Press, New York. pp. 11–49.

MUKHERJEE, K. L., and ZABKA, G. G. 1964. Studies in the myxomycete *Didymium iridis*. Can. Jour. Bot. *42*: 1459–1466.

NAGAI, R., and KAMIYA, N. 1966. Movement of the myxomycete plasmodium. II. Electron microscope studies on fibrillar structures in the plasmodium. Proc. Jap. Acad. *42*: 934–939.

NAIR, P., and ZABKA, G. G. 1966. Pigmentation and sporulation in selected Myxomycetes. Am. Jour. Bot. *53*: 887–892.

NAKAJIMA, H. 1956. Some properties of a contractile protein in the slime mold. (Japanese.) Seitano-Kagaku (Medical Science) *7*: 256–259. (cf. Kamiya, 1959.)

————. 1957. A contractile protein in the myxomycete plasmodium. 22nd Ann. Meet. Bot. Soc. Japan.

————. 1964. The mechanochemical system behind streaming in *Physarum*, in "Primitive Motile Systems in Cell Biology" (Allen and Kamiya, ed.). pp. 111–120. Academic Press, New York.

NAKAJIMA, H., and ALLEN, R. D. 1965. The changing patterns of birefringence in plasmodia of the slime mold, *Physarum polycephalum*. Jour. Cell. Biol. *25*: 361–374.

NAKAJIMA, H., and HATANO, S. 1962. Acetylcholinesterase in the plasmodium of the myxomycete, *Physarum polycephalum*. Jour. Cell. and Comp. Physiol. *59*: 259–264.

NAUSS, R. 1943. Observations on the culture of *Hemitrichia vesparium* with special reference to its black plasmodial color. Bull. Torrey Bot. Club *70*: 152–163.

————. 1947. My garden of slime molds. Jour. N. Y. Bot. Gard. *48*: 101–109.

————. 1949. *Reticulomyxa filosa* gen. et sp. nov. a new primitive plasmodium. Bull. Torrey Bot. Club *76*: 161–173.

NIKLOWITZ, W. 1957. Über den Feinbau der Mitochondrien des Schleimpilzes *Badhamia utricularis*. Exptl. Cell. Res. *13*: 591–595.

NYGAARD, O. F., GUTTES, S., and RUSCH, H. P. 1960. Nucleic acid metabolism in a slime mold with synchronous mitosis. Biochim. et Biphys. Acta *38*: 298–306.

OHTA, J. 1952a. Experimental studies on the protoplasmic streaming in the myxomycete plasmodium. I. Some observations on the motive force of protoplasmic streaming. Cytologia *17*: 210–218.

————. 1952b. Experimental studies on the protoplasmic streaming in the myxomycete plasmodium. II. The effects of some respiratory poisons and reduced oxygen tensions on the motive force of protoplasmic streaming. Cytologia *17*: 300–310.

————. 1954. Studies on the metabolism of the myxomycete plasmodium. Jour. Biochem. *39*: 489–497.

OLIVE, E. W. 1907a. Evidence of sexual reproduction in the slime molds. Science *25*: 266–267.

————. 1907b. Cytological studies on *Ceratiomyxa*. Trans. Wisconsin Acad. Sci. *15*: 753–773.

OLIVE, L. S. 1960. *Echinostelium minutum*. Mycologia *52*: 159–161.

————. 1967. The Protostelida—a new order of the Mycetozoa. Mycologia *59*: 1–29.

OOSAWA, F., KASAI, M., HATANO, S., and ASAKURA, S. 1966. Polymerization of actin and flagellin, in "Principles of Biomolecular Organization," pp. 273–307. Little, Brown and Co. Boston.

PARK, D., and ROBINSON, P. M. 1967. Internal water distribution and cytoplasmic streaming in *Physarum polycephalum*. Ann. Bot. (London) N.S., *31*: 731–738.

PARKER, H. 1946. Studies in the nutrition of some aquatic Myxomycetes. Jour. Elisha Mitchell Sci. Soc. *62*: 231–247.

PARRIS, G. K. 1940. A check list of fungi, bacteria, nematodes and viruses occurring in Hawaii, and their hosts. Plant Dis. Rep. Suppl. 121, pp. 37–39.

PETERSON, J. E. 1952. Myxomycetes developed on bark of living trees in moist chamber culture. Master's thesis. Michigan State Univ., East Lansing.

PETTERSSON, B. 1940. Experimentelle Untersuchungen über die euanemochore Verbreitung der Sprepflanzen. Act Bot. Fenn. *25*: 1–103. (cf. P. H. Gregory. 1961. The microbiology of the atmosphere. Interscience Publ. Inc., New York.)

PFEFFER, W. 1906. The physiology of plants. English ed. Oxford.

PINOY, E. 1902. Nécessité de la présence d'une bactérie pour obtenir la culture de certains Myxomycètes. Bull. Soc. Mycol. France *18*: 288–289.

———. 1903. Nécessité d'une symbiose microbienne pour obtenir la culture des Myxomycètes. Compt. Rend. Acad. Sci. Paris *137*: 580–581.

———. 1907. Role des bactéries dans le developpement de certains Myxomycètes. Ann. Inst. Pasteur *21*: 622–656, 686–700.

———. 1908. Sur l'existence d'un dimorphisme sexuel chez un myxomycète. C. R. Soc. Biol. *64*: 630–631.

———. 1915. Nutrition et coloration des Myxomycètes. C. R. Soc. Biol. *78*: 172–174.

POBEQUIN T. 1954. Contribution à l'étude des carbonates de calcium. Ann. Sci. Nat. Bot. *15*: 29–104.

POTEAT, W. L. 1937. A lawn marvel. Science *86*: 155–156.

PROWAZEK, S. 1904. Kernveränderung in Myxomycetenplasmodien. Oester. Bot. Zeit. *54*: 278–281.

RAKOCZY, L. 1961. Observation on the regeneration of the plasmodium of the Myxomycete *Didymium xanthopus* (Ditm.) Fr. Acta Soc. Bot. Poloniae *30*: 443–456.

———. 1962. The effect of light on the fructification of the slime mold *Physarum nudum* Macbride as influenced by the age of the culture. Acta Soc. Bot. Poloniae *31*: 651–665.

———. 1963. Influence of monochromatic light on the fructification of *Physarum nudum*. Bull. Acad. Polon. Sci. Ser. Sci. Biol. *11*: 559–562.

———. 1967. Antagonistic action of light in sporulation of the myxomycete *Physarum nudum*. Acta Soc. Bot. Poloniae 36: 153–159.

RASHEVSKY, N. 1948. Mathematical Biophysics. 2nd ed. Univ. of Chicago Press. Chicago, Illinois.

REINHARD, H. F. 1952. Über die Physiologie der Sporenbildung und der Sporenkeimung bei *Didymium eunigripes*. Dokt.-Dissert., Univ. Koln. (cf. Stosch, 1965).

RHEA, R. P. 1966a. Electron microscopic observations on the slime mold *Physarum polycephalum* with specific reference to fibrillar structures. Jour. Ultra. Res. *15*: 349–379.

———. 1966b. Microcinematographic, electron microscopic and electrophysiological studies on shuttle streaming in the slime mold *Physarum polycephalum*. pp. 35–58 in "Dynamics of Fluids and Plasmas." Academic Press, Inc., New York.

ROSANOFF, S. 1868. De l'influence de l'attraction terrestre sur la direction des plasmodia des Myxomycètes. Mem. Soc. Sci. Nat. Cherbourg. *19*: 149–172 (cf. Hawker, 1952).

ROSEN, F. 1893. Beitrage zur Kenntniss der Pflanzenzellen. II. Studien über die Kerne und die Membranbildung bei Myxomyceten und Pilzen. Beitr. Biol. Pflanzen *6*: 237–266.

Ross, I. K. 1957a. Capillitial formation in the Stemonitaceae. Mycologia *49*: 808–819.

——. 1957b. Syngamy and plasmodium formation in the Myxogastres. Am. Jour. Bot. *44*: 843–850.

——. 1959. Fruiting in the Myxomycetes. IXth Intern. Bot. Congr. Vol. 2, p. 333.

——. 1960. Sporangial development in *Lamproderma arcyrionema*. Mycologia *52*: 621–627.

——. 1961. Further studies on meiosis in the Myxomycetes. Am. Jour. Bot. *48*: 244–248.

——. 1964. Pure cultures of some Myxomycetes. Bull. Torrey. Bot. Club *91*: 23–31.

——. 1966. Chromosome numbers in pure and gross cultures of Myxomycetes. Am. Jour. Bot. *53*: 712–718.

—— 1967a. Syngamy and plasmodium formation in the myxomycete *Didymium iridis*. Protoplasma *64*: 104–119.

——. 1967b. Growth and development of the myxomycete *Perichaena vermicularis*. I. Cultivation and vegetative nuclear divisions. Am. Jour. Bot. *54*: 617–625.

——. 1967c. Growth and development of the myxomycete *Perichaena vermicularis*. II. Chromosome numbers and nuclear cycles. Am. Jour. Bot. *54*: 1231–1236.

——. 1967d. Abnormal cell behavior in the heterothallic myxomycete *Didymium iridis*. Mycologia *59*: 235–245.

Ross, I. K., and Cummings, R. J. 1967. Formation of amoeboid cells from the plasmodium of a myxomycete. Mycologia *59*: 725–732.

Ross, I. K., and Sunshine, L. D. 1965. The effect of quinic acid and similar compounds on the growth and development of *Physarum flavicomum* in pure culture. Mycologia *57*: 360–367.

Rostafinski, J. T. 1875. Śluzowce (Mycetozoa). Monografia. Paryz.

Rusch, H. P. 1968. Some biochemical events in the life cycle of *Physarum polycephalum*. *in* Advances in Cell Biology. Vol. I. (ed. D. M. Prescott). Appleton-Century-Crofts.

Rusch, H. P., and Sachsenmaier, M. 1964. Time of mitosis in relation to synthesis of DNA and RNA in *Physarum polycephalum*. Acta Union Inter. Contre le Cander *20*: 1282–1284.

Sachsenmaier, W., and Rusch, H. P. 1964. The effect of 5-fluoro-2′-deoxyuridine on synchronous mitosis in *Physarum polycephalum*. Expt. Cell. Res. *36*: 124–133.

Sansome, Eva R., and Dixon, P. A. 1965. Cytological studies of the myxomycete *Ceratiomyxa fruticulosa*. Arch. Mikrobiol. *52*: 1–9.

Sansome, Eva R., and Sansome, F. W. 1961. Observations on *Ceratiomyxa* in West Africa. Jour. W. Afr. Sci. Assoc. *7*: 93–100.

Santesson, R. 1948. *Listerella paradoxa* Jahn Och *Orcadella singularis* (Jahn) no. comb., två för Sverige nye Myxomyceter. Svensk. Bot. Tidskr. *42*: 42–50.

Schin, K. S. 1965a. Meiotische Prophase und Spermatidenreifung bei *Gryllus domesticus*, mit besonderer Berücksichtigung der Chromosomenstrucktur. Zeit. Zellforsch. *65*: 481–513.

——. 1965b. Core-Strukturen in den meiotischen und post-meiotischen Kernen der Spermatogenese von *Gryllus domesticus*. Chromosoma (Berl.) *16*: 436–452.

Schinz, H. 1920. Myxogastres, in Rabenhorst's "Kryptogamen-Flora," X Abt., Leipzig.

Schmitz, F. 1879. Untersuchungen über die Zellkerne der Thallophyten. Niederrh. Gesell. F. Natur. und Heilkunde, Bonn. In Naturw. Ver Preuss. Rheinlande und Westfalens, Verhandl. *36*: 345–376.

Scholes, P. M. 1962. Some observations on the cultivation, fruiting and germination of *Fuligo septica*. Jour. Gen. Microbiol. *29*: 137–148.

Schünemann, E. 1930. Untersuchungen über die Sexualitat der Myxomyceten. Planta Arch. Wiss. Bot. *9*: 645–672.

Schure, P. S. J. 1949. Nuclear divisions in the fructifications of some Myxomycetes and a method of culture to obtain fructifications. Antonie van Leeuwenhoek Jour. Micro. and Serol. *15*: 143–161.

SCHUSTER, F. 1964a. Electron microscope observations on spore formation in the true slime mold *Didymium nigripes*. Jour. Protozool. *11*: 207–216.

———. 1964b. Ultrastructural and growth studies on slime molds. Argonne Nat. Lab. ANL-6971: 70–74.

———. 1965a. A deoxyribose nucleic acid component in mitochondria of *Didymium nigripes*, a slime mold. Exptl. Cell. Res. *39*: 329–345.

———. 1965b. Ultrastructure and morphogenesis of solitary stages of true slime molds. Protistologica *1*: 49–62.

SEIFRIZ, W. 1937. A theory of protoplasmic streaming. Science *86*: 397–398.

———. 1943. Protoplasmic streaming. Bot. Rev. *9*: 49–123.

———. 1944. Exotoxins from slime molds. Science *100*: 74–75.

———. 1953. Mechanism of protoplasmic movement. Nature *171*: 1136–1138.

SEIFRIZ, W., and EPSTEIN, N. 1941. Shock anaesthesia in Myxomycetes. Biodynamica *3*: 191–197.

SEIFRIZ, W., and RUSSELL, M. 1936. The fruiting of Myxomycetes. New Phyt. *35*: 472–478.

SEIFRIZ, W., and URBACH, F. 1944. Physical activities and respiration in slime molds. Growth *8*: 221–233.

SEIFRIZ, W., and ZETZMANN, M. 1935. A slime-mold pigment as indicator of acidity. Protoplasma *23*: 175–179.

SINOTO, Y., and YUASA, A. 1934. Studies in the cytology of reproductive cells. I. On the planocytes in five forms of Myxomycetes. Bot. Mag. Tokyo. *48*: 720–729.

SKUPIENSKA, ALINA. 1953. Influence du substratum sur le développement du myxomycète *Didymium nigripes*. Fr. Bull. Soc. Sci. Lettres Lodz *4(7)*: 1–2.

SKUPIENSKI, F. X. 1917. Sur la sexualité de Champignons Myxomycètes. Compt. Rend. Acad. Sci. Paris *165*: 118–121.

———. 1920. Recherches sur le cycle évolutif de certains Myxomycètes. Imprimerie M. Flinikowski, Paris.

———. 1926. Sur le cycle évolutif chez une espèce de myxomycète endosporée. C. R. Acad. Sci. Paris. *182*: 150–152.

———. 1927. Sur le cycle évolutif chez une espèce de myxomycète endosporée *Didymium difforme*. Etude cytologique. C. R. Acad. Sci. Paris. *184*: 1341–1344.

———. 1928. Badania Bio-cytolicze nad *Didymium difforme*. Czesc pierwsza. (Étude bio-cytologique du *Didymium difforme*. Première partie.) Acta Soc. Bot. Poloniae *5*: 255–336.

———. 1929. Sur la coloration vitale de *Didymium nigripes*. Acta Soc. Bot. Poloniae *6*: 203–213.

———. 1930. Influence de la temperature sur la fructification de *Didymium nigripes*. Acta Soc. Bot. Poloniae *7*: 241–249.

———. 1933. Influence du milieu de culture sur le développement des Myxomycètes. Acta Soc. Bot. Poloniae. *10*: 113–127.

———. 1934. Sur l'existence de races physiologiques chez les Myxomycètes. Ann. Protistol. *4*: 121–132.

———. 1939. Races physiologiques chez les myxomycètes *Didymium squamulosum* Fries. C. R. Soc. Biol. *131*: 355–357.

———. 1953. Faculté régéneratrice du plasmode de *Didymium squamulosum* Fries. Contribution à l'étude cytologique de *Myxomycètes*. Bull. Soc. Sc. Lettr. Lodz. classe III, *4*: 1–3. (cf., Rakoczy, 1961.)

SMART, R. F. 1937. Influence of certain external factors on spore germination in the Myxomycetes. Am. Jour. Bot. *24*: 145–159.

SMITH, E. C. 1929a. Longevity of myxomycete spores. Mycologia *21*: 321–323.

———. 1929b. Some phases of spore germination in myxomycetes. Am. Jour. Bot. *16*: 645–650.

———. 1931. Ecological observations on Colorado Myxomycetes. Torreya. *31*: 42–44.

SMITH, F., and GRENAN, M. M. 1949. Some factors influencing the spreading of plasmodial protoplasm. Biodynamica *6*: 225–230.

SOBELS, J. C. 1950. Nutrition de quelques Myxomycètes en cultures pures et associées et leurs propriétés antibiotiques. N. V. Drukkerij v/h Koch and Knuttel, Gouda Netherlands.

SOBELS, J. C., and VAN DER BRUGGE, H. F. H. 1950. Influence of daylight on the fruiting of two orange-yellow pigmented myxomycete plasmodia. Konink. Nederl. Akad. Wetens. *53*: 1610–1616.

SOLACOLU, T. 1932. Sur les matières colorantes de quelques Myxomycètes. Le Botaniste *24*: 107–140.

SOLIS, B. C. 1962. Studies on the morphology of *Physarum nicaraguense* Macbr. M. S. Thesis, Univ. of Iowa, Iowa City.

SOTELO, J. R., and WETTSTEIN, R. 1964. Electron microscope study on meiosis. The sex chromosome in spermatocytes, spermatids and oocytes of *Gryllus argentinus*. Chromosoma (Berl.) *15*: 389–415.

SPONSLER, O. L., and BATH, J. D. 1953. A view of submicroscopic components of protoplasm as revealed by the electron microscope. Protoplasma *42*: 69–76.

———. 1954. Some micellar components of *Physarum polycephalum* as revealed by the electron microscope. Protoplasma *44*: 259–265.

STAHL, E. 1884. Zur Biologie der Myxomyceten. Bot. Zeit. *42*: 145–156, 161–176, 187–191.

STEWART, P. A., and STEWART, B. T. 1959. Protoplasmic movement in slime mold plasmodia: the diffusion drag force hypothesis. Expt. Cell. Res. *17*: 44–58.

———. 1960a. Protoplasmic streaming and the fine structure of slime mold plasmodia. Expt. Cell. Res. *18*: 374–377.

———. 1960b. Electron microscopical studies of plasma membrane formation in slime molds. Norelco Reporter *7*: 21–22, 67.

———. 1961a. Circular streaming patterns in a slime mold plasmodium. Nature *192*: 1206–1207.

———. 1961b. Membrane formation during sclerotization of *Physarum polycephalum* plasmodia. Exptl. Cell Res. *23*: 471–478.

STILL, C. C. 1964. The enzymic binding of indole-3-acetic acid and morphogenesis in the slime mold, *Physarum polycephalum*. Ph.D. Thesis, Temple University, Philadelphia, Pa.

STILL, C. C., and WARD, J. M. 1963. Photo-indole-3-acetic acid effects on morphogenesis in *Physarum polycephalum*. Bact. Proc. P. 68.

STOSCH, H. A. VON. 1935. Untersuchungen über die Entwicklungsgeschichte der Myxomyceten. Sexualität und Apogamie bei Didymiaceen. Planta *23*: 623–656.

———. 1937. Über den Generationwechsel der Myxomyceten, eine Erwiderung. Ber. deutsch. bot. Ges. *55*: 362–369.

———. 1965. Wachstums- und Entwicklungsphysiologie der Myxomyceten. Handbuch der Pflanzenphysiologie *15* (Pt. 1): 641–679.

STOSCH, H. A. VON, VAN ZUL-PISCHINGER, M., and DERSCH, G. 1964. Nuclear phase alternance in the myxomycete *Physarum polycephalum*. Abstracts Xth Intern. Bot. Congr., Edinburgh, August 1964, pp. 481–482.

STRASBURGER, E. 1880. Zellbildung und Zelltheilung. (cf. Camp, 1937.)

———. 1884. Zur Entwickelungsgeschichte der Sporangien von *Trichia fallax*. Bot. Zeit. *42*: 305–316, 321–326.

STRAUB, J. 1954. Das Licht bei der Auslösung der Fruchtkörperbildung von *Didymium nigripes* und die Uberstragung der Lichtwirkung durch Plasma. Naturwiss. *41*: 219–220.

STURGIS, W. C. 1912. A guide to the botanical literature of the Myxomycetes from 1875 to 1917. Colo. Coll. Publ., Sci. Ser. *12*: 285–433.

SULLIVAN, A. J., JR. 1953. Some aspects of the biochemistry of dormancy in the myxomycete *Physarum polycephalum*. Physiol. Plant. *6*: 804–815.

SZENT-GYÖRGYI, A. 1951. Chemistry of muscular contraction. 2nd ed. Academic Press, New York and London.

TAKATA, T., NAGAI, R., and KAMIYA, N. 1967. Movement of the myxomcete plasmodium. III. Artificial polarization in endoplasm distribution in a plasmodium and its bearing on protoplasmic streaming. Proc. Jap. Acad. 43: 45–50.

TERADA, T. 1962. Electron microscope studies on the slime mold Physarum polycephalum. Faculty of Science, Osaka Univ., Osaka, Japan. 1962: 47–58.

THERRIEN, C. D. 1966a. Microspectrophotometric analysis of nuclear deoxyribonucleic acid in some Myxomycetes. Ph.D. Dissertation, University of Texas at Austin.

———. 1966b. Microspectrophotometric measurement of nuclear deoxyribonucleic acid content in two Myxomycetes. Can. Jour. Bot. 44: 1667–1675.

THOM, C., and RAPER, K. B. 1930. Myxamoebae in soil and decomposing crop residues. Jour. Wash. Acad. Sci. 20: 362–370.

TIMNICK, M. B. 1947. Culturing myxomycete plasmodia for classroom use. Proc. Iowa Acad. Sci. 53: 191–193.

TORREND, C. 1909. Flore des Myxomycètes. Etude des espèces connues jusqu'ici. Broteria, Ser. Bot. 7: 1–270.

TS'O, P. O. P., BONNER, J., EGGMAN, L., and VINOGRAD, J. 1956a. Observations on an ATP-sensitive protein system from the plasmodia of a myxomycete. J. Gen. Physiol. 39: 325–347.

TS'O, P. O. P., EGGMAN, L., and VINOGRAD, J. 1956b. The isolation of myxomysin, an ATP-sensitive protein from the plasmodium of a myxomycete. J. Gen. Physiol. 39: 801–812.

———. 1956c. Myxomyosin, a protein related to structure and streaming of cytoplasm. Fed. Proc. 15(1):373.

———. 1957a. Physical and chemical studies of myxomyosin, an ATP-sensitive protein in cytoplasm. Biochem. et Biophys. Acta 25: 532–542.

———. 1957b. The interaction of myxomyosin with ATP. Arch. Biochem. and Biophys. 66: 64–70.

ULRICH, R. 1943. Les constituents de la membrane chez les champignons. Rev. Mycol. (Paris) Mém. Hors-Ser. No. 3. 1–44.

VAN OVEREEM, M. A. 1937. On green organisms occurring in the lower troposphere. Rec. Trav. Bot. Neerl. 34: 388–442.

VOUK, V. 1910. Untersuchungen über di Bewegungen der Plasmodien. I. Die Rhythmik der Protoplasmaströmung. S. B. kais. Akad. Wiss. Wien, meth.-naturw. Kl. 119: 853–876.

———. 1911. Über den Generationswechsel bei Myxomyceten. Oesterr. Bot. Zeits. 61: 131–139. (cf. Martin, 1940.)

———. 1913a. Die Lebensgemeinschaften der Bakterien mit einigen höheren und niederen Pflanzen. Naturwiss. 1: 81–87.

———. 1913b. Untersuchungen über die Bewegungen der Plasmodien. II. Studien über die Protoplasmastromung. Denkschr. kais. Akad. Wiss. Wien, meth.-naturw. Kl. 88: 652–692.

WARCUP, J. H. 1950. The soil-plate method for isolation of fungi from soil. Nature (London) 166: 117–118.

WARD, J. M. 1954. Enzymes in the slime mold Physarum polycephalum. 1. An atypical ascorbic acid oxidase. 2. Succinoxidase. Diss. Abs. 14: 754–755.

———. 1955. The enzymatic oxidation of ascorbic acid in the slime mold, Physarum polycephalum. Plant Physiol. 30: 58–67.

———. 1956. Comparative cytochrome oxidase and atypical ascorbic acid oxidase activities in the vegetative and spore stages of the slime mold, Physarum polycephalum. (Abst.) Pl. Physiol. 31 (suppl.): xxix.

———. 1958a. Biochemical systems involved in differentiation of the Fungi. 4th Int. Cong. of Biochem. Vienna. Symposium No. VI, pp. 1–26.

———. 1958b. Shift of oxidases with morphogenesis in the slime mold, Physarum polycephalum. Science 127: 596.

WARD, J. M., and HAVIR, E. A. 1957a. Sulfhydrils, melanin formation, and cell division during morphogenesis in the slime mold *Physarum polycephalum*. (Abst.) Pl. Physiol. 32 (suppl.): xxiv–xxv.

————. 1957b. The role of 3:4 dihydroxytoluene, sulfhydril groups and cresolase during melanin formation in a slime mold. Biochem. et Biophys. Acta 25: 440–442.

WARD, MARSHALL. 1884. The morphology and physiology of an aquatic Myxomycete. Qurt. Jour. Micr. Sci. N. S. *24*: 64–86.

WATANABE, A. 1932. On the plasmodium of the Myxomycetes. (trans. title). Kagaku *10*: 418–421.

WATANABE, A., KADATI, M., and KINOSHITA, S. 1938. Über die negative Galvanotaxis der Myxomyceten-Plasmodien. Bot. Mag. (Tokyo) *52*: 441–445.

WELDEN, A. 1955. Capillitial development in the Myxomycetes *Badhamia gracilis* and *Didymium iridis*. Mycologia *47*: 714–728.

WETTSTEIN, F. VON. 1921. Das Vorkommen von Chitin und seine Verwertung als systematischphytogenetisches Merkmal in Pflanzenreich. Sitzver, Akad. Wiss. Wien, Math.-Naturw. Kl. Abt. I, 130–133.

WILSON, C. M., and ROSS, I. K. 1955. Meiosis in the Myxomycetes. Am. Jour. Bot. *42*: 743–749.

WILSON, M., and CADMAN, E. J. 1928. The life history and cytology of *Reticularia lycoperdon*. Trans. Roy. Soc. Edinburgh 55: 555–608.

WINER, B. J., and MOORE, A. R. 1941. Reactions of the plasmodium *Physarum polycephalum* to physico-chemical changes in the environment. Biodynamica 3: 323–345.

WOHLFARTH-BOTTERMANN, K. E. 1962. Weitreichende, fibrillare Protoplasmadifferenzierungen und ihre Bedeutung fur die Protoplasmastromung. I. Elektronenmikroskopischer Nachweis und Feinstruktur. Protoplasma *54*: 514–539.

————. 1964. Differentiations of the ground cytoplasm and their significance for the motive force of amoeboid movement, in "Primitive Motile Systems in Cell Biology" (Allen and Kamiya, ed.), pp. 79–109. Academic Press, New York.

WOLF, F. T. 1959. Chemical nature of the photoreceptor pigment inducing fruiting of plasmodia of *Physarum polycephalum*. In "Photoperiodism and related phenomena in plants and animals." AAAS. Washington, D. C. pp. 321–326.

WOLLMAN, CONSTANCE. 1966. Cultural studies of selected species of Myxomycetes. Ph.D. Dissertation, Univ. of Texas, Austin.

WOLLMAN, CONSTANCE, and ALEXOPOULOS, C. J. 1964. Spore to spore cultivation in agar culture of three Myxomycetes: *Comatricha laxa, Perichaena depressa,* and *Licea biforis*. Southwest. Natural. *9*: 160–165.

————. 1967. The plasmodium of *Licea biforis* in agar culture. Mycologia *59*: 423–430.

————. 1968. *Comatricha nodulifera* a new myxomycete from Texas. Can. Jour. Bot. *46*: 157–159.

WOLSTENHOLME, D. R., and MEYER, G. F. 1966. Some facts concerning the nature and formation of axial core structures in spermatids of *Gryllus domesticus*. Chromosoma *18*: 272–286.

YOUNGGREN, N. A. 1958. A spectrophotometric investigation for enzymes containing iron-porphyrines in the plasmodium of the slime-mold *Physarum polycephalum*. Diss. Abst. *19*: 157–158.

ZELDIN, M. H., and WARD, J. M. 1963a. Acrilamide electrophoresis and protein pattern during morphogenesis in a slime mold. Nature *198*: 389–390.

————. 1963b. Protein changes during photo-induced morphogenesis in *Physarum polycephalum*. Bact. Proc. P. 80.

ZUKAL, H. 1893. Über zwei neue Myxomyceten. Oester. Bot. Zeitschr. *43*: 73–77, 133–137.

ZURZYCKI, J. 1951. The influence of temperature on the protoplasmic streaming in *Elodea densa* Casp. Acta Soc. Bot. Poloniae *21*: 241–264.

Author Index

Boldface page numbers indicate illustrations.

Index of Genera and Species of Myxomycetes

Boldface page numbers indicate illustrations.

Subject Index

Boldface page numbers indicate illustrations.